Holt

Georgia Performance Standards Exploration and Mastery Worktext

For use with *Holt Mathematics* Course 3
and *Mathematics in Context*® Level 3

HOLT, RINEHART AND WINSTON

A Harcourt Education Company

Orlando • **Austin** • New York • San Diego • London

ISBN 0-03-096254-4

14 15   1409   12
4500367019

Table of Contents

Each chapter opens with a hands-on Project and closes with Chapter Big Ideas. Both activities are designed to support the Georgia Performance Standards for Grade 8 addressed in the individual lessons.

The table below states which pages in **Holt Mathematics** *Course 3* and in **Mathematics in Context** *Level 3* support Worktext lessons. All Worktext lessons contain Exploration activities, Review for Mastery worksheets, and Homework and Practice worksheets. Lessons denoted with (*) also contain Hands-On Labs and lessons with (†) also contain Technology Labs.

Chapter 1 · Principles of Algebra

Holt Mathematics Course 3	Worktext Lesson	Mathematics in Context Level 3
1-1	**1A**	Algebra Rules: C
1-2	**1B**	Patterns and Figures: A, B Algebra Rules: A
1-4	**1C**	Algebra Rules: A
1-5	**1D**	Algebra Rules: A
1-7	**1E**	Algebra Rules: D
1-8	**1F**	Algebra Rules: D
1-9	**1G**	Graphing Equations: A
--	**1H**	Algebra Rules: D

Holt Mathematics

Chapter 2 · Rational Numbers

Holt Mathematics Course 3	Worktext Lesson	Mathematics in Context Level 3
2-3	2A	--
2-5	2B	Revisiting Numbers: C, D
2-6	2C	--
2-7	2D	--
2-8	2E	Graphing Equations: D Algebra Rules: D
--	2F	--

Holt Mathematics

Chapter 3 · Graphs, Functions, and Sequences

Holt Mathematics Course 3	Worktext Lesson	Mathematics in Context Level 3
3-1	**3A**	Revisiting Numbers: E
3-2	**3B**	Revisiting Numbers: E Ups and Downs: A-E
--	**3C**	Ups and Downs: B, C
3-4	**3D**	Ups and Downs: B, C
3-5	**3E**	Ups and Downs: A, C
3-6	**3F**	Ups and Downs: B Patterns and Figures: A, B, D

Holt Mathematics

Chapter 4 · Exponents and Roots

Worktext			GPS

Holt Mathematics Course 3	Worktext Lesson	Mathematics in Context Level 3
4-1	4A	--
4-2	4B	Revisiting Numbers: A, B
4-3	4C	Revisiting Numbers: A, B
4-4	4D	Revisiting Numbers: A, B
4-5	4E	Revisiting Numbers: E Patterns and Figures: C
4-6	4F	Revisiting Numbers: A, E
4-7	4G	Revisiting Numbers: E
4-8	4H	It's All the Same: D Looking at an Angle: E
--	4I	--
--	4J	--

Holt Mathematics

Chapter 5 · Ratios, Proportions, and Similarity

Holt Mathematics Course 3	Worktext Lesson	Mathematics in Context Level 3
5-4	**5A**	Looking at an Angle: D
5-7	**5B**	Looking at an Angle: A-D
5-8	**5C**	Looking at an Angle: A-D

Holt Mathematics

Chapter 6 · Percents

Holt Mathematics Course 3	Worktext Lesson	Mathematics in Context Level 3
6-3	**6A**	Great Predictions: A, B
6-4	**6B**	Great Predictions: C
6-6	**6C**	It's All the Same: B Ups and Downs: E
6-7	**6D**	--

Holt Mathematics

Chapter 7 · Foundations of Geometry

Holt Mathematics Course 3	Worktext Lesson	Mathematics in Context Level 3
7-2	**7A**	It's All the Same: A, C, E
--	**7B**	It's All the Same: A
7-5	**7C**	It's All the Same: E Graphing Equations: A
7-6	**7D**	It's All the Same: A

Holt Mathematics

Chapter 8 · Perimeter, Area, and Volume

Holt Mathematics Course 3	Worktext Lesson	Mathematics in Context Level 3
8-1	8A	Algebra Rules: E Ups and Downs: C
8-2	8B	--
8-3	8C	Ups and Downs: C Algebra Rules: B
8-5	8D	--
8-6	8E	--
8-7	8F	--
8-8	8G	--
8-9	8H	--
8-10	8I	--

Holt Mathematics

Chapter 9 · Data and Statistics

Holt Mathematics Course 3	Worktext Lesson	Mathematics in Context Level 3
9-7	**9A**	Insights Into Data: A, E, F
--	**9B**	Insights Into Data: A-E

Holt Mathematics

Chapter 10 · Probability

Holt Mathematics Course 3	Worktext Lesson	Mathematics in Context Level 3
10-1	**10A**	Great Predictions: A
10-2	**10B**	Great Predictions: C, D
10-3	**10C**	Insights Into Data: B Great Predictions: E
10-4	**10D**	Great Predictions: D
10-5	**10E**	Great Predictions: B, D, E
10-6	**10F**	Great Predictions: C
10-7	**10G**	--
10-8	**10H**	Great Predictions: B
10-9	**10I**	--

Holt Mathematics

Chapter 11 · Multi-Step Equations and Inequalities

Holt Mathematics Course 3	Worktext Lesson	Mathematics in Context Level 3
11-1	**11A**	Algebra Rules: A, E
11-2	**11B**	Graphing Equations: D Algebra Rules: D
11-3	**11C**	Algebra Rules: D Graphing Equations: D
--	**11D**	--
--	**11E**	--
11-4	**11F**	--
11-5	**11G**	--
--	**11H**	Graphing Equations: E
11-6	**11I**	Graphing Equations: E Algebra Rules: D

Holt Mathematics

Chapter 12 · Graphing Lines

Holt Mathematics Course 3	Worktext Lesson	Mathematics in Context Level 3
12-1	**12A**	Graphing Equations: B, C Algebra Rules: B
12-2	**12B**	Graphing Equations: B Algebra Rules: B
12-3	**12C**	Graphing Equations: C Algebra Rules: B
12-4	**12D**	--
12-5	**12E**	--
12-6	**12F**	--
--	**12G**	--
12-7	**12H**	Insights Into Data: F

Holt Mathematics

Chapter 13 · Sequences and Functions

Holt Mathematics Course 3	Worktext Lesson	Mathematics in Context Level 3
13-1	13A	Patterns and Figures: A, B Algebra Rules: A
13-2	13B	Ups and Downs: C, E
13-3	13C	Patterns and Figures: A-D
13-4	13D	Graphing Equations: C Algebra Rules: B
--	13E	Patterns and Figures: A, B
13-5	13F	Ups and Downs: C, E
13-6	13G	Ups and Downs: E
13-7	13H	--
--	13I	--
--	13J	--
--	13K	--

Holt Mathematics

Chapter 14 · Polynomials

Holt Mathematics Course 3	Worktext Lesson	Mathematics in Context Level 3
14-1	**14A**	--
14-2	**14B**	Algebra Rules: E Patterns and Figures: A, B
14-3	**14C**	Algebra Rules: A Patterns and Figures: A, B
14-4	**14D**	Algebra Rules: A Patterns and Figures: A, B
14-5	**14E**	Algebra Rules: A Patterns and Figures: A, B
14-6	**14F**	Algebra Rules: E

Holt Mathematics

CHAPTER 1

Project
Algebra: Fire Drills

Career: Firefighter

A firefighter approaching a fires should be aware of ventilation, space, what is burning, and what could be ignited. Oxygen, fuel, heat, and chemical reactions are at the core of a fire, but the amounts and materials differ.

In this chapter project...you will research the amount of pollution in the air. You will:

- Learn about different toxic gases that can be released in a fire and how much of each is considered dangerous.

- Research the amount of pollutants in the air or water of your town, county, or state. Many local governments publish yearly reports on pollutants found in the air and water, and list the pollutants by how many parts per million or billion found.

- Create a graph showing the amount of pollutants found in your community. Also graph the level of each pollutant that is considered dangerous, and compare the two graphs.

To get started, work through the Space Spaces worksheet on the next page.

This chapter project reinforces your understanding of these Georgia Performance Standards:

M8P4.c Recognize and apply mathematics in contexts outside of mathematics.

M8P5.c Create and use representations to organize, record, and communicate mathematical ideas.

go.hrw.com
Chapter Project Online
KEYWORD: MT7 Ch1

Holt Mathematics

Project Recording Sheet
Principles of Algebra

Firefighting

What toxic gases are created in a fire? The table lists some of the
gases that are formed when different materials are burned.

Fire-Caused Toxic Gases

Gas	Dangerous Level (ppm)	Burning Source
Carbon dioxide (CO_2)	40,000	Complete burning of wood, paper
Carbon monoxide (CO)	1200	Incomplete burning
Hydrogen chloride (HCl)	50	Plastics
Hydrogen cyanide (HCN)	50	Wool, nylon, polyurethane foam, rubber, paper
Nitrogen dioxide (NO_2)	20	Grains, some plastics
Phosgene ($COCl_2$)	2	Refrigerants

The unit ppm stands for "parts per million." This means the number of
molecules of gas there are in every million molecules of air. For
example, 1200 parts per million of carbon monoxide means that for
every one million molecules of air, 1200 molecules are carbon dioxide
and the remaining 998,000 are similar to the air in the atmosphere.

Use the table for Exercises 1–4.

1. Which gas released by a fire is the most dangerous? Why do
   you think so?

   _____

   _____

2. How many times more dangerous is the most dangerous gas
   compared to the least dangerous?

   _____

   _____

3. Which toxic gas is most likely to be found in a common house
   fire? Why do you think so?

   _____

   _____

   _____

4. Write an algebraic equation that compares the toxicity of all of
   the gases. (For example: 50 HCL = 1200 CO.)

   _____

   _____

Holt Mathematics

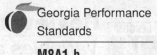
Georgia Performance
Standards

M8A1.b

1A Variables and Expressions

Catherine's dance team is planning a spring trip to the coast. Catherine is saving money in a bank account to pay for the trip. Her parents started her account with $100. She sells Christmas plants and adds $2.50 to her account for each plant she sells.

How much will be in her account if she sells 50 plants?

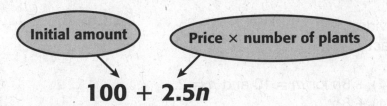

Initial amount   Price × number of plants

$100 + 2.5n$

Evaluate the expression $100 + 2.5n$ by substituting 50 for n.

$$100 + 2.5(50)$$
$$100 + 125$$
$$225$$

There will be $225.00 in Catherine's account if she sells 50 plants.

Evaluate the expression $100 + 2.5n$ for each value of n.

1. $n = 10$ $100 + 2.5(10)$

2. $n = 25$ $100 + 2.5(\ \ )$

3. $n = 75$ $100 + 2.5(\ \ )$

Think and Discuss

4. Explain what n represents.

5. Describe how you evaluated the expression for different values of n.

Holt Mathematics

Name _____ Date _____ Class _____

LESSON
Review for Mastery
1A Variables and Expressions

An **algebraic expression** uses at least one letter, or **variable,** which represents a value that can change.

A number that multiplies a variable is its **coefficient.** A **constant** is a specific number, whose value does not change.

To **evaluate** an algebraic expression, **substitute** a given number for a variable, and find the value of the resulting numerical expression.

Algebraic Expression

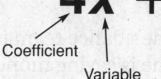

$$4x + 7$$

Coefficient   Variable   Constant

Follow the order of operations:
1. Parentheses
2. Multiply or Divide
3. Add or Subtract

Evaluate $5(m + 1) + 8n$ for $m = 10$ and $n = 2$.

$5(m + 1) + 8n$	
$5(10 + 1) + 8(2)$	Substitute 10 for m and 2 for n.
$5(11) + 8(2)$	Parentheses, simplify inside.
$55 + 16$	Multiply, from left to right.
71	Add.

Complete to evaluate each expression.

1. $9 + 7z$ for $z = 3$

$9 + 7 \cdot$ _____

$9 +$ _____

_____

2. $5(q - 8)$ for $q = 17$

$5 \cdot ($ _____ $- 8)$

$5 \cdot ($ _____ $)$

_____

3. $25 - 2x$ for $x = 8$

$25 - 2 \cdot ($ _____ $)$

$25 -$ _____

_____

4. $2(x + 6) + 4$ for $x = 9$

$2($ _____ $+ 6) + 4$

$2($ _____ $) + 4$

_____ $+ 4$

_____

5. $42 - 3(x + 1)$ for $x = 3$

$42 - 3 \cdot ($ _____ $+ 1)$

$42 - 3 \cdot ($ _____ $)$

$42 -$ _____

_____

6. $22 + 5(2z)$ for $z = 4$

$22 + 5 \cdot (2 \cdot$ _____ $)$

$22 + 5 \cdot ($ _____ $)$

$22 +$ _____

_____

Holt Mathematics

LESSON 1A Homework and Practice
Variables and Expressions

Evaluate each expression for the given value of the variable.

1. $5x - 3$ for $x = 4$

2. $23 - b$ for $b = 16$

_____

_____

3. $\frac{1}{2}y$ for $y = 22$

4. $19 - 3x$ for $x = 6$

_____

_____

5. $7b - 9$ for $b = 9$

6. $8.6 + 9y$ for $y = 7$

_____

_____

7. $78 - 14k$ for $k = 5$

8. $9(a + 3)$ for $a = 6$

_____

_____

Evaluate each expression for the given value of the variables.

9. $3x + y$ for $x = 6$ and $y = 9$

10. $5a - b$ for $a = 6$ and $b = 8$

_____

_____

11. $7m - 8n$ for $m = 10$ and $n = 7$

12. $7r + 6s$ for $r = 12$ and $s = 14$

_____

_____

13. $10(x - y)$ for $x = 14$ and $y = 8$

14. $m(18 - x)$ for $m = 9$ and $x = 6$

_____

_____

A caterer determines $\frac{1}{4}$ pound of roast beef is needed to serve each guest at a party. How many pounds of roast beef are needed for each number of guests?

15. 8 guests   **16.** 12 guests   **17.** 18 guests   **18.** 25 guests

_____   _____   _____   _____

Holt Mathematics

EXPLORATION

1B Algebraic Expressions

Georgia Performance Standards

M8A1.a, M8A1.b

The table shows the prices for different activities at a park.

Activity	Price
Park ride	$1.25 per ride
Jet ski rental	$25.00 + $5.00 per hour
Scooter rental	$10.00 + $2.50 per hour
Bike rental	$5.00 + $2.00 per hour
Bay cruise	$25.00 per person

An algebraic expression for this cost is 1.25r.

Use a variable to write an expression for each cost.

	Activity	Cost	Variable	Expression
	Park ride	$1.25 per ride	r (rides)	1.25r
1.	Jet ski rental	$25.00 + $5.00 per hour	h (hours)	
2.	Scooter rental	$10.00 + $2.50 per hour	h (hours)	
3.	Bike rental	$5.00 + $2.00 per hour	h (hours)	
4.	Bay cruise	$25.00 per person	p (people)	

To find the cost of renting a jet ski for 5 hours, evaluate the expression $25 + 5h$ by substituting 5 for h.

$$25 + 5(5) = 25 + 25 = 50$$

5. Use your expressions from above to evaluate the cost of a 5-hour scooter rental and of a 5-hour bike rental.

Think and Discuss

6. **Describe** a real-world situation in which you might use the expression $50 + 2x$.

7. **Explain** what you need to write an algebraic expression.

Holt Mathematics

Review for Mastery

LESSON 1B *Algebraic Expressions*

What words tell you to add, subtract, multiply, or divide?

Add $n + 6$	**Subtract** $n - 6$	**Multiply** $6n$	**Divide** $n \div 6$
n plus 6	n minus 6	n times 6	n divided by 6
the sum of n and 6	the difference between n and 6	the product of n and 6	the quotient of n and 6
6 added to n	6 subtracted from n	6 multiplied by n	6 equal shares of n
n increased by 6	6 less than n		
	n decreased by 6		

Write the algebraic expression that represents the word expression.

1. the quotient of n and 3

_____

2. 3 more than n

_____

3. the product of 3 and n

_____

4. n decreased by 3

_____

5. 3 less than n

_____

6. the product of n and 3

_____

7. n increased by 3

_____

8. one-third times n

_____

Write a word phrase for each algebraic expression.

9. $4n$

_____

10. $2 + n$

_____

11. $n - 5$

_____

12. $n \div 3$

_____

13. $n + 9$

_____

14. $\dfrac{n}{2}$

_____

Holt Mathematics

Homework and Practice

Writing Algebraic Expressions

Write an expression for each word phrase.

1. a number x divided by 7

2. the sum of 10 and a number n

_____

_____

3. a number b decreased by 14

4. the product of a number x and 8

_____

_____

5. 12 times the difference of a number r and 7

6. 11 minus the product of 5 and a number k

_____

_____

7. a. Grace wants to divide the job of writing x invitations to the party equally among 4 committee members. Write an expression to determine the number of invitations she will have each committee member write.

_____

b. If Grace has 220 invitations for the committee members to write, how many will she have each member write?

_____

Write an algebraic expression and use it to evaluate each word problem.

8. Arturo purchased a package of 50 blank CDs. After he used x CDs, he had x less than 50 CDs remaining. How many CDs did he have left after using 31 CDs?

_____

9. At the grocery store, Henry bought c pounds of cashews for $4.99 per pound. If he buys 2 pounds, how much will they cost?

_____

Holt Mathematics

EXPLORATION

1C Adding Integers

Georgia Performance
Standards

M8A1.b

You can use a thermometer to model addition of integers.

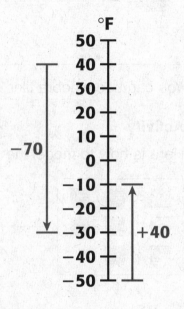

1. Suppose the temperature starts at −50°F and increases 40° during the day. Complete the addition statement to show the new temperature.

$$-50° + 40° = \underline{\quad}$$

2. Suppose the temperature starts at 40°F and drops 70° overnight. Complete the addition statement to show the new temperature.

$$40° + (-70°) = \underline{\quad}$$

Complete the addition statement modeled by each number line.

3. $-4 + \underline{\quad} = 5$

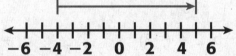

4. $-1 + (\underline{\quad}) = -8$

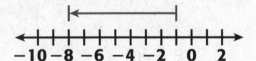

Think and Discuss

5. Explain how to add integers on a number line.

9

Holt Mathematics

LESSON 1C Hands-On Lab
Model Adding Integers

KEY	REMEMBER:
▢ = 1 ▢ = −1	The sum of two or more numbers can be positive, negative, or zero. The sum of an integer and its opposite is zero.

You can use algebra tiles to help you add integers.

Activity

Here is how to model the solution to the problem 3 + (−5).

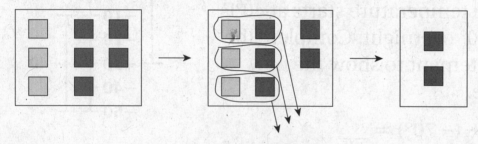

3 + −5   Remove pairs
                that equal zero

1. Use algebra tiles to model and find each sum

a. 4 + (−2) _____   **b.** 2 + (−3) _____   **c.** −3 + 3 _____

d. −2 + 5 _____   **e.** −3 + (−3) _____   **f.** −4 + (−1) _____

Holt Mathematics

LESSON 1C Hands-On Lab
Model Adding Integers, continued

The same technique works with problems involving three or more
addends, such as $-3 + 2 + (-4) + 1$.

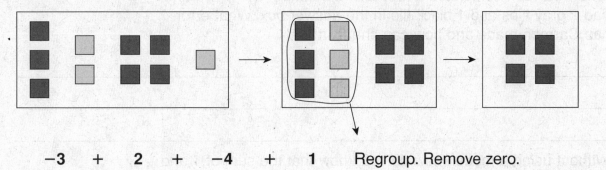

-3 $+$ 2 $+$ -4 $+$ 1 Regroup. Remove zero.

2. Use algebra tiles to model and find each sum

a. $3 + 2 + (-2) + (-2)$ _____   **b.** $2 + (-1) + (-4) + (-2)$ _____

c. $-3 + (-1) + (-2) + (-3)$ _____   **d.** $-2 + (-1) + 3 + (-3) + (-2) + 1$ _____

Holt Mathematics

LESSON 1C

Hands-On Lab

Model Adding Integers, continued

Think and Discuss

1. When Carmen completed a model of the sum of 3 + (−2), she had 2 gray tiles and 1 black tile in the answer box. What error has Carmen made and how can she fix it?

_____

_____

_____

2. Without using a model, how do you know that the sum of 1 and −5 is a negative integer? How can you use this information to check the accuracy of your model?

_____

_____

_____

3. What would you conclude about a sum if all of the algebra tiles were paired off and removed from a model?

_____

4. Can three numbers sum to zero? If so, give an example. If not, explain why not.

_____

Try This

Use algebra tiles to model and find each sum.

1. 5 + (−3) _____   **2.** 2 + (−4) + (−1) _____

3. −1 + 3 + (−2) + (−3) _____   **4.** −1 + (−1) + (−2) + 4 _____

5. −2 + (−4) + (−1) + (−1) _____   **6.** 2 + (−2) + 4 + (−1) + (−2) + 1 _____

Holt Mathematics

Name _____ Date _____ Class _____

Review for Mastery
Adding Integers

You can model integer addition using two-color counters. Use the yellow side for 1 and the red side for −1. Remember that one yellow counter and one red counter are opposites, so their sum is zero.

$7 + 5 =$ Ⓨ Ⓨ Ⓨ Ⓨ Ⓨ Ⓨ Ⓨ = 12 yellow counters = 12
Ⓨ Ⓨ Ⓨ Ⓨ Ⓨ

$7 + (−5) =$ Ⓨ Ⓨ Ⓨ Ⓨ Ⓨ Ⓨ Ⓨ = 2 yellow counters = 2
Ⓡ Ⓡ Ⓡ Ⓡ Ⓡ

$−7 + (−5) =$ Ⓡ Ⓡ Ⓡ Ⓡ Ⓡ Ⓡ Ⓡ = 12 red counters = −12
Ⓡ Ⓡ Ⓡ Ⓡ Ⓡ

$−7 + 5 =$ Ⓡ Ⓡ Ⓡ Ⓡ Ⓡ Ⓡ Ⓡ = 2 red counters = −2
Ⓨ Ⓨ Ⓨ Ⓨ Ⓨ

If the given integers were added, state whether the result would be positive or negative.

1. $−4 + (−6)$　　　　**2.** $−3 + 8$　　　　**3.** $−5 + 2$

_____　　　　_____　　　　_____

Notice if the counters are the same color, you add the absolute values of the integers. The answer is the sign of the integers. If the counters are both colors, you subtract the absolute values of the integers. Use the sign of the integer with the greater absolute value.

To add the given integers, state whether you need to add or subtract absolute values.

4. $8 + 3$　　　　　　**5.** $−4 + (−1)$　　　　**6.** $3 + (−6)$

_____　　　　_____　　　　_____

Complete to find each sum.　　**7.** $5 + (−9) = ?$　　**8.** $−6 + (−4) = ?$

Are the signs the same or different?　_____　_____

Which sign will you use for the sum?　_____　_____

Will you add or subtract absolute values?　_____　_____

Write the sum.　_____　_____

Holt Mathematics

Name _____ Date _____ Class _____

Homework and Practice
Adding Integers

Use a number line to find the sum.

1. 2 + 3

2. −5 + 3

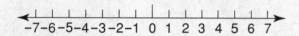

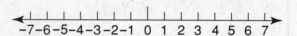

_____

_____

Add.

3. −6 + 15   **4.** −28 + (−7)   **5.** 31 + (−19)   **6.** −34 + 21

_____   _____   _____   _____

Evaluate each expression for the given value of the variables.

7. a + 9 for a = 5   **8.** x + 7 for x = 8   **9.** y + 6 for y = 13

_____   _____   _____

10. −5 + r for r = −7   **11.** −9 + w for w = −12   **12.** m + 8 for m = −11

_____   _____   _____

13. −6 + k for k = −9   **14.** t + (−5) for t = −8   **15.** b + (−7) for b = −7

_____   _____   _____

16. −11 + x for x = 15   **17.** g + (−15) for g = 15   **18.** −16 + j for j = −18

_____   _____   _____

19. The music club had 328 members. This year 103 new members
joined. How many members does the music club have now?

_____

20. Rosetta is playing a board game with her friends. She rolls
doubles of five on her first roll of the number cubes. If a player
rolls doubles, they roll again after moving forward. However if
they roll doubles again they must move backwards. Rosetta rolls
doubles of six on her second roll. How many spaces is Rosetta
from her starting place?

_____

Holt Mathematics

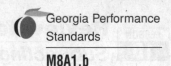
Georgia Performance
Standards

M8A1.b

1D Subtracting Integers

You can use a number line to model subtracting integers.

To subtract 10 from 50, begin at the number being subtracted, 10, and count the number of units to the number 50.

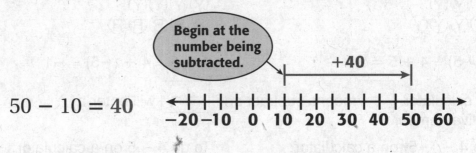

$$50 - 10 = 40$$

The direction is **right,** so the difference is **positive.**

To subtract -10 from -70, begin at the number being subtracted, -10, and count the number of units to the number -70.

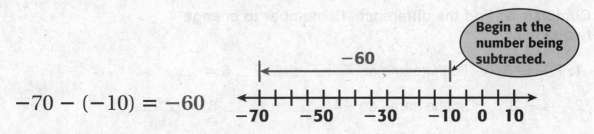

$$-70 - (-10) = -60$$

The direction is **left,** so the difference is **negative.**

Use the number line to complete each subtraction statement.

1. $5 - (-4) =$ ___

2. $-8 - (-1) =$ ___

Think and Discuss

3. Discuss a different strategy for subtracting integers.

15

Holt Mathematics

Name _____ Date _____ Class _____

To subtract one integer from another, rewrite the subtraction as the
addition of an opposite. Then use the rules for adding integers.

$4 - (-5)$ **Subtracting a Negative** $4 - 5$ **Subtracting a Positive**
Change subtraction to $4 - (+5)$ Change subtraction to
$4 + (+5)$ addition of a positive. $4 + (-5)$ addition of a negative.

ⓎⓎⓎⓎ   ⓎⓎⓎⓎ
ⓎⓎⓎⓎⓎ   ⓇⓇⓇⓇⓇ

$4 - (-5) = 4 + 5 = 9$ $4 - 5 = 4 + (-5) = -1$

On a calculator, ⎯ means subtract and +/− will enter a
negative number.

To do $4 - (-5)$ on a calculator: To do $4 - 5$ on a calculator:

Input: 4 ⎯ 5 +/− =   Input: 4 ⎯ 5 =

Display: 9   Display: -1

**Complete to find the difference. Remember to change
two signs.**

1. $7 - (-6)$ is the same as 7 _____ _____ 6 = _____

2. $-4 - 3$ is the same as -4 _____ _____ 3 = _____

3. $-2 - (-9)$ is the same as -2 _____ _____ 9 = _____

4. $14 - 16$ is the same as 14 _____ _____ 16 = _____

5. $7 - (-10)$ is the same as 7 _____ _____ 10 = _____

6. $-8 - (-19)$ is the same as -8 _____ _____ 19 = _____

7. $-5 - 12$ is the same as -5 _____ _____ 12 = _____

Find each difference. Use a calculator to check.

8. $7 - 12 =$ _____   **9.** $-3 - 8 =$ _____   **10.** $17 - (-4) =$ _____

11. $-14 - (-3) =$ _____   **12.** $5 - 8 =$ _____   **13.** $-6 - 4 =$ _____

Holt Mathematics

Homework and Practice

LESSON
1D

Subtracting Integers

Subtract.

1. 9 − 3

_____

2. 12 − 4

_____

3. 9 − 16

_____

4. 19 − 12

_____

5. 7 − 15

_____

6. 18 − 4

_____

7. −8 − 12

_____

8. −11 − 14

_____

9. 25 − 49

_____

10. 18 − 36

_____

11. −101 − 52

_____

12. −76 − (−12)

_____

Evaluate each expression for the given value of the variables.

13. $a − 10$ for $a = 7$

_____

14. $x − 13$ for $x = 20$

_____

15. $17 − y$ for $y = 6$

_____

16. $15 + b$ for $b = −9$

_____

17. $14 − t$ for $t = −18$

_____

18. $d − 24$ for $d = −17$

_____

19. $−16 − w$ for $w = −15$

_____

20. $−10 − r$ for $r = −22$

_____

21. $−14 − g$ for $g = −19$

_____

22. $x − (−18)$ for $x = −25$

_____

23. $y − (−14)$ for $y = −14$

_____

24. $n − (−17)$ for $n = 21$

_____

25. The largest island in the world is Greenland with an area of
839,999 square miles. The second largest island is New Guinea
with an area of 316,615 square miles. What is the difference in
the areas of the two islands?

_____

26. Justin weighed 223 pounds and lost 45 pounds. What is Justin's
new weight?

_____

Holt Mathematics

1E Solving Equations by Adding or Subtracting

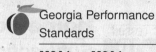

Georgia Performance Standards

M8A1.a, M8A1.c

Evaluate the expressions for each given value of *x*.

1.

x	*x* + 1
0	
1	
2	
3	

2.

x	*x* − 2
3	
4	
5	
6	

Each expression below has been evaluated. Find the value of *x*.

3.

x	*x* + 2
	3
	4
	5
	6

4.

x	*x* − 5
	0
	1
	2
	3

Think and Discuss

5. Explain how you evaluated the expressions in Problems 1 and 2.

6. Explain how you found the values of *x* in Problems 3 and 4.

Holt Mathematics

LESSON 1E Hands-On Lab
Model Solving Equations by Subtracting

KEY		REMEMBER:
▢ = 1	▯ = x	It will not change the value of an equation if you subtract the same number from each side.
▪ = −1		

You can use algebra tiles to help you solve equations.

Activity

To solve the equation $x + 3 = 5$, you need x alone on one side of the equal sign. You can achieve this goal by adding −3 to the left side of the equation. You can perform this operation if you add −3 to the right side as well.

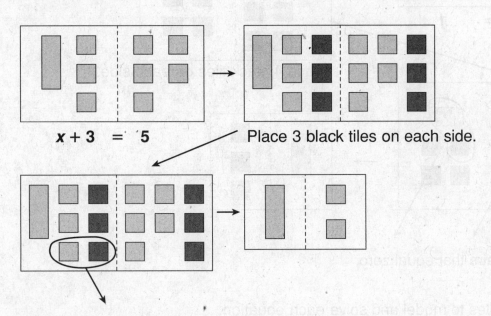

$x + 3 = 5$ Place 3 black tiles on each side.

Each black/gray pair equals zero.

Holt Mathematics

Hands-On Lab

LESSON 1E *Model Solving Equations by Subtracting, continued*

1. Use algebra tiles to model and solve each equation

a. $x + 2 = 4$ _____

b. $x + 3 = 5$ _____

c. $x + 1 = 5$ _____

d. $5 + x = 6$ _____

The same technique works to model the solution to the equation
$x + 4 = 1$, where there are fewer tiles on the right side than the left.

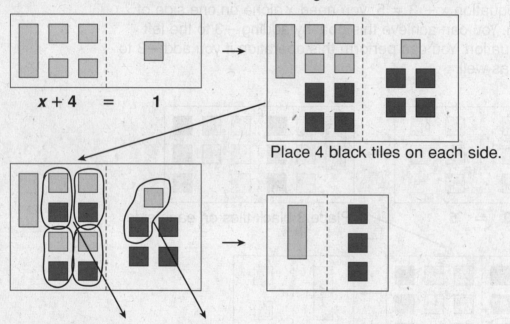

$x + 4 = 1$

Place 4 black tiles on each side.

Remove all pairs that equal zero.

2. Use algebra tiles to model and solve each equation.

a. $x + 4 = 3$ _____

b. $x + 5 = 2$ _____

c. $x + 3 = 1$ _____

d. $x + 3 = 3$ _____

Holt Mathematics

LESSON 1E **Hands-On Lab**
Model Solving Equations by Subtracting, continued

Think and Discuss

1. How do you know how many black tiles to place on each side?

   _____

   _____

2. Why is it important to add the same number of black tiles to both sides of the model?

   _____

   _____

3. Why are you allowed to remove pairs of black and gray tiles from the model?

   _____

4. How is solving the equation $x + 1 = 3$ different from solving $x + 3 = 1$? How is it the same?

   _____

   _____

   _____

Try This

Use algebra tiles to model and solve each equation.

1. $x + 1 = 2$ _____   2. $x + 3 = 5$ _____   3. $x + 2 = 7$ _____

4. $x + 3 = 2$ _____   5. $x + 4 = 2$ _____   6. $x + 2 = 1$ _____

7. $x + 1 = -1$ _____   8. $x + 1 = 0$ _____   9. $x + 2 = -1$ _____

Holt Mathematics

LESSON 1E

Review for Mastery
Solving Equations by Adding or Subtracting

To solve an addition equation, use subtraction.

Solve $x + 5 = 12$.

$$
\begin{array}{rr}
x + 5 = & 12 \\
-5 \quad & -5 \\
\hline
x = & 7
\end{array}
$$

Subtract the number added to the variable.

To solve a subtraction equation, use addition.

Solve $9 = w - 3$.

$$
\begin{array}{rr}
9 = & w - 3 \\
+3 \quad & +3 \\
\hline
12 = & w
\end{array}
$$

Add the number subtracted from the variable.

Tell what you would add or subtract to solve the equation.

1. $a + 2 = 7$ **2.** $x - 2 = 4$ **3.** $6 + y = 9$ **4.** $34 = b + 13$

_____   _____   _____   _____

5. $21 = z - 9$ **6.** $14 + r = 20$ **7.** $18 = d - 11$ **8.** $6 = 5 + p$

_____   _____   _____   _____

Complete to solve the equation. In Exercises 9–11 check the solution.

9.
$$
\begin{array}{rr}
x - 2 = & 15 \\
+2 \quad & +2 \\
\hline
\end{array}
$$

$x - \underline{\ \ } \overset{?}{=} \underline{\ \ }$

$x \overset{?}{=} \underline{\ \ }$

Check: $x - 2 = 15$

$\underline{\ \ } - 2 \overset{?}{=} 15$

$\underline{\ \ } \overset{?}{=} 15\ \checkmark$

10.
$$
\begin{array}{rr}
z + 6 = & 14 \\
\hline
\end{array}
$$

$z + \underline{\ \ } \overset{?}{=} \underline{\ \ }$

$z \overset{?}{=} \underline{\ \ }$

Check: $z + 6 = 14$

$\underline{\ \ } + 6 \overset{?}{=} 14$

$\underline{\ \ } \overset{?}{=} 14\ \checkmark$

11.
$$
\begin{array}{rr}
7 = & 4 + n \\
\hline
\end{array}
$$

$\underline{\ \ } \overset{?}{=} \underline{\ \ } + n$

$\underline{\ \ } \overset{?}{=} n$

Check: $7 = 4 + n$

$7 \overset{?}{=} 4 + \underline{\ \ }$

$7 \overset{?}{=} \underline{\ \ }\ \checkmark$

12.
$$
\begin{array}{rr}
t + 5 = & 16 \\
\hline
\end{array}
$$

$t + \underline{\ \ } = \underline{\ \ }$

$t = \underline{\ \ }$

13.
$$
\begin{array}{rr}
a - 7 = & 13 \\
\hline
\end{array}
$$

$a - \underline{\ \ } = \underline{\ \ }$

$a = \underline{\ \ }$

14.
$$
\begin{array}{rr}
28 = & 9 + b \\
\hline
\end{array}
$$

$\underline{\ \ } = \underline{\ \ } + b$

$\underline{\ \ } = b$

Holt Mathematics

Name _____ Date _____ Class _____

Homework and Practice
Solving Equations by Adding or Subtracting

Determine which value is a solution of the equation.

1. $x - 8 = 14$; $x = 6, 20,$ or 22

_____

2. $8 + a = 19$; $a = 7, 11,$ or 27

_____

3. $y - 14 = 22$; $y = 8, 12,$ or 36

_____

4. $d + 17 = 52$; $d = 25, 35,$ or 69

_____

Solve.

5. $m - 9 = 14$

_____

6. $7 + x = 16$

_____

7. $k + 12 = 31$

_____

8. $y - 14 = 46$

_____

9. $13 + r = 29$

_____

10. $17 + t = 19$

_____

11. $b + 39 = 57$

_____

12. $p + 27 = 27$

_____

13. $0 = w - 45$

_____

14. $8.7 + s = 12.1$

_____

15. $x - 3.7 = 0.8$

_____

16. $n - 3.41 = 5.40$

_____

17. The school library is combining books from two storage units into a newly designed area for the library. The first original unit held 186 books and the second unit had 307 books. Write and solve an equation to find the number of books in the new area of the library.

_____

18. Amelia wanted to buy a new computer and printer which had a total cost of $1099.95. She had saved $389.85 for her purchase. How much more does she need to save to buy the computer and printer she wants?

_____

Holt Mathematics

Georgia Performance Standards

M8A1.a, M8A1.c

1F Solving Equations by Multiplying or Dividing

Evaluate the expressions for each given value of x.

1.

x	$2x$
0	
1	
2	
3	

2.

x	$\dfrac{x}{2}$
0	
2	
4	
6	

Each expression below has been evaluated. Find the value of x.

3.

x	$3x$
	3
	6
	9
	12

4.

x	$\dfrac{x}{4}$
	0
	1
	2
	3

Think and Discuss

5. **Explain** how you evaluated the expressions in Problems 1 and 2.

6. **Explain** how you found the values of x in Problems 3 and 4.

Holt Mathematics

LESSON
1F # Hands-On Lab
Model Solving Equations by Dividing

KEY	REMEMBER:
▢ = 1 ▪ = −1 ▯ = x	It will not change the value of an equation if you divide both sides by the same number.

You can use algebra tiles to help you solve equations.

Activity

To solve the equation $2x = 4$, you need x alone on one side of the equal sign. You can achieve this goal by dividing the left side of the equation by 2. You can divide as long as you divide the same way on both sides.

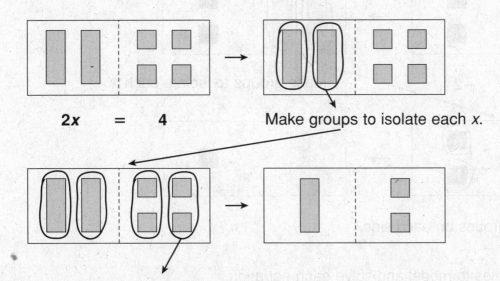

$2x = 4$ Make groups to isolate each x.

Make the same number of groups.

25   **Holt Mathematics**

LESSON 1F Hands-On Lab
Model Solving Equations by Dividing, continued

1. Use algebra tiles to model and solve each equation.

a. $2x = 8$ _____   **b.** $3x = 9$ _____

c. $4x = 8$ _____   **d.** $2x = 6$ _____

Solving the equation $2x = -2$ is not much different. You can use tiles to represent negative numbers just as you can use them for positive numbers. Once you set up the equation using the x-tiles and the negative tiles, the method for solving is the same.

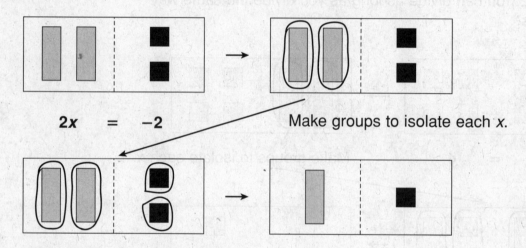

$2x \quad = \quad -2$ Make groups to isolate each x.

Make equal groups on each side.

2. Use algebra tiles to model and solve each equation.

a. $3x = -6$ _____   **b.** $4x = -4$ _____

c. $2x = -4$ _____   **d.** $3x = -9$ _____

Holt Mathematics

LESSON
1F # Hands-On Lab
Model Solving Equations by Dividing, continued

Think and Discuss

1. When you group tiles, how do you know how many groups to make?

   _____

   _____

2. How is solving the equation $2x = 4$ different from solving $2x = -4$? How is it the same?

   _____

   _____

3. Write an equation with a positive solution that would require you to make 3 groups.

   _____

4. Explain how you would model a solution to the equation $2x = -6$.

   _____

   _____

   _____

Try This

Use algebra tiles to model and solve each equation.

1. $2x = 6$ _____

2. $3x = 6$ _____

3. $4x = 12$ _____

4. $2x = -8$ _____

5. $4x = -4$ _____

6. $4x = -12$ _____

7. $3x = -6$ _____

8. $2x = 8$ _____

9. $4x = -8$ _____

Holt Mathematics

Review for Mastery

LESSON 1F

Solving Equations by Multiplying or Dividing

To solve a multiplication equation, use division.

Solve $3x = 24$.

$$3x = 24$$
$$\frac{3x}{3} = \frac{24}{3}$$
$$x = 8$$

To solve a division equation, use multiplication.

Solve $\frac{x}{4} = 20$.

$$\frac{x}{4} = 20$$
$$4 \cdot \frac{x}{4} = 20 \cdot 4$$
$$x = 80$$

When an equation has two operations, undo addition or subtraction first. Then undo multiplication or division.

Solve $2x + 11 = 35$.

$$
\begin{array}{rl}
2x + 11 = & 35 \\
\underline{-11} \quad & \underline{-11} \quad \text{Undo the addition.} \\
2x = & 24 \\
\frac{2x}{2} = & \frac{24}{2} \quad \text{Undo the multiplication.} \\
x = & 12
\end{array}
$$

Tell what number you would multiply or divide by to solve the equation.

1. $5a = 60$

2. $\frac{x}{6} = 12$

3. $144 = 12f$

_____   _____   _____

Solve.

4. $6x = 42$

$$\frac{6x}{\underline{\quad}} = \frac{42}{\underline{\quad}}$$

$$x = \underline{\quad}$$

5. $\frac{a}{3} = 9$

$$\underline{\quad} \cdot \frac{a}{3} = 9 \cdot \underline{\quad}$$

$$a = \underline{\quad}$$

6. $25 = \frac{k}{5}$

$$\underline{\quad} \cdot 25 = \frac{k}{5} \cdot \underline{\quad}$$

$$\underline{\quad} = k$$

7. $2x + 3 = 11$

___ ___

$$\frac{2x}{\underline{\quad}} = \frac{\underline{\quad}}{\underline{\quad}}$$

$$x = \underline{\quad}$$

8. $\frac{b}{4} + 5 = 6$

___ ___

$$\underline{\quad} \cdot \frac{b}{4} = \underline{\quad} \cdot \underline{\quad}$$

$$b = \underline{\quad}$$

9. $5t - 9 = 36$

___ ___

$$\frac{5t}{\underline{\quad}} = \frac{\underline{\quad}}{\underline{\quad}}$$

$$t = \underline{\quad}$$

Holt Mathematics

LESSON 1F Homework and Practice
Solving Equations by Multiplying or Dividing

Solve.

1. $-x + 8 = 3$

2. $\dfrac{y}{3} - 4 = 9$

3. $7w = 35$

_____

_____

_____

4. $\dfrac{n}{-2} = 8$

5. $-8 + 5t = -6$

6. $\dfrac{a}{-6} = 7$

_____

_____

_____

7. $-9 + 3k = -15$

8. $-9d = 36$

9. $\dfrac{c}{4} - 8 = -17$

_____

_____

_____

10. $\dfrac{m}{7} = 8$

11. $-8 + \dfrac{b}{5} = -11$

12. $-2x - 19 = 19$

_____

_____

_____

13. $-5x = 65$

14. $\dfrac{r}{-6} = -4$

15. $\dfrac{h}{-5} - 17 = -12$

_____

_____

_____

16. $\dfrac{x}{-6} = -6$

17. $3s - 15 = -15$

18. $-64 = -8v$

_____

_____

_____

19. Peter went camping and rode his mountain bike 52 miles. This was 4 times as many miles as he rides in a normal week. How many miles does Peter ride in a normal week?

_____

20. Mr. Otten saved $32 each week for 26 weeks. How much did he save in that time?

_____

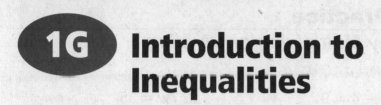

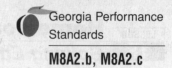

Georgia Performance
Standards

M8A2.b, M8A2.c

1G Introduction to Inequalities

To raise money for a school trip, Angela sells cookies for $2.50 per box. She has to raise at least $100 from the cookie sales in order to go on the trip.

1. Which of the numbers of boxes of cookies shown gives Angela the following amounts of money?

   a. Less than her goal of $100

   b. Exactly $100

   c. More than her goal of $100

25 boxes
30 boxes
40 boxes
50 boxes

2. Name another number of boxes that Angela could sell that would give her less than her goal of $100.

3. Name another number of boxes that Angela could sell that would give her more than her goal of $100.

Think and Discuss

4. **Describe** the strategies you used to solve Problem 1.

5. **Explain** how you found numbers of boxes in order to solve Problems 2 and 3.

Holt Mathematics

Review for Mastery

LESSON 1G *Introduction to Inequalities*

A **solution of an inequality** is a number that makes the inequality true. An inequality usually has more than one solution. All the solutions are contained in the **solution set.**

As with equations, solve a simple inequality by using inverse operations to isolate the variable.

Solve and graph $x + 4 > 9$.

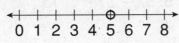
0 1 2 3 4 5 6 7 8

Draw an open circle at 5 to show that 5 is not included in the solution set.

$$x + 4 > 9$$
$$\underline{-4 \quad -4} \quad \text{Subtract 4.}$$
$$x > 5$$

0 1 2 3 4 5 6 7 8

Draw an arrow to the right of 5 to show that all numbers greater than 5 are included in the solutions.

According to the graph, 6 should be a solution and 4 should not be a solution.

Check:

$$x + 4 > 9 \qquad\qquad x + 4 > 9$$
$$6 + 4 \overset{?}{>} 9 \qquad\qquad 4 + 4 \overset{?}{>} 9$$
$$10 > 9 \qquad\qquad\quad 8 \not> 9$$

So, 6 *is* in the solution set and 4 *is not* in the solution set.
Thus, the solution set for the inequality $x + 4 > 9$ is $x > 5$.

Write *true* or *false*.

1. $7 < 4$

_____

2. $0 \leq 9$

_____

3. $-3 > 4$

_____

Using the variable *n*, write the inequality shown by each graph.

4.
0 1 2 3 4 5 6 7 8

_____

5.
-7 -6 -5 -4 -3 -2 -1 0 1

_____

Complete. Is the given value in the solution set? Answer *is* or *is not*.

6. 3 _____ in the solution set of $x - 1 > 5$.

$$x - 1 > 5$$
$$\underline{\quad} - 1 \overset{?}{>} 5$$
$$\underline{\quad\quad} > 5$$

7. 0 _____ in the solution set of $z + (-4) \geq -4$.

$$z + (-4) \geq -4$$
$$\underline{\quad} + (-4) \geq -4$$
$$\underline{\quad} \geq -4$$

8. 14 _____ in the solution set of $w + 10 \leq 25$.

$$w + 10 \leq 25$$
$$\underline{\quad} + 10 \leq 25$$
$$\underline{\quad} \leq 25$$

Holt Mathematics

Name _____ Date _____ Class _____

Homework and Practice
Solving Simple Inequalities

Use <, >, or = to compare each inequality.

1. 8 + 13 ☐ 20

2. 23 ☐ 3(7)

3. 28 − 9 ☐ 18

4. 67 ☐ 9(8)

5. 52 − 37 ☐ 15

6. 78 ☐ 12(6)

Solve and graph each inequality.

7. x + 3 > 7

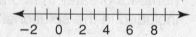

_____

8. y − 5 ≤ 1

_____

9. 4n ≥ 20

_____

10. h − 1 ≥ 6

_____

11. $\frac{x}{5}$ < 3

_____

12. $\frac{t}{3}$ ≥ 4

_____

13. 9d > 45

_____

14. 17 + m < 23

_____

15. 128 ≥ 16x

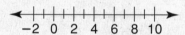

_____

16. Philippe wants to drink at least 72 ounces of water every day while at work. He works 6 hours a day. How many ounces of water must Philippe drink each hour? Write and solve an inequality to answer the question.

_____

17. Glynn's car has a 18 gallon gas tank. He travels 450 miles. What is the least miles per gallon Glynn's car will get on this trip? Write and solve an inequality to answer the question.

_____

Holt Mathematics

**EXPLORATION**

1H Solving for a Variable

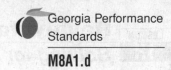Georgia Performance Standards

M8A1.d

Melanie wants to plant a rectangular vegetable garden. She wants the area of the garden to be 24 ft². The formula for the area of a rectangle is $A = \ell w$, so Melanie can use $24 = \ell w$ to find possible lengths and widths for her garden.

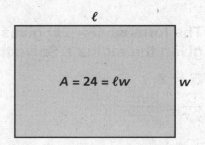

1. Melanie considers several different lengths for the plot. Complete the table to show the width for each possible length.

Length ℓ (ft)	Width w (ft)	Area A (ft²)
2	12	24
3		24
4		24
6		24
8		24

2. Explain how you found each width.

3. Write an equation that gives the width w of the plot for any length ℓ.

Think and Discuss

4. **Describe** how the equation you wrote in Problem 3 is related to the original equation $24 = \ell w$.

5. **Explain** how you can use your equation to find the width of Melanie's garden if the length is 12 feet.

6. **Explain** how to solve the equation $A = \ell w$ for ℓ.

Holt Mathematics

Review for Mastery

LESSON 1H

Solving for a Variable

Solving for a variable in a formula can make it easier to use the formula. To solve a formula for a variable, use inverse operations to isolate the variable.

The formula $C = 2\pi r$ gives the circumference of a circle C given the radius r. Solve the formula for r.

$C = 2\pi r$	r is multiplied by 2π.
$\dfrac{C}{2\pi} = \dfrac{2\pi r}{2\pi}$	Divide both sides by 2π.
$\dfrac{C}{2\pi} = r$	Simplify.

Solve the formula for V.

$B = V - 10$	10 is subtracted from V.
$B + 10 = V - 10 + 10$	Add 10 to both sides.
$B + 10 = V$	Simplify.

State the inverse operation to perform when solving for the indicated variable.

1. $P = 4s$; for s _____

2. $y = x + z$; for x _____

3. $d - 2r = 0$; for d _____

The formula for distance traveled is $d = rt$, where r is the rate of travel and t is the time spent traveling.

4. Solve the formula for t. _____

5. A car travels at a rate of 60 miles/hr over a distance of 240 miles. How much time does the trip take? _____

Holt Mathematics

Review for Mastery

LESSON 1H *Solving for a Variable   continued*

Solving for a variable sometimes requires two or more inverse operations.

The formula $P = 2\ell + 2w$ gives the perimeter of a rectangle P with length ℓ and width w. Solve the formula for w.

$$P = 2\ell + 2w$$
$$P - 2\ell = 2\ell + 2w - 2\ell \qquad \text{Subtract } 2\ell \text{ from both sides.}$$
$$P - 2\ell = 2w$$
$$\frac{P - 2\ell}{2} = \frac{2w}{2} \qquad \text{Divide both sides by 2.}$$
$$\frac{P - 2\ell}{2} = w \qquad \text{Simplify.}$$

State the inverse operation to perform when solving for the indicated variable.

6. $3d + f = 0$; for d _____

7. $\frac{a}{3} - b = c$; for a _____

8. $\frac{h - j}{k} = 2$; for h _____

The formula $F = \frac{9}{5}C + 32$ converts a temperature C in degrees Celsius to the corresponding temperature F in degrees Fahrenheit.

9. Solve the formula for C. _____

10. The temperature on a summer day is 77°F. Find the temperature in degrees Celsius. _____

Holt Mathematics

LESSON 1H Homework and Practice
Solving for a Variable

State the first inverse operation to perform when solving for the indicated variable.

1. $-3f = g$; for f _____

2. $D = \frac{m}{v}$; for m _____

3. $\frac{n}{2} + p = 1$; for n _____

Solve each formula for the indicated variable.

4. $K = C + 273$ for C 5. $\frac{a}{b} = d$ for a 6. $y = mx + b$ for m

_____   _____   _____

7. The formula $A = \frac{1}{2}bh$ gives the area of a triangle.
   Solve the formula for b.   _____

8. The formula for the volume of a pyramid is $V = \frac{1}{3}Bh$. V is the
   volume, B is the area of the base, and h is the height of the
   pyramid.

   a. Solve the formula for h.   _____

   b. A pyramid has a volume of 12 cm³
      and a base with area 9 cm². What
      is the height of the pyramid?   _____

9. The formula $c = 5p + 215$ gives the total cost in dollars, c, for
   hosting a birthday party at a miniature golf course. p is the total
   number of people attending the party.

   a. Solve the formula for p.   _____

   b. If Jonas's parents are willing to
      spend $300 for a party, how
      many people can attend?   _____

Holt Mathematics

Answer these questions to summarize the important concepts from Chapter 1 in your own words.

1. Explain why $|7| = |-7|$.

2. Explain how to add integers when the signs are the same and when the signs are different.

3. Explain how to subtract integers.

4. Explain how to multiply and divide two integers.

5. Explain the difference between an open circle and a solid circle when graphing inequalities.

For more review of Chapter 1:

- Complete the Chapter 1 Study Guide and Review on pages 52–54 of your textbook.

- Complete the Ready to Go On quizzes on pages 30 and 48 of your textbook.

Holt Mathematics

Project
Rational Numbers: Eat Up

Career: Nutritionist

Nutritionists use their knowledge of the nutrient content of food to help promote healthful eating. Together with food scientists, they develop guidelines for people who must follow medically necessary diets as well as for people who just want to improve their eating habits.

In this chapter project...you will calculate the amount of nutrients you would get from a junk food diet. You will:

• Use the nutrition information label on junk food (for example, packages of chips or cookies) to determine how much vitamins and nutrients you get from eating them.

• Research the daily requirements for those vitamins and nutrients.

• Calculate how much junk food you would need to eat to satisfy the daily minimum requirements for the vitamins and nutrients and graph your results.

To get started, work through the Food for Thought worksheet on the next page.

This chapter project reinforces your understanding of these Georgia Performance Standards:

M8A1.a Represent a given situation using algebraic expressions or equations in one variable.

M8P5.a Create and use representations to organize, record, and communicate mathematical ideas.

---

go.hrw.com
Chapter Project Online
KEYWORD: MT7 Ch2

Holt Mathematics

CHAPTER 2

Project Recording Sheet
Rational Numbers

Food For Thought

Nutritionists work in many situations in the development and use of foods. One of the nutrients that have been studied is sodium, which is part of common table salt. The recommendations for amounts of sodium are Girls and Boys 9–13: 1900–3000 mg; Girls 14–18: 3000 mg; Boys 14–18: 2400–2700 mg

The chart lists the sodium content of some common food products.

Prepared Food	Sodium Content (mg)	Prepared Food	Sodium Content (mg)
Barbeque beans	570	Oatmeal cookies	150
Chicken noodle soup	890	Orange juice	0
Chili, canned	1220	Pasta sauce	500
Ice cream	35	Peas, canned	390
Cranberry juice	35	Peas, frozen	105
Donuts, powdered	280	Potato chips	180
French fries, frozen	270	Spaghetti, dry	10
Fruit cocktail	10	Sports drink	110
Hot dogs, beef	570	Turkey, sliced	300
Ketchup	190	Vegetable juice	630
Mustard	55	Waffle, frozen	420

Create some meals that meet the following requirements:

- 100% of the daily sodium requirement for your gender and age
- a low-sodium meal with $\frac{1}{2}$ of the normal requirement
- a meal with $\frac{3}{4}$ of the normal requirements
- a breakfast that contains about $\frac{1}{3}$ of your requirements
- a meal that contains at least twice as much sodium as the recommended daily requirement

Research: What other nutrients are important for good health? What are the daily minimum requirements? Create a chart that shows your results.

Holt Mathematics

2A Adding and Subtracting Rational Numbers

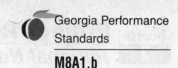

Georgia Performance
Standards

M8A1.b

Beckie has $454.96 in a checking account. She needs to pay bills in the amounts $25.95, $313.00, $45.76, and $87.95.

Beckie estimates the following:

Account: $454.96 ≈ $455.00

Bills: $25.95 ≈ $ 25.00
              $313.00 = $310.00
                $45.76 ≈ $ 45.00
                $87.95 ≈ $ 90.00
                          $470.00

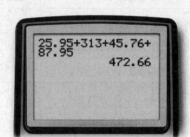

Beckie determines that she does not have enough money in her account to pay her bills. She then checks her estimate with a calculator.

Estimate the solution to each expression in the table. Then use a calculator to solve.

		Estimate	Actual
1.	120 − 9.8		
2.	45 − 17.8 + 15.9 + 16.1 − 1.07		
3.	88.10 + 109.85		
4.	34.12 − 18.30 + 65.25		

Think and Discuss

5. Describe the estimation strategies you used.

Holt Mathematics

LESSON 2A **Hands-On Lab**
Adding and Subtracting Rational Numbers

Activity

Susi is a dolphin who likes to jump. She jumps $5\frac{1}{2}$ feet out of the water. Then she falls back into the water, covering a total distance of $9\frac{1}{4}$ feet. How far is Susi now below the water's surface?

Draw Susi's jumps.

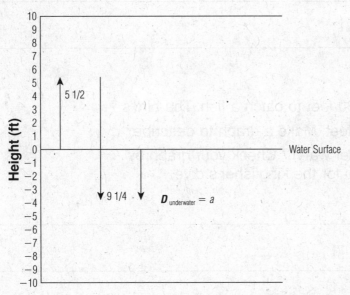

The graph shows that the dolphin is $3\frac{3}{4}$ feet under water.

Check your graph by writing and evaluating an expression for Susi's jumps:

$$D_{\text{underwater}} = 5\frac{1}{2} + \left(-9\frac{1}{4}\right) = \frac{11}{2} - \frac{37}{4} = \frac{22}{4} - \frac{37}{4} = -\frac{15}{4} = -3\frac{3}{4}$$

Holt Mathematics

Hands-On Lab
Adding and Subtracting Rational Numbers, continued

Think and Discuss

Susi continues to dive 50 more feet to the bottom of the ocean. How deep is the ocean and how do you know?

_____

_____

_____

Try This

A kingfisher dives from a height of 30 feet to catch a fish. The bird's dive covers a total distance of $40\frac{1}{3}$ feet. Make a graph to describe the situation. How far is the fish under water? Check your graph by writing and evaluating an expression for the kingfisher's dive.

_____

_____

_____

Holt Mathematics

Name _____ Date _____ Class _____

Review for Mastery
Adding and Subtracting Rational Numbers

To add fractions that have the same denominator:
- Use the common denominator for the sum.
- Add the numerators to get the numerator of the sum.
- Write the sum in simplest form.

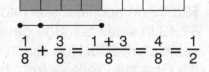

$$\frac{1}{8} + \frac{3}{8} = \frac{1+3}{8} = \frac{4}{8} = \frac{1}{2}$$

To subtract fractions that have the same denominator:
- Use the common denominator for the difference.
- Subtract the numerators.
    Subtraction is addition of an opposite.
- Write the difference in simplest form.

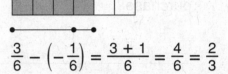

$$\frac{3}{6} - \left(-\frac{1}{6}\right) = \frac{3+1}{6} = \frac{4}{6} = \frac{2}{3}$$

Complete to add the fractions.

1. $\frac{3}{14} + \frac{4}{14} =$ _____ = _____

2. $\frac{2}{10} + \left(-\frac{4}{10}\right) =$ _____ = _____

3. $-\frac{5}{12} + \left(-\frac{3}{12}\right) =$ _____ = _____

Complete to subtract the fractions.

4. $\frac{8}{9} - \frac{2}{9} =$ _____ = _____

5. $\frac{9}{15} - \left(-\frac{3}{15}\right) =$ _____ = _____

6. $-\frac{10}{24} - \left(-\frac{2}{24}\right) =$ _____ = _____

To add or subtract decimals, line up the decimal points and then
add or subtract from right to left as usual.

12.83	35.78
+24.17	−14.55
37.00	21.23

Complete to add the decimals.

7. $14.23 + 3.56 =$ _____

8. $44.02 + 8.07 =$ _____

9. $1.39 + 13.6 =$ _____

Complete to subtract the decimals.

10. $124.33 - 13.16 =$ _____

11. $33.47 - 0.6 =$ _____

12. $25.15 - 25.06 =$ _____

Holt Mathematics

Homework and Practice

LESSON 2A *Adding and Subtracting Rational Numbers*

1. Gretchen bought a sweater for $23.89. In addition, she had to pay $1.43 in sales tax. She gave the sales clerk $30. How much change did Gretchen receive from her total purchase?

_____

2. Jacob is replacing the molding around two sides of a picture frame. The measurements of the sides of the frame are $4\frac{3}{16}$ in. and $2\frac{5}{16}$ in. What length of molding will Jacob need?

_____

Use a number line to find each sum.

3. $-0.5 + 0.4$

_____

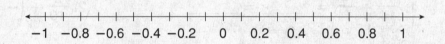

4. $-\frac{2}{7} + \frac{6}{7}$

_____

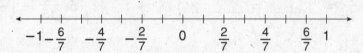

Add or subtract. Simplify.

5. $\frac{3}{8} + \frac{1}{8}$

6. $-\frac{1}{10} + \frac{7}{10}$

7. $\frac{5}{14} - \frac{3}{14}$

8. $\frac{4}{15} + \frac{7}{15}$

_____   _____   _____   _____

9. $\frac{5}{18} - \frac{7}{18}$

10. $-\frac{8}{17} - \frac{2}{17}$

11. $-\frac{1}{16} + \frac{5}{16}$

12. $\frac{3}{20} + \frac{1}{20}$

_____   _____   _____   _____

Evaluate each expression for the given value of the variable.

13. $38.1 + x$ for $x = -6.1$

14. $18.7 + x$ for $x = 8.5$

15. $\frac{8}{15} + x$ for $x = -\frac{4}{15}$

_____   _____   _____

Holt Mathematics

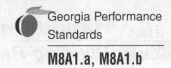

Georgia Performance
Standards
M8A1.a, M8A1.b

2B Dividing Rational Numbers

You can use your calculator to investigate division of rational numbers.

1. Use your calculator to complete the table by dividing the rational numbers. The first one has been filled in as an example.

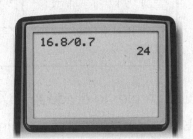

16.8/0.7
24

$\frac{16.8}{0.7} = 24$	$\frac{168}{7} =$	$\frac{1680}{70} =$
$\frac{4.1}{0.5} =$	$\frac{41}{5} =$	$\frac{410}{50} =$
$\frac{0.026}{0.04} =$	$\frac{0.26}{0.4} =$	$\frac{2.6}{4} =$
$\frac{75}{0.06} =$	$\frac{750}{0.6} =$	$\frac{7500}{6} =$
$\frac{16.32}{1.02} =$	$\frac{163.2}{10.2} =$	$\frac{1632}{102} =$

2. How are the division problems in each row related to each other?

Think and Discuss

3. **Show** how you can use the pattern in the first row of the table to write a new division problem whose quotient is equal to 24.

4. **Explain** how to write a division problem that is equivalent to $145 \div 16.5$ but that involves dividing by a whole number.

Holt Mathematics

Name _____ Date _____ Class _____

Hands-On Lab
Dividing Rational Numbers

You can use a ruler to divide rational numbers, both in fractional and in decimal form.

Activity

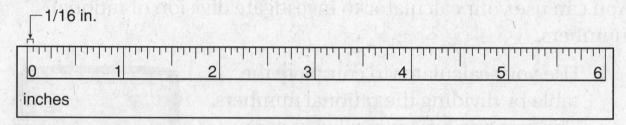
1/16 in.

inches

Use a ruler to divide $4\frac{1}{2}$ by $\frac{3}{4}$.

Use the ruler to draw a thin box $4\frac{1}{2}$ in. long and half an inch high.

Measure $\frac{3}{4}$ in. from the left end of the box and place a vertical

dividing line. Measure another $\frac{3}{4}$ in. from the dividing line and place

a second dividing line. Continue measuring till you get to the end of the box. Did you come out even? How many segments did you divide the box into?

_____

For decimal numbers, use a metric ruler to divide 13.3 by 1.9. Draw a box 13.3 cm long and 1 cm high. Use the metric ruler to divide it into segments 1.9 cm long. How many segments did you divide the box into?

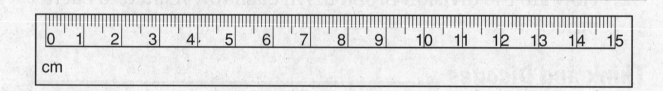
cm

Holt Mathematics

Hands-On Lab

LESSON 2B

Dividing Rational Numbers, continued

Think and Discuss

1. When a positive number is divided by a positive rational number, does the number become smaller or larger? Under what circumstances will it become smaller or larger?

_____

_____

_____

2. You should "divide by a fraction" by changing it to a multiplication problem. Multiply by the reciprocal of the fraction. Could you use that principle when dividing by 0.3?

_____

_____

_____

Try This

Using the metric ruler draw a box 12 cm long. Make it 4 cm tall, with horizontal lines along the length dividing it into 4 sections, one on top of the other. Divide the first section into segments of 0.8 cm, the second into sections of 1.2 cm, the third into sections of 1.5 cm, and the fourth into sections of 2.0 cm. At the end of each row of segments write the division it represents: "12 ÷ 0.8 = ?", and so on.

Name _____ Date _____ Class _____

Review for Mastery
Dividing Rational Numbers

To write the **reciprocal** of a fraction,
interchange the numerator and denominator.

The product of a number and its reciprocal is 1.

$$\frac{2}{3} \times \frac{3}{2} = 1$$

$\frac{2}{3}$ ⤬ $\frac{3}{2}$

Fraction   Reciprocal

Write the reciprocal of each rational number.

1. The reciprocal of $\frac{3}{5}$ is: **2.** The reciprocal of 6 is: **3.** The reciprocal of $2\frac{1}{3}$ is:

_____   _____   _____

To divide by a fraction, multiply by its reciprocal.

$$\frac{2}{3} \div 6$$

$$\frac{2}{3} \times \frac{1}{6}$$

$$\frac{1 \times 1}{3 \times 3} = \frac{1}{9}$$

$$\frac{3}{5} \div \frac{9}{10}$$

$$\frac{3}{5} \times \frac{10}{9}$$

$$\frac{\overset{1}{3} \times \overset{2}{10}}{\underset{1}{5} \times \underset{3}{9}} = \frac{2}{3}$$

Complete to divide and simplify.

4. $\frac{3}{8} \div 12 = \frac{3}{8} \times$ _____ = _____   **5.** $\frac{4}{3} \div 16 =$ _____

6. $\frac{5}{7} \div \frac{20}{21} = \frac{5}{7} \times$ _____ = _____   **7.** $-\frac{3}{4} \div \left(\frac{9}{8}\right) = -\frac{3}{4} \times$ _____ = _____

Change a decimal divisor to a whole number.
Using the number of places in the divisor,
move the decimal point to the right in both
the divisor and the dividend.

$0.7\overline{)4.34} \rightarrow 0.7.\overline{)4.3.4} \rightarrow 7\overset{6.2}{\overline{)43.4}}$

Rewrite each division with a whole-number divisor.
Then, do the division.

8. $0.6\overline{)1.14} \rightarrow$ _____ = _____   **9.** $0.3\overline{)4.56} \rightarrow$ _____ = _____

10. $0.02\overline{)7.12} \rightarrow$ _____ = _____   **11.** $0.08\overline{)57.28} \rightarrow$ _____ = _____

Holt Mathematics

LESSON 2B Homework and Practice
Dividing Rational Numbers

Divide. Write each answer in simplest form.

1. $\dfrac{1}{4} \div \dfrac{5}{8}$

2. $-\dfrac{5}{6} \div \dfrac{5}{12}$

3. $-\dfrac{2}{5} \div \dfrac{7}{10}$

4. $-\dfrac{3}{14} \div \left(-\dfrac{6}{7}\right)$

_____ _____ _____ _____

5. $\dfrac{7}{9} \div \left(\dfrac{5}{6}\right)$

6. $\dfrac{9}{20} \div \left(-\dfrac{3}{4}\right)$

7. $-\dfrac{11}{12} \div \left(-\dfrac{44}{54}\right)$

8. $-\dfrac{13}{30} \div \left(\dfrac{39}{45}\right)$

_____ _____ _____ _____

9. $20 \div \dfrac{4}{9}$

10. $\dfrac{7}{8} \div (-21)$

11. $-10 \div \dfrac{4}{5}$

12. $-\dfrac{21}{25} \div (-14)$

_____ _____ _____ _____

Divide.

13. $32 \div 0.4$

14. $-6.58 \div 0.08$

15. $7.26 \div (-0.03)$

16. $3.333 \div 0.66$

_____ _____ _____ _____

17. $0.0096 \div (-1.2)$

18. $-25.28 \div 1.6$

19. $17.5 \div 0.07$

20. $279.4 \div 12.7$

_____ _____ _____ _____

21. $71.46 \div 9$

22. $36.3 \div (-1.6)$

23. $-984.6 \div 2.4$

24. $-601.96 \div 2.02$

_____ _____ _____ _____

Evaluate each expression for the given value of the variable.

25. $\dfrac{52}{x}$ for $x = -0.16$

26. $\dfrac{-14.52}{x}$ for $x = 5.5$

27. $\dfrac{-54.72}{x}$ for $x = -0.003$

_____ _____ _____

28. A 3.6-pound beef roast cost $10.62. What is the cost of the beef roast per pound?

_____

Holt Mathematics

EXPLORATION

2C Adding and Subtracting with Unlike Denominators

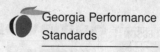
Georgia Performance Standards

M8A1.b

You can use models to show addition and subtraction of fractions with unlike denominators. Look at the models for $\frac{1}{2} + \frac{1}{3}$ and $\frac{1}{2} - \frac{1}{3}$.

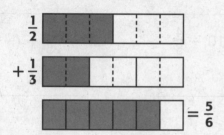
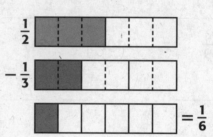

1. Draw a picture to show that $\frac{1}{2} + \frac{4}{5} = 1\frac{3}{10} = 1.3$.

2. Draw a picture to show that $\frac{1}{2} + \frac{2}{3} = \frac{7}{6} = 1\frac{1}{6}$.

3. Complete each addition problem. Simplify your answers.

    a. $\frac{7}{10} + \frac{4}{5}$ **b.** $\frac{3}{5} + \frac{3}{4}$

Think and Discuss

4. **Explain** how to add and subtract fractions with unlike denominators.

5. **Discuss** why the fraction that results from adding or subtracting fractions with unlike denominators has a different denominator than the fractions.

Holt Mathematics

Name _____ Date _____ Class _____

LESSON 2C

Review for Mastery
Adding and Subtracting with Unlike Denominators

To model $\frac{1}{2} + \frac{1}{3}$, use two rectangles of the same size and shape.

A. 1st rectangle: Shade $\frac{1}{2}$ vertically.

$\frac{1}{2}$

B. 2nd rectangle: Shade $\frac{1}{3}$ horizontally.

$\frac{1}{3}$

C. Separate the shaded portions into parts of equal size.

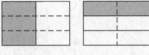

$\frac{1}{2} = \frac{3}{6}$ $\frac{1}{3} = \frac{2}{6}$

D. Use a new rectangle to show the sum.

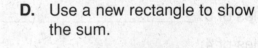

$\frac{1}{2} + \frac{1}{3} = \frac{3}{6} + \frac{2}{6} = \frac{5}{6}$

Model $\frac{1}{2} + \frac{2}{5}$. Write the result.

1.

Model $\frac{1}{3} + \frac{3}{5}$. Write the result.

2.

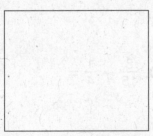

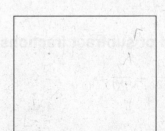

51

Holt Mathematics

Name _____ Date _____ Class _____

Review for Mastery
Adding and Subtracting with Unlike Denominators (continued)

To add fractions with different denominators, first write the fractions with common denominators. To find the LCD of denominators 5 and 6, list the multiples of each.

Multiples of 5: 5, 10, 15, 20, 25, (30)
Multiples of 6: 12, 18, 24, (30)
So, the LCD of 5 and 6 is 30.

Complete to find the LCD for each set of denominators.

3. The LCD of 6 and 4 is: _____

Multiples of 6: _____

Multiples of 4: _____

4. The LCD of 3 and 7 is: _____

Multiples of 3: _____

Multiples of 7: _____

To add fractions with different denominators:

Add: $\dfrac{1}{2} + \dfrac{1}{3} \cdot \dfrac{1 \cdot 3}{2 \cdot 3} = \dfrac{3}{6}$

$\dfrac{1 \cdot 2}{3 \cdot 2} = \dfrac{2}{6}$

So, $\dfrac{1}{2} + \dfrac{1}{3} = \dfrac{3}{6} + \dfrac{2}{6} = \dfrac{5}{6}$

Complete to add fractions. Simplify.

5. $\dfrac{1}{4} = \dfrac{}{20}$

$+ \dfrac{3}{5} = \dfrac{}{20}$

$= \underline{\qquad}$

6. $\dfrac{3}{4} = \dfrac{}{16}$

$+ \dfrac{5}{16} = \dfrac{}{16}$

$= \underline{\qquad} = \underline{\qquad}$

7. $5\dfrac{1}{3} = 5\dfrac{}{24}$

$+ 2\dfrac{5}{8} = 2\dfrac{}{24}$

$= \underline{\qquad}$

Add or subtract fractions. Simplify.

8. $\dfrac{1}{4} + \dfrac{7}{20} =$

9. $\dfrac{4}{9} - \dfrac{1}{5} =$

10. $\dfrac{8}{15} - \dfrac{1}{4} =$

Holt Mathematics

Homework and Practice

LESSON 2C

Adding and Subtracting with Unlike Denominators

Add or subtract. Write the answer in simplest form.

1. $\frac{1}{2} - \frac{3}{8}$

2. $\frac{3}{5} + \frac{1}{4}$

3. $\frac{7}{9} - \frac{5}{12}$

4. $-\frac{5}{9} + \frac{2}{3}$

5. $\frac{3}{10} - \left(-\frac{1}{2}\right)$

6. $\frac{7}{12} + \left(-\frac{5}{15}\right)$

7. $-\frac{4}{15} - \frac{2}{5}$

8. $\frac{5}{12} - \frac{2}{5}$

9. $-\frac{7}{8} + \frac{5}{12}$

10. $-2\frac{1}{8} - 3\frac{1}{4}$

11. $-4\frac{3}{5} + 1\frac{2}{3}$

12. $6\frac{1}{3} - 4\frac{5}{6}$

13. $7 - 5\frac{7}{8}$

14. $8\frac{1}{6} + \left(-\frac{7}{12}\right)$

15. $-16 + \left(-\frac{8}{9}\right)$

16. $4\frac{7}{10} - 11$

Evaluate each expression for the given value of the variable.

17. $-2\frac{5}{8} + x$ for $x = 3\frac{1}{4}$

18. $1\frac{1}{2} + x$ for $x = -2\frac{5}{6}$

19. $-7\frac{4}{9} - x$ for $x = -7$

20. $9\frac{5}{8} + x$ for $x = 6\frac{3}{4}$

21. $-15\frac{3}{8} + x$ for $x = 1\frac{3}{4}$

22. $-15\frac{2}{9} - x$ for $x = -12\frac{2}{3}$

23. Brendan practiced soccer for $1\frac{1}{2}$ hours on Monday, $1\frac{1}{4}$ hours on Tuesday, $1\frac{1}{6}$ hours on Wednesday and $\frac{3}{4}$ hours on Thursday in preparation for the game on Friday. How many total hours did Brendan practice soccer in this week?

Holt Mathematics

EXPLORATION

2D Solving Equations with Rational Numbers

Georgia Performance
Standards

M8A1.a, M8A1.c

A box of cookies has 6 servings. Each serving contains 40.5 calories. How many calories are in the whole box?

40.5	40.5	$= 81$
40.5	40.5	$= 81$
40.5	40.5	$\dfrac{= 81}{243}$

Equation

$40.5 \cdot 6 = c$

$243 = c$

Estimate the solution for each equation. Then use a calculator to solve.

	Equation	Estimate	Actual
1.	$124.75 - x = 50$		
2.	$x + 16.9 = 15.5$		
3.	$0.6x = 15$		
4.	$\dfrac{x}{1.25} = 8$		

Think and Discuss

5. Describe how you estimated the solutions for the equations in Problems 1–4.

6. Discuss whether it is easier to estimate the solutions of some equations than the solutions of others.

Holt Mathematics

Name _____ Date _____ Class _____

LESSON
Review for Mastery

2D
Solving Equations with Rational Numbers

Solving equations with rational numbers is basically the same as
solving equations with integers or whole numbers:

Use inverse operations to isolate the variable.

$\frac{1}{4}z = -16$

$4 \cdot \frac{1}{4}z = -16 \cdot 4$

$z = -64$

Multiply each side by 4.

$y - \frac{3}{8} = \frac{7}{8}$

$+ \frac{3}{8} \quad + \frac{3}{8}$

$y \quad = \frac{10}{8} = 1\frac{2}{8} = 1\frac{1}{4}$

Add $\frac{3}{8}$ to each side.

$x + 3.5 = -17.42$

$\underline{\quad - 3.5 \quad\quad - 3.5}$

$x \quad = -20.92$

Subtract 3.5 from each side.

$-26t = 317.2$

$\frac{-26t}{-26} = \frac{317.2}{-26}$

$t = -12.2$

Divide each side by −26.

Tell what you would do to isolate the variable.

1. $x - 1.4 = 7.82$

2. $\frac{1}{4} + y = \frac{7}{4}$

3. $3z = 5$

_____

_____

_____

Solve each equation.

4. $14x = -129.5$

5. $\frac{1}{3}y = 27$

6. $265.2 = \frac{z}{22.1}$

_____

_____

_____

7. $x + 53.8 = -1.2$

8. $25 = \frac{1}{5}k$

9. $m - \frac{2}{3} = \frac{3}{5}$

_____

_____

_____

Holt Mathematics

LESSON 2D

Homework and Practice

Solving Equations with Rational Numbers

Solve.

1. $y - 3.2 = -4.7$

2. $x + 5.61 = 3.89$

3. $0.4d = 8.2$

_____

_____

_____

4. $b - 2 = 17.5$

5. $a + 101 = -14.2$

6. $3.3x = -108.9$

_____

_____

_____

7. $-19.48 + x = -28.03$

8. $\dfrac{m}{10.1} = 3.5$

9. $217.25 = 39.5w$

_____

_____

_____

10. $\dfrac{t}{4.7} = -14.7$

11. $b - 29.15 = -17.73$

12. $\dfrac{r}{-7.6} = 3.05$

_____

_____

_____

Solve. Write each in simplest form.

13. $\dfrac{5}{8} + y = 2\dfrac{3}{8}$

14. $\dfrac{12}{25} m = -\dfrac{9}{50}$

15. $\dfrac{6}{35} r = \dfrac{18}{25}$

_____

_____

_____

16. $x - \left(-\dfrac{7}{10}\right) = 3\dfrac{3}{5}$

17. $y - \dfrac{11}{18} = 4\dfrac{2}{9}$

18. $-\dfrac{9}{24} w = \dfrac{18}{32}$

_____

_____

_____

19. Jessica baked 10 dozen cookies. She left $\dfrac{1}{8}$ of the baked
cookies home and took the rest to school for the bake sale. How
many cookies did Jessica take to school?

_____

20. Doug must take 1.25 milliliters of medicine every day. How many
days will the medicine last if Doug was given a prescription of
the medicine in a bottle containing 50 milliliters?

_____

Holt Mathematics

Georgia Performance Standards

M8A1.a, M8A1.c

2E Solving Two-Step Equations

Felipe has a 750-gallon tank full of water on his ranch for his livestock. The livestock use 15 gallons of water per day, and no rain is expected to refill the tank during the dry season.

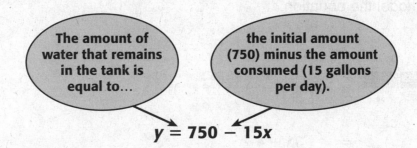

The amount of water that remains in the tank is equal to...

the initial amount (750) minus the amount consumed (15 gallons per day).

$$y = 750 - 15x$$

Use the equation $y = 750 - 15x$ to answer each question.

1. How much water is in the tank after the first day ($x = 1$)?

2. How much water is in the tank after 25 days ($x = 25$)?

3. What will be equal to zero in the equation $y = 750 - 15x$ when the tank is empty?

4. After how many days will the tank be empty?

Think and Discuss

5. **Discuss** what it means when 750 gallons (the initial amount) is exactly the same as $15x$ gallons (the amount consumed).

Holt Mathematics

Name _____ Date _____ Class _____

Hands-On Lab
Solving Two-Step Equations

Activity

Shelley shopped online in hopes of ordering cookies for a party. She found the cookies she wanted at 2 stores. Store X offered a discount of $5 if Shelley purchased 4 dozen cookies. Store Y will sell 3 dozen cookies at the same total price as the 4 dozen from Store X, including $4 for shipping. Using x as the cost of one dozen cookies, then $4x - 5$ is the total cost of the purchase from Store X, and $3x + 4$ is the total cost of the purchase from Store Y. Solve the equation below for x to find the price for a dozen cookies. Use algebra tiles to model the equation.

$4x - 5 = 3x + 4$

$4x - 5$ $=$ $3x + 4$

Step 1 $\quad 4x - 5 = 3x + 4$ Given
Step 2 $4x - 5 - 3x = 3x + 4 - 3x$ Subtraction Property of Equality
Step 3 $\quad\quad x - 5 = 4$ Simplify

Step 4 $\quad x - 5 + 5 = 4 + 5$ Addition Property of Equality

Step 5 $x = 9$ Addition Property of Equality

Holt Mathematics

LESSON 2E Hands-On Lab
Solving Two-Step Equations, continued

Think and Discuss

What is meant by the Subtraction Property of Equality?

_____

_____

_____

_____

_____

_____

Try This

Solve and check the equation $7m - 3 = 2m + 27$, using algebra tiles.

_____

Holt Mathematics

LESSON
2E

Review for Mastery
Solving Two-Step Equations

To solve an equation, it is important to first note how it is formed.

Then, work backward to undo each operation.

$4z + 3 = 15$	$\frac{z}{4} - 3 = 7$	$\frac{z + 3}{4} = 7$
The variable is multiplied by 4 and then 3 is added.	The variable is divided by 4 and then 3 is subtracted.	3 is added to the variable and then the result is divided by 4.
To solve, first subtract 3 and then divide by 4.	To solve, first add 3 and then multiply by 4.	To solve, multiply by 4 and then subtract 3.

Describe how each equation is formed.
Then, tell the steps needed to solve.

1. $3x - 5 = 7$

The variable is _____ and then _____.

To solve, first _____ and then _____.

2. $\frac{x}{3} + 5 = 7$

The variable is _____ and then _____.

To solve, first _____ and then _____.

3. $\frac{x + 5}{3} = 7$

5 is _____ and then the result is _____.

To solve, first _____ and then _____.

4. $10 = -3x - 2$

The variable is _____ and then _____.

To solve, first _____ and then _____.

5. $10 = \frac{x - 2}{5}$

2 is _____ the variable and then the result is _____.

To solve, first _____ and then _____.

Holt Mathematics

Name _____ Date _____ Class _____

LESSON 2E **Review for Mastery**
Solving Two-Step Equations (continued)

To isolate the variable, work backward using inverse operations.

The variable is multiplied by 2 and then 3 is added.

$2x + 3 = 11$ To undo addition,
$\underline{-3 \quad -3}$ subtract 3.
$2x \quad = 8$ To undo multiplication,
$\dfrac{2x}{2} = \dfrac{8}{2}$ divide by 2.
$x = 4$

Check: Substitute 4 for x.
$2(4) + 3 \overset{?}{=} 11$
$8 + 3 \overset{?}{=} 11$
$11 = 11$ ✔

The variable is divided by 2 and then 3 is subtracted.

$\dfrac{x}{2} - 3 = 11$ To undo subtraction,
$\underline{\phantom{\dfrac{x}{2}}+3 \; + \; 3}$ add 3.
$\dfrac{x}{2} = 14$ To undo division,
$2 \cdot \dfrac{x}{2} = 2 \cdot 14$ multiply by 2.
$x = 28$

Check: Substitute 28 for x.
$\dfrac{28}{2} - 3 \overset{?}{=} 11$
$14 - 3 \overset{?}{=} 11$
$11 = 11$ ✔

Complete to solve and check each equation.

6. $3t + 7 = 19$ To undo addition, subtract.   **Check:** $3t + 7 = 19$
$\underline{} \quad \underline{}$ $3(\underline{}) + 7 \overset{?}{=} 19$ Substitute for t.
$3t = \underline{}$ To undo multiplication, divide. $\underline{} + 7 \overset{?}{=} 19$
$3t \div \underline{} = \underline{} \div \underline{}$ $\underline{}$
$t = \underline{}$

7. $\dfrac{w}{3} - 7 = 5$ To undo subtraction, add.   **Check:** $\dfrac{w}{3} - 7 = 5$
$\underline{} \quad \underline{}$ $\dfrac{}{3} - 7 \overset{?}{=} 5$ Substitute.
$\dfrac{w}{3} = \underline{}$ To undo division, multiply. $\underline{} - 7 \overset{?}{=} 5$
$\underline{} \cdot \dfrac{w}{3} = \underline{} \cdot 12$ $\underline{}$
$w = \underline{}$

8. $\dfrac{z-3}{2} = 8$ To undo division, multiply.   **Check:** $\dfrac{z-3}{2} = 8$
$\underline{} \cdot \dfrac{z-3}{2} = \underline{} \cdot 8$ $\dfrac{-3}{2} \overset{?}{=} 8$ Substitute.
$z - 3 = \underline{}$ To undo subtraction, $\dfrac{}{2} \overset{?}{=} 8$
$\underline{} \quad \underline{}$ add. $\underline{}$

Holt Mathematics

Name _____ Date _____ Class _____

LESSON 2E

Homework and Practice
Solving Two-Step Equations

Write and solve a two-step equation to answer the following questions.

1. Sue wants to buy a new printer that costs $189. She has $125 saved. She has a job that pays $8 an hour. How many hours must she work to earn enough to buy the printer?

_____

_____

_____

_____

2. Corbin's car payment is $289. This is $37 less than $\frac{1}{3}$ of his monthly income. What is Corbin's monthly income?

_____

_____

_____

_____

Solve.

3. $13 = 3a - 14$ 4. $\frac{1}{3}k - 4 = 1$ 5. $-8 = \frac{x}{3} - 5$ 6. $6 - 5d = 1$

_____   _____   _____   _____

7. $15y + 9 = -36$ 8. $\frac{1}{4}x + 6 = 11$ 9. $\frac{w}{4} - 9 = -3$ 10. $0.3m - 5 = 7$

_____   _____   _____   _____

11. $\frac{x-5}{7} = -3$ 12. $7 - \frac{a}{4.2} = 3.5$ 13. $\frac{5r-3}{2} = -4$ 14. $-12.9 = 5.7 + 3d$

_____   _____   _____   _____

15. Nineteen more than five times a number is eighty-four. Find the number.

_____

16. Mr. Cruz buys some wood and pays $245. Each bundle of wood costs $15 and there is a delivery charge of $35. How many bundles of wood did Mr. Cruz buy?

_____

Holt Mathematics

Georgia Performance
Standards

M8A1.c

2F Absolute Value Equations

The absolute value of a number is equal to its distance from zero on the number line. You can explore the solutions to absolute value equations using the number line.

4 units   4 units

−5 −4 −3 −2 −1 0 1 2 3 4 5

$|x| = 4$

Which points are 4 units from 0?

$x = -4$ or $x = 4$

2   2
units   units

−5 −4 −3 −2 −1 0 1 2 3 4 5

$|x - 1| = 2$

Which points are 2 units from 1?

$x = -1$ or $x = 3$

1. The equation on the right above has solutions −1 and 3. Substitute these values into the equation to verify that both result in a true equation.

2. The equation $|x - 1| = 2$ has solutions that are 2 units from 1 on the number line. Describe in words the solutions to the absolute value equation $|x - 3| = 5$. Then write the solutions.

3. The equation $|x| = 4$ has solutions that are 4 units from 0 on the number line. Rewrite this equation with the zero in it.

Think and Discuss

4. **Discuss** absolute value equations of the form $|x - a| = b$. Why would you expect no solutions to this equation when b is negative?

5. **Discuss** in words the solutions to the equation $|x - a| = b$ for $b > 0$. Does your answer change if a is positive, negative, or zero?

Holt Mathematics

LESSON 2F Review for Mastery
Solving Absolute-Value Equations

To solve absolute-value equations, the first step is always to isolate the absolute-value expression. Do not assume there is no solution just because there is a negative number on the right hand side of the original equation.

$$2 - 3|x| = -1$$

$$2 - 3|x| = -1$$

$\underline{-2 \qquad\qquad -2}$	Subtract 2 from each side.
$-3|x| = -3$	Simplify.
$\dfrac{-3|x|}{-3} = \dfrac{-3}{-3}$	Divide by -3.
$|x| = 1$	
$|x| = -1$ or $|x| = 1$	*Rewrite the equation as 2 cases.*

The solutions are -1 and 1.

Check:

$2 - 3|x| = -1$	$2 - 3|x| = -1$
$2 - 3|-1| = -1$	$2 - 3|1| = -1$
$2 - 3(1) = -1$	$2 - 3(1) = -1$
$2 - 3 = -1$	$2 - 3 = -1$
$-1 = -1 ✔$	$-1 = -1 ✔$

Solve each absolute-value equation. Check your answer.

1. $7 - |x| = -5$

2. $-2|x| = -10$

Holt Mathematics

LESSON 2E

Review for Mastery

Solving Absolute-Value Equations (continued)

Some absolute-value equations have expressions inside the absolute value signs. After isolating the absolute-value expression and rewriting it as 2 cases, you can use the steps for solving a two-step equation.

$|3x - 2| - 6 = 5$

$\underline{ +6 \quad +6}$ *Add 6 to each side to isolate the absolute value expression.*

$|3x - 2| = 11$

$3x - 2 = 11$ or $3x - 2 = -11$ *Rewrite the equation as 2 cases.*

$\underline{+2 \quad +2 \qquad +2 \quad +2}$

$3x = 13$ or $3x = -9$

$\dfrac{3x}{3} = \dfrac{13}{3}$ or $\dfrac{3x}{3} = \dfrac{-9}{3}$ *Solve the two-step equations.*

$x = \dfrac{13}{3}$ or $x = -3$ *Simplify.*

The solutions are -3 and $\dfrac{13}{3}$.

Check:

$|3x - 2| - 6 = 5$	$|3x - 2| - 6 = 5$
$|3(-3) - 2| - 6 = 5$	$\left|3\left(\dfrac{13}{3}\right) - 2\right| - 6 = 5$
$|-9 - 2| - 6 = 5$	$|13 - 2| - 6 = 5$
$|-11| - 6 = 5$	$|11| - 6 = 5$
$11 - 6 = 5$	$11 - 6 = 5$
$5 = 5$ ✔	$5 = 5$ ✔

Solve each absolute-value equation. Check your answer.

3. $|2x + 1| = 9$ **4.** $2|3 - 5x| = 4$

65
Holt Mathematics

LESSON 2F Homework and Practice
Absolute-Value Equations

Solve each absolute-value equation. Check your answer.

1. $2 + |x| = 5$

2. $-3|x| + 2 = -10$

3. $|8x - 14| = 6$

4. $|1 - x| - 1 = 1$

5. Boris notices that the current temperature in his town is exactly 63°F from both the record low and record high temperatures for his town. If the current temperature is 36°F, what are the record low and high temperatures? Solve the equation $|T - 36| = 63$ to find the temperatures.

_____

6. Your teacher places the numbers –3, –2, –1, 0, 1, 2, and 3 in a hat. She then pulls a number out of the hat without looking. The number has the property shown below. List the numbers that could be the number pulled out of the hat.

a. Its absolute value is 2.

_____

b. The number is equal to its absolute value.

_____

c. The absolute value of the number is positive.

_____

Holt Mathematics

Answer these question to summarize the important concepts from Chapter 2 in your own words.

1. Explain how to write -2.54 as a fraction in simplest terms.

2. Explain how to add $\frac{4}{9}$ and $\frac{2}{9}$.

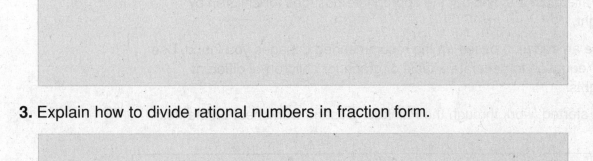

3. Explain how to divide rational numbers in fraction form.

4. Explain how to solve the equation $x - \frac{1}{5} = \frac{4}{15}$.

For more review of Chapter 2:

- Complete the Chapter 2 Study Guide and Review on pages 106–108 of your textbook.

- Complete the Ready to Go On quizzes on pages 90 and 102 of your textbook.

Holt Mathematics

Project

Graphs, Functions, and Sequences: Healthy Dosage

Career: Pharmacist

In addition to dispensing medicine that has been prescribed by doctors, pharmacists advise patients about the uses and possible side effects of medications. Pharmacists may also make recommendations to help patients manage conditions such as diabetes and high blood pressure. Although many pharmacists work in drugstores, others work closely with doctors and nurses in hospitals.

In this chapter project...you will calculate the amount of medication appropriate for children of different weights. You will:

- Learn how the weight of a child is related to how much aspirin the child should be given.

- Research another medication, such as medicines for upset stomachs and allergies, and find out the appropriate dosages for children by weight.

- Write an equation based on the recommended dosages you found. Use your equation to generate a table or graph for children of different weights.

To get started, work through the Painkiller Dosage worksheet on the next page.

This chapter project reinforces your understanding of these Georgia Performance Standards:

M8A1.a Represent a given situation using algebraic expressions or equations in one variable.

M8P5.a Create and use representations to organize, record, and communicate mathematical ideas.

---

go.hrw.com
Chapter Project Online
KEYWORD: MT7 Ch3

Holt Mathematics

CHAPTER 3 Project Recording Sheet
Graphs, Functions, and Sequences

Painkiller Dosage

Paracetamol and ibuprofen are commonly used to relieve pain and fever. The table shows the recommended dose of each drug for children of various weights.

Recommended Doses for Children		
Weight of Child (lb)	Dose of Paracetamol (mg)	Dose of Ibuprofen (mg)
25	135	55
30	162	66
35	189	77

1. To find the number of milligrams of paracetamol that should be given to a child who weighs x pounds, use the equation $y = 5.4x$. Make a table of ordered pairs to show the recommended dose of paracetamol for children who weigh 25 lb, 30 lb, 35 lb, 40 lb, 45 lb, and 50 lb.

2. Use your table to graph the equation on a coordinate plane.

3. A pharmacist is advising a doctor on the correct dose of paracetamol for a child who weighs 37 lbs. Explain how you can use the graph to estimate the dose.

_____

_____

4. To find the number of milligrams of ibuprofen that should be given to a child who weighs x pounds, use the equation $y = 2.2x$. Make a table of ordered pairs, and then graph the equation.

5. Explain how the graph of ibuprofen doses is similar to the graph of paracetamol doses. How are the graphs different?

_____

_____

Holt Mathematics

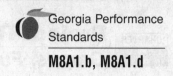

Georgia Performance
Standards

3A Ordered Pairs

M8A1.b, M8A1.d

At the GasCo station, gasoline costs $3 per gallon. Let x represent the number of gallons of gasoline that you buy and let y represent the total cost of the gasoline.

1. Complete the table.

Number of Gallons, x	Total cost, y
1	$3
2	
3	
4	
5	
6	

2. Each row of the table contains an ***ordered pair.*** An ordered pair lists an x-value and its corresponding y-value. For example, the first row of the table contains the ordered pair (1, 3). Write the ordered pairs in the other rows of your table.

3. The equation $y = 3x$ gives the cost of x gallons of gasoline. Use the equation to find the cost of 12 gallons of gasoline.

4. Write the ordered pair from Problem 3.

Think and Discuss

5. Describe how you could find a new ordered pair for the above situation.

6. Explain whether you think the ordered pair (1, 3) is the same as (3, 1).

Holt Mathematics

Technology Lab

LAB 3A *Create a Table of Solutions*

The *Table* feature on a graphing calculator can help you make a table of values quickly.

Activity

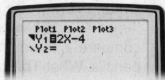

1 Make a table of solutions of the equation $y = 2x - 3$. Then find the value of y when $x = 29$.

To enter the equation, press the **Y=** . Then

press 2 **X,T,θ,n** **−** 3.

Press **2nd** **WINDOW** (TBLSET) to go to the Table Setup menu.
In this menu, **TblStart** shows the starting *x*-value, and **ΔTbl** shows how the *x*-values increase. If you need to change these values, use the arrow keys to highlight the number you want to change and then type a new number.

Press **2nd** **GRAPH** (TABLE) to see the table of values.

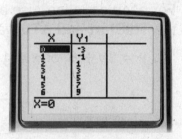

On this screen, you can see that $y = 7$ when $x = 5$.

Use the arrow keys to scroll down the list. You can see that $y = 55$ when $x = 29$.

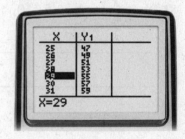

To check, substitute 29 into $y = 2x - 3$.
$y = 2x - 3$

$\quad = 2(29) - 3 = 58 - 3 = 55$

Holt Mathematics

Technology Lab
LAB 3A *Create a Table of Solutions, continued*

Think and Discuss

1. On an Internet site, pencils can be purchased for 17¢ each, but they only come in boxes of 12. You decide to make a table to compare x, the number of pencils, to y, the total cost of the pencils. What **TblStart** and **ΔTbl** values will you use? Explain.

_____

_____

_____

Try This

For each equation, use a table to find the y-values for the given x-values. Give the **TblStart** and **ΔTbl** values you used.

1. $y = 3x + 6$ for $x = 1$, 3, and 7

_____

_____

2. $y = \frac{x}{4}$ for $x = 5$, 10, 15, and 20

_____

_____

_____

Holt Mathematics

Review for Mastery

LESSON 3A *Ordered Pairs*

An **ordered pair** can be used to write a solution for a two-variable equation. For the equation $y = x + 5$, a solution is (0, 5). When the x-value is 0, the y-value is 5.

(0, 5)

x-value   y-value

Which of the ordered pairs (5, 3) or (3, 5) is a solution of $y = 2x - 1$?

$y = 2x - 1$
$3 \overset{?}{=} 2(5) - 1$ Substitute 5 for x
                              and 3 for y.
$3 \overset{?}{=} 10 - 1$
$3 \neq 9$

So, (5, 3) *is not* a solution
of $y = 2x - 1$.

$y = 2x - 1$
$5 \overset{?}{=} 2(3) - 1$ Substitute 3 for x
                              and 5 for y.
$5 \overset{?}{=} 6 - 1$
$5 = 5$

So, (3, 5) *is* a solution
of $y = 2x - 1$.

Determine whether each ordered pair is a solution of the given equation. Write *is* or *is not*.

1. $y = 4x + 3$; (1, 6)

2. $y = 4x + 3$; (0, 3)

3. $y = x + 3$; (3, 0)

_____

_____

_____

4. $y = 5x$; (3, 15)

5. $y = 3x - 4$; (5, 3)

6. $y = 6 - x$; (4, 2)

_____

_____

_____

A two-variable equation has infinitely many solutions. Use a table to find and record some solutions to a given equation. Use $x = 1, 2$, and 3, for example, to make a table of values for $y = 5x - 1$. Substitute each given value of x in the expression for x. Evaluate the expression to find the value of y that completes the ordered pair.

x	5x – 9 = y	(x, y)
1	5(1) – 1 = 4	(1, 4)
2	5(2) – 1 = 9	(2, 9)
3	5(3) – 1 = 14	(3, 14)

Complete each table.

7. $y = 4x$

x	4x = y	(x, y)
0	4(0) =	(0,)
1	4( ) =	(1,)
2	4( ) =	(2,)

8. $y = 5x - 3$

x	5x – 3 = y	(x, y)
1	5( ) – 3 =	(1,)
2	5( ) – 3 =	(2,)
3	5( ) – 3 =	(3,)

Holt Mathematics

LESSON
3A

Homework and Practice
Ordered Pairs

Determine whether each ordered pair is a solution of $y = 5 + 3x$.

1. (1, 8)   **2.** (3, 7)   **3.** (2, 10)   **4.** (0, 5)

_____   _____   _____   _____

Determine whether each ordered pair is a solution of $y = 4x - 1$.

5. (0, 1)   **6.** (1, 3)   **7.** (3, 11)   **8.** (5, 19)

_____   _____   _____   _____

Use the given values to complete the table of solutions.

9. $y = x + 4$ for $x = 0, 1, 2, 3, 4$

x	x + 4	y	(x, y)
0			
1			
2			
3			
4			

10. $y = 2x + 3$ for $x = 0, 1, 3, 5, 7$

x	2x + 3	y	(x, y)
0			
1			
3			
5			
7			

11. $y = 4x - 1$ for $x = 1, 2, 4, 5, 8$

x	4x − 1	y	(x, y)
1			
2			
4			
5			
8			

12. $y = 5x + 2$ for $x = 0, 2, 4, 6, 8$

x	5x + 2	y	(x, y)
0			
2			
4			
6			
8			

13. Mrs. Frank had 150 customers when she began her delivery route. Each month she adds 5 new customers. The equation that gives the total number of customers, *t*, in her route is $t = 150 + 5m$, where *m* is the number of months since she began the route. How many customers will Mrs. Frank have after 12 months?

_____

Holt Mathematics

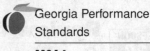
Georgia Performance
Standards

M8A4.c

3B Graphing on a Coordinate Plane

You are about to give directions to the locations labeled on the grid. The only restrictions are the following:

● You can move only horizontally (sideways) or vertically (up and down).

● Your first move should be horizontal. Use the directions *left* or *right*.

● Your second move should be vertical. Use the directions *up* or *down*.

Give directions to go to each location.

1. the museum

2. the park

3. the mall

4. the zoo

5. the planetarium

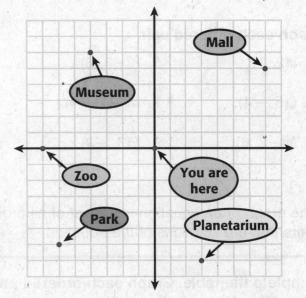

Think and Discuss

6. **Explain** how to write the directions for the locations in Problems **1–5** using *ordered-pair* notation. (*Hint:* the museum is at (−4, 6).)

Holt Mathematics

LESSON 3B — Review for Mastery
Graphing on a Coordinate Plane

Point *A* is described by the ordered pair (3, −2). The first number, 3, is the **x-coordinate** and the second number, −2, is the **y-coordinate**.

Using a grid to represent a **coordinate plane,** graph point *A* by starting at the **origin,** where the **x-axis** and **y-axis** intersect. The *x*-coordinate, 3, tells you to go *right* 3. The *y*-coordinate, −2, tells you to go *down* 2.

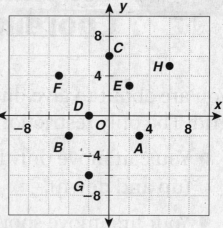

Write an ordered pair to describe each point on the coordinate plane above.

1. point *C* _____ **2.** point *F* _____ **3.** point *G* _____

Graph each ordered pair.

4. *J*(2, 1) **5.** *K*(−3, 0)

6. *L*(5, −4) **7.** *M*(−4, −4)

8. *N*(−2, 6) **9.** *P*(3, −2)

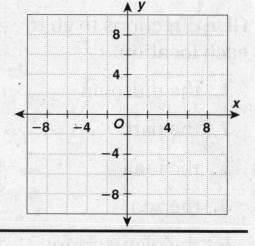

The graph of an equation is the set of all ordered pairs that are solutions of the equation.

Complete the table. Graph each ordered pair. Draw a line through the points.

10. $y = 4x$

x	4x = y	(x, y)
0	4( ) =	(0,)
1	4( ) =	(1,)
2	4( ) =	(2,)

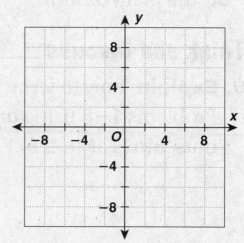

Holt Mathematics

Name _____ Date _____ Class _____

LESSON 3B Homework and Practice
Graphing on a Coordinate Plane

Give the coordinates of each point.

1. A

2. D

3. H

4. C

5. B

6. T

7. M

8. R

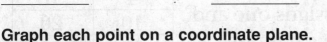

Graph each point on a coordinate plane.
Label points A–F.

9. A(3, 5)

10. B(−6, 3)

11. C(0, −4)

12. D(−4, −6)

13. E(5, −2)

14. F(2, 0)

Complete the table of ordered pairs. Graph the
equation on a coordinate plane.

15. y = 2x

x	2x	y	(x, y)
1			
2			
3			

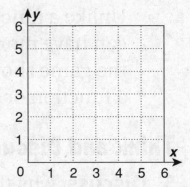

16. A doctor sees 4 patients each hour. Use the equation y = 4x,
where the y-value represents the many patients that the doctor
may see in x hours. Graph, if necessary. How many patients will
the doctor see in a 5-hour day?

Holt Mathematics

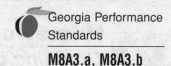

Georgia Performance
Standards

M8A3.a, M8A3.b

3C Relations and Functions

Mila and Greg are playing a guessing game. Mila tells Greg a number, and Greg changes it into another number according to a rule that only he knows. To win, Mila has to guess Greg's rule.

1. The table shows Mila's numbers and Greg's responses. What rule is Greg using to change the numbers?

Mila	Greg
1	2
3	6
4	8
10	20
20	40

2. A *function* is a rule that assigns one and only one output value to each input value. If Mila's numbers are the inputs, is Greg's rule a function? Explain.

3. During another game, Mila said "2" twice, but Greg gave different answers each time. Is he still using a function as a rule? Explain.

4. A *relation* is a rule that pairs numbers in one set with number in another set. Unlike a function, an input in a relation can have more than one output. In the game shown at right, is Greg using a function or a relation?

Mila	Greg
1	4
2	3
1	5
3	6

Think and Discuss

5. Discuss why the guessing game does not work if Greg is using a relation, not a function.

Holt Mathematics

Name _____ Date _____ Class _____

Review for Mastery
Functions

A **relation** is a set of ordered pairs.	{(1, 2), (3, 4), (5, 6)}
The **domain** of a relation is the set of all <u>first components</u> of the ordered pairs.	{1, 3, 5}
The **range** of a relation is the set of all <u>second components</u> of the ordered pairs.	{2, 4, 6}

Write the domain and range for each relation.

1. relation: {(−1, 1), (−2, 3), (−3, 5)}

   domain: {−1, _____

   range: { 1, _____

2. relation: {(a, 1), (b, 2), (c, 3)}

   domain: { a, _____

   range: {1, _____

A **function** is a relation in which each element of the domain corresponds to *exactly one* element of the range.

The relation below is a function.

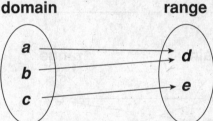

function: {(a, d), (b, d), (c, e)}
   a has only one partner, d.
   b has only one partner, d.
   c has only one partner, e.

The relation below is not a function.

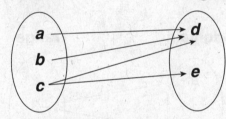

relation: {(a, d), (b, d), (c, d), (c, e)}
   a has only one partner, d.
   b has only one partner, d.
   c has two partners, d and e.

Tell if each relation is a function. Explain.

3. domain   range

_____

_____

4. domain   range

_____

_____

Holt Mathematics

Name _____ Date _____ Class _____

Homework and Practice
Relations and Functions

Write the domain and range for each relation.

1. relation: {(0, 4), (1, 5), (2, 6)}

domain: _____

range: _____

2. relation: {(−3, 6), (−2, 3), (−1, 0)}

domain: _____

range: _____

Tell if each relation is a function. Explain.

3.

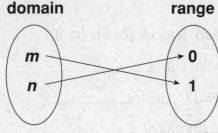

_____

_____

4.

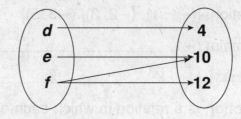

_____

_____

5.

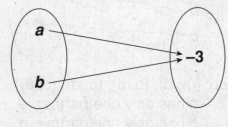

_____

_____

6.

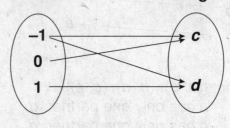

_____

_____

Tell if each relation is a function. Explain.

7. {(1, 4), (2, 7), (1, 10), (3, 0)}

_____

_____

8. {(−3, 2), (−2, 2), (−1, 2), (0, 2)}

_____

_____

Holt Mathematics

3D Functions

Georgia Performance Standards

M8A1.b, M8A3.b, M8A3.c, M8A3.d, M8A3.i

A *function* is a rule that assigns one *output* value for each *input* value. An input/output table is a convenient way of representing functions.

1. Complete the table by applying the rule to each input value.

Input x	Rule: $2000 - 25x$	Output y
0	$2000 - 25(0) = 2000$	2000
1		
2		
3		

2. Determine the rule that produces the following output values from the given input values.

Input x	Rule	Output y
2		0
4		2
6		4
8		6

Think and Discuss

3. Explain the relationship between the input values, a rule, and the output values.

4. Discuss whether the output values have to be different from the input values.

Holt Mathematics

Name _____ Date _____ Class _____

LESSON
3D
Review for Mastery
Functions

From a given rule for a relation, you can write a table of values.

　Choose convenient *x*-values (domain or input).
　Get corresponding *y*-values (range or output).

$y = 2x - 1$

x	2x − 1	y
−2	2(−2) − 1 = −5	−5
−1	2(−1) − 1 = −3	−3
0	2(0) − 1 = −1	−1
1	2(1) − 1 = 1	1
2	2(2) − 1 = 3	3

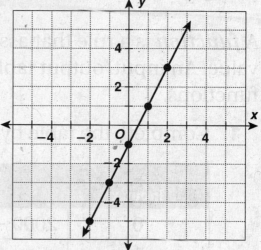

Write a table of values for each function and graph.

1. $y = x - 1$

x	x − 1	y
−2	−2 − 1 = −3	−3
−1	−1 − 1 =	
0	− 1 =	
1	− 1 =	
2	− 1 =	

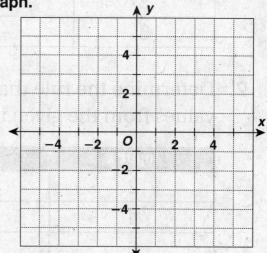

2. $y = 2x + 1$

x	2x + 1	y
−2	2( ) + 1 =	
−1		
0		
1		
2		

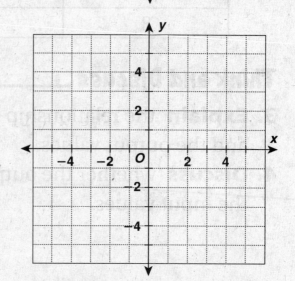

Holt Mathematics

Review for Mastery

LESSON 3D

Functions (continued)

A function has exactly one output for each input. You can check to see if a relation is a function by making sure each value in the domain is associated with only one value in the range. You can use the vertical line test on a graph.

Determine if the relation is a function. Explain.

x	y
1	10
2	20
3	30
4	40
5	50

The relation is a function.
Each *x* value has only one *y* value.

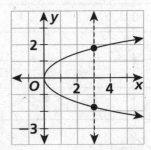

The relation is not a function.
A vertical line intersects the graph at two points.

Determine if the relation is a function. Explain.

3.

x	y
−2	5
−1	7
0	9
−1	6
−2	4

_____

_____

4.

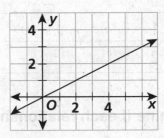

_____

_____

5.

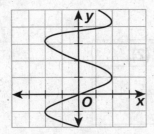

_____

_____

6.

x	y
1	1
2	1
3	1
4	1
5	1

_____

_____

Holt Mathematics

Name _____ Date _____ Class _____

Homework and Practice
Functions

Complete the table and graph each function.

1. $y = 3x + 4$

x	3x + 4	y
−3		
−2		
−1		
0		
1		

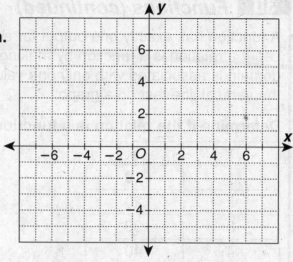

2. $y = 2x^2 - 1$

x	2x² − 1	y
−2		
−1		
0		
1		
2		

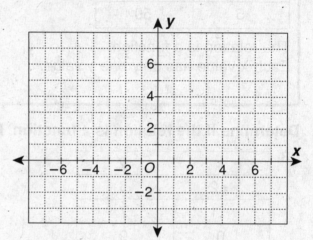

Determine if each relationship represents a function.

3. $y^2 = 4x - 3$

4.

x	2	4	6	8
y	−1	−2	−3	−4

_____   _____

5. For each function, find $f(0)$, $f(-1)$, and $f(2)$.

Function	f (0)	f (−1)	f (2)
$y = -5x + 2$			
$y = 3x^2 - 8$			

6. Given the function $f(x) = -4x^2 - 5$ and the domain
$\{-3, -2, -1, 0, 1, 2, 3\}$. Find the range of the function.

_____

84   **Holt Mathematics**

3E Equations, Tables, and Graphs

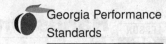
Georgia Performance Standards

M8A1.b, M8A1.d,
M8A3.i, M8A4.c,
M8A4.e, M8A4.f

Jerome is driving at a constant speed of 50 mi/h. You can use an equation, a table, and a graph to represent the distance d that Jerome travels in t hours.

1. Complete the table.

Time (hr), t	distance (mi), d
0.5	
1	50
1.5	
2	
2.5	
3	

2. Plot the points in your table and then connect the points to make a graph that shows Jerome's distance as a function of time.

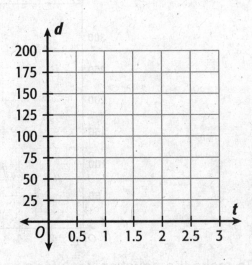

Think and Discuss

3. Describe the graph that you made.

4. Explain how distance is related to time. How can you use this to write an equation relating d and t?

Holt Mathematics

Name _____ Date _____ Class _____

Hands-On Lab
Equations, Tables, and Graphs

Activity

Relationships can be represented as equations, tables, or graphs.
Each representation shows the same data, but in a different way.

A cheetah can run 50 miles an hour. You can show that relationship
in an equation, a table, and a graph. First, fill in the table to show
the relationship. Then use the table to make a graph and write an
equation.

Hour (h)	$50h$	Distance (d)
0	0	0
1	50(1)	50
2		
3		
4		
5		

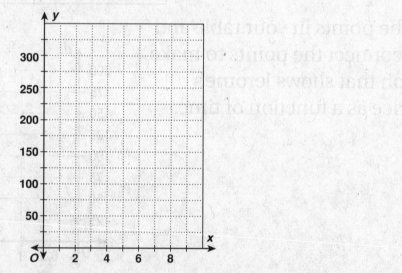

To make the equation, look for a pattern in the values.

> **Remember:** The hour, h, is the input value. The distance, d, is the output value.

_____

Holt Mathematics

LESSON 3E Hands-On Lab
Equations, Tables, and Graphs, continued

Think and Discuss

1. What pattern did you see in the table?

_____

_____

2. If the cheetah ran 60 miles an hour instead of 50, how would that affect the graph, the table, and the equation?

_____

_____

_____

Try This

A factory can make 25 basketballs a minute. How many basketballs can the factory make in 6 minutes? Make a table, a graph, and an equation to show that relationship.

Minutes	Basketballs made

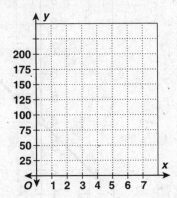

1. Equation: _____

2. How many basketballs can the factory make in 6 minutes?

_____

Holt Mathematics

LESSON 3E Review for Mastery
Equations, Tables, and Graphs

Follow these steps to write an equation from its graph.

Step 1 Select points on the graph to make a table of values. Use the *x*-coordinate for the *x*-value and the *y*-coordinate for the *y*-value.

x	y
0	2
1	3
2	4
3	5

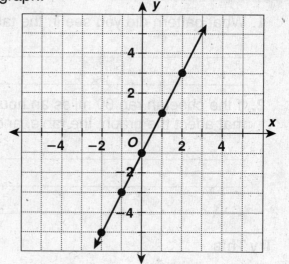

Step 2 Look for a pattern in the values that relates *y* to *x*.

Each value of *y* is 2 more than the value of *x*.

x	y
0 + 2	= 2
1 + 2	= 3
2 + 2	= 4
3 + 2	= 5

Step 3 Use the pattern to write an equation. $y = x + 2$

Complete the table and find a pattern to write an equation of the graph.

1.

x	y
0	4
1	
2	
3	

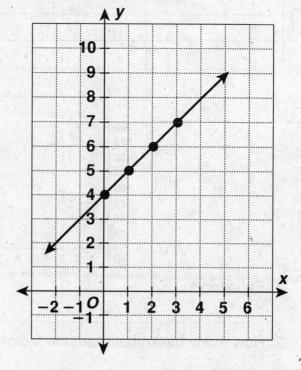

2.   *x*   *y*

    0 + _____ = 4

    1 + _____ = _____

   _____

   _____

3. Write the equation.

   _____

Holt Mathematics

Name _____ Date _____ Class _____

Homework and Practice
Equations, Tables, and Graphs

Use each table to make a graph and to write an equation.

1.

x	y
−3	4
−1	2
1	0
3	−2

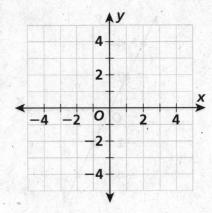

_____

2.

x	y
2	−5
4	−3
6	−1
8	1

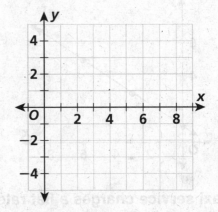

_____

3. Fatima takes a shower every morning before school. The equation $g = 6m$ represents the number of gallons g that she uses for a shower that lasts m minutes. Complete the table and sketch a graph of the equation.

m	6m	g
10	6(10)	
15	6(15)	
20		
25		
30		
35		

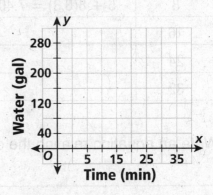

Holt Mathematics

Name _____ Date _____ Class _____

LESSON
3E
Homework and Practice
Equations, Tables, and Graphs continued

Use each graph to make a table and to write an equation.

4.

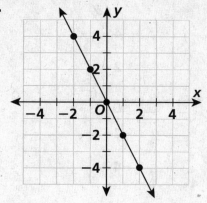

x					
y					

_____

5.

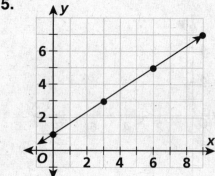

x			
y			

_____

A taxi service charges a flat rate of $5, plus an additional 30 cents per mile, for each ride. Use this information to answer Exercises 6 and 7.

6. Complete the table for the cost of a taxi ride. Then sketch a graph.

miles	cost ($)
8	5 + 8(0.3) = 7.40
16	
24	
32	

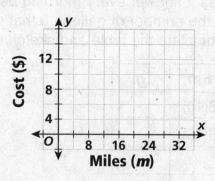

7. Write an equation relating the cost *c* and miles *m* for a taxi ride.

_____

Holt Mathematics

3F Arithmetic Sequences

Georgia Performance Standards

M8A1.b, M8A3.e, M8A3.f

Maya is a structural engineer. She is designing support structures for a bridge. As shown in the figures, the structures consist of regular beams (the horizontal and vertical beams) and cross beams (the diagonal beams).

One section

Two sections

Three sections

1. Maya makes a table showing the number of cross beams needed for various numbers of sections. Complete the table.

Number of Sections	1	2	3	4	5
Number of Cross Beams	2	4			

2. She also makes a table showing the number of regular beams needed for various numbers of sections. Complete the table.

Number of Sections	1	2	3	4	5
Number of Regular Beams	4	7			

Think and Discuss

3. **Describe** any patterns you notice in the table for the number of cross beams.

4. **Explain** how you could find the number of regular beams needed to make 6 sections based on the patterns in your table.

Holt Mathematics

Hands-On Lab
Arithmetic Sequences

Activity

A **sequence** is an ordered list of numbers or objects. In an
arithmetic sequence, the difference between one term and the
next is always the same. This difference is called the **common
difference,** and it is added to each term to get the next term.

A group of 32 students wants to order pizza for dinner, one large
pizza for every 4 students. Find an ad for a large pizza in the paper,
or call a local pizza company to find how much a large pizza costs.
Use this information to fill in the chart and use an arithmetic
sequence to determine the total cost for the pizzas.

Number of students	4	8	16	20	24	28	32
Total cost of pizza							

Use the grid below to model an arithmetic sequence. This time
3 students will share a pizza. Each square in the grid represents
one student. Lightly color in groups of 3 to represent each pizza,
until you have colored in enough groups of 3 to represent the total
number of pizzas the students will need. Then write the sequence of
numbers in the group of 3 squares that represent each pizza.

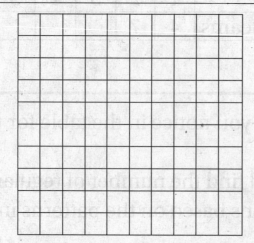

LESSON
3F

Hands-On Lab
Arithmetic Sequences, continued

Think and Discuss

1. How does an arithmetic sequence work?

_____

_____

_____

2. How can you find the common difference in an arithmetic sequence?

_____

_____

_____

Try This

1. Find the missing terms in this arithmetic sequence.

17		23	26		32		

What is the common difference in this sequence?

_____

2. Find a function in the arithmetic sequence below. Use y to identify each term in the sequence and *n* to identify each term's position.

Sequence:

4, 8, 12, 16, 20

n	y = f (n)
1	4
2	8
3	12
4	16
5	20

What is the function?

_____

_____

Holt Mathematics

Name _____ Date _____ Class _____

Review for Mastery
Arithmetic Sequences

In an **arithmetic sequence**, the difference between one term and the next term is always the same. That difference is called the **common difference**.

If the terms increase, the common difference is positive.	If the terms decrease, the common difference is negative.
2, 6, 10, 14, …	50, 47, 44, 41, …
Look at pairs of differences:	Look at pairs of differences:
$6 - 2 = 4$	$47 - 50 = -3$
$10 - 6 = 4$	$44 - 47 = -3$
$14 - 10 = 4$	$41 - 44 = -3$
The common difference is 4.	The common difference is −3.
To find next term in the sequence, add 4 to the last term.	To find next term in the sequence, add −3 to the last term.
$14 + 4 = 18$	$41 + (-3) = 38$
So, the next term is 18.	So, the next term is 38.

Complete to find the common difference of each arithmetic sequence. Then find the next term in the sequence.

1. 3, 9, 15, 21, …   **2.** 44, 42, 40, 38, …   **3.** 4, 9, 14, 19, …

$9 - 3 =$ _____ $42 - 44 =$ _____   _____

$15 - 9 =$ _____   _____   _____

$21 - 15 =$ _____   _____   _____

Common difference: Common difference: Common difference:

_____   _____   _____

Next term: Next term: Next term:

$21 +$ _____ $=$ _____   _____   _____

Holt Mathematics

Homework and Practice

LESSON 3F

Arithmetic Sequences

Find the common difference in each arithmetic sequence.

1. 6, 19, 32, 45, …

_____

2. 12, 19, 26, 33, …

_____

3. 2, 3.4, 4.8, 6.2, …

_____

4. 0, −8, −16, −24, …

_____

5. 25, 16, 7, −2, …

_____

6. −33, −20, −7, 6, …

_____

Find the next three terms in the arithmetic sequence.

7. 14, 21, 28, 35, …

_____

8. $\frac{1}{4}$, $\frac{3}{4}$, $1\frac{1}{4}$, $1\frac{3}{4}$, …

_____

9. 31, 42, 53, 64, …

_____

10. 8, 4.3, 0.6, −3.1, …

_____

11. $-5\frac{2}{3}$, $-5\frac{1}{3}$, -5, $-4\frac{2}{3}$

_____

12. 25, 42, 59, 76, …

_____

Find the missing term in the arithmetic sequence.

13. 21, 37, 53, 69, ___, …

_____

14. −30, −21, ___, −3, 6, …

_____

15. ___, 2.9, −1, −4.9, −8.8, …

_____

16. 0.7, ___, 3.5, 4.9, 6.3, …

_____

17. $\frac{1}{8}$, $\frac{3}{8}$, $\frac{5}{8}$, ___, $1\frac{1}{8}$, …

_____

18. $\frac{5}{6}$, $1\frac{1}{6}$, ___, $1\frac{5}{6}$, $2\frac{1}{6}$

_____

Holt Mathematics

Big Ideas

Answer these questions to summarize the important concepts from Chapter 3 in your own words.

1. Explain why (4, 37) is a solution to the function $y = 3x + 25$.

2. Explain how to graph the ordered pair $(-5, 2.5)$. Give the quadrant of the point.

3. Explain how to tell if a relationship is a function using the vertical line test.

4. Explain how to write an equation from data in a table.

5. Explain why 145, 126, 107, 88, . . . is an arithmetic sequence. Find the next three terms.

For more review of Chapter 3:

- Complete the Chapter 3 Study Guide and Review on pages 150–152 of your textbook.

- Complete the Ready to Go On quizzes on pages 132 and 146 of your textbook.

Holt Mathematics

Exponents and Roots: The Tiniest Pieces

Career: Nuclear Physicist

The atom was defined by the ancient Greeks as the smallest particle of matter. We now know that atoms are made up of many smaller particles. Nuclear physicists study these particles using large machines—such as linear accelerators, synchrotrons, and cyclotrons—that can smash atoms to uncover their component parts. Nuclear physicists use mathematics along with the data they discover to create models of the atom and the structure of matter.

In this chapter project…you will create a scale model or drawing of an atom. You will:

- Learn to change numbers between standard notation and scientific notation, which is helpful in describing the very small distances in an atom.

- Research the distances in an atom. You will find that the *nucleus* (center) of an atom is very small, and the distance to the electrons outside of the nucleus is relatively large.

- Make a scale model of an atom outside, using your classmates as electrons. Use a circle of paper that is 0.5 cm in diameter to represent the nucleus. Your teacher will help you use proportions and the information you collected to calculate how far one of the human electrons should be from the nucleus in your model. Setting up your human atom will be easier if you use a football field, because you can use the distances marked on the field.

To get started, work through the The Lives of Particles worksheet on the next page.

This chapter project reinforces your understanding of these Georgia Performance Standards:

M8N1.j Express and use numbers in scientific notation.

M8P5.a Create and use representations to organize, record, and communicate mathematical ideas.

---

go.hrw.com
Chapter Project Online
KEYWORD: MT7 Ch4

Holt Mathematics

Project Recording Sheet
CHAPTER 4

Exponents and Roots

The Lives of Particles

Complete the table to show the life spans of the subatomic particles listed without using exponents.

Life Spans of Some Subatomic Particles

Subatomic Particle	Independent Life Span (s)	Life Span in Standard Notation (s)
Electron	Stable	Stable
Proton	Stable	Stable
Neutron	920	920
Mu meson	2.2×10^{-6}	
Pi meson	2.6×10^{-3}	
Sigma baryon	1.5×10^{-10}	
Tau lepton	3.4×10^{-13}	
Upsilon meson	1×10^{-20}	
Quark	Unknown	Unknown

1. List the atomic particles from the table in order from shortest life span to longest.

_____

_____

2. Which atomic particles have independent life spans longer than one second?

_____

3. About how many life spans of a mu meson would be as long as a pi meson?

_____

_____

Holt Mathematics

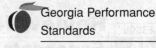
Georgia Performance
Standards

M8N1.i, M8A1.b

4A Exponents

You can multiply $(-5) \cdot (-5) \cdot (-5) \cdot (-5) \cdot (-5) \cdot (-5)$ using exponents and a calculator.

The number -5 is a factor 6 times, so you can write it as $(-5)^6$.

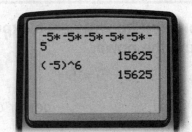

The expressions are equivalent because they have the same value.

$(-5) \cdot (-5) \cdot (-5) \cdot (-5) \cdot (-5) \cdot (-5) =$ 15,625 and $(-5)^6 = 15{,}625$

Write each of the following using exponents. Then use a calculator to find the value of the expression.

1. $2 \cdot 2 \cdot 2 \cdot 2$

2. $8 \cdot 8 \cdot 8 \cdot 8 \cdot 8 \cdot 8$

3. $(-4) \cdot (-4) \cdot (-4)$

4. $(-5) \cdot (-5)$

5. $3 \cdot 3 \cdot 3 \cdot 3 \cdot 3 \cdot 3 \cdot 3 \cdot 3 \cdot 3$

6. $9 \cdot 9 \cdot 9$

Think and Discuss

7. Discuss whether 3^9 is the same as 9^3.

8. Explain why 4^6 is greater than 4^5.

Holt Mathematics

Name _____ Date _____ Class _____

Review for Mastery
Exponents

exponent

base

The fifth power of 3 $3^5 = 3 \cdot 3 \cdot 3 \cdot 3 \cdot 3$

3 used as a factor 5 times

Complete to write each expression using an exponent. State the power.

1. $5 \cdot 5 \cdot 5 \cdot 5 = 5^{\_\_}$

the _____ power of 5

2. $(-7) \cdot (-7) \cdot (-7) = (-7)^{\_\_}$

the _____ power of ____

Complete to evaluate each expression.

3. $(-2)^3 = (-2)(-2)(-2) = $ _____

4. $10^4 = $ ____ $\cdot$ ____ $\cdot$ ____ $\cdot$ ____ $= $ _____

5. $(-5)^4 = ($____$)($____$)($____$)($____$) = $ _____

When an expression is a product that includes a power, you simplify the power first.

$3 \cdot 2^3 = 3 \cdot 2 \cdot 2 \cdot 2 = 3 \cdot 8 = 24$

Complete to simplify each expression.

6. $4 \cdot (-2)^3 = 4($____$)($____$)($____$) = $ _____

7. $5 \cdot 3^3 = $ ____ $\cdot$ ____ $\cdot$ ____ $\cdot$ ____ $= $ _____

8. $(3 \cdot 2)^3 = 6^3 = $ ____ $\cdot$ ____ $\cdot$ ____ $= $ _____

9. $(-4(-2))^3 = ($____$)^3 = ($____$)($____$)($____$) = $ _____

10. $25 - 3(4 \cdot 3^2)$

$= 25 - 3(4 \cdot $ _____$)$

$= 25 - 3($_____$)$

$= 25 - $ _____

$= $ _____

11. $-100 - 2(3 \cdot 4)^2$

$= -100 - 2($_____$)^2$

$= -100 - 2($_____$)$

$= -100 - $ _____

$= $ _____

12. $15 - 4(3 + 3^2)$

$= 15 - 4(3 + $ _____$)$

$= 15 - 4($_____$)$

$= 15 - $ _____

$= $ _____

Holt Mathematics

Name _____ Date _____ Class _____

LESSON 4A Homework and Practice
Exponents

Write using exponents.

1. $8 \times 8 \times 8 \times 8 \times$
$8 \times 8 \times 8$

2. $(-5) \times (-5) \times$
$(-5) \times (-5)$

3. $9 \times 9 \times 9 \times$
$9 \times 9 \times 9$

_____ _____ _____

Evaluate.

4. 10^4

5. $(-4)^3$

6. $(-6)^2$

7. 9^2

_____ _____

8. 14^2

9. $(-8)^2$

10. $(-12)^2$

11. $(-3)^4$

_____ _____

Simplify.

12. $3^3 - 15$

13. $(-4)^4 + 7$

14. $7^2 - 2^5$

15. $78 - 6^2$

_____ _____ _____

16. $11^2 - 3^4 + 3$

17. $16 - 3^3 \times 4$

18. $6^2 + 10 \times 2^4$

19. $-3 (4^3 + 9^2)$

_____ _____ _____

Evaluate for the given value of the variable.

20. x^3 for $x = -3$

21. $6y^2$ for $y = 4$

22. $w^4 - 17$ for $w = 3$

_____ _____ _____

23. Write an expression for eight times a number used as a factor
four times.

_____

24. If the length of a side of a regular cube is 12 cm, find its volume.
(Hint: $V = l^3$).

_____

Holt Mathematics

4B Look for a Pattern in Integer Exponents

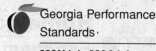

Georgia Performance
Standards·

M8N1.i, M8A1.b

Suppose the height of a magic plant doubles every hour, beginning with a height of 1 inch at the "zero hour."

Use the bar graph to think about how tall the plant was 1 hour before (−1) and 2 hours before (−2) the zero hour.

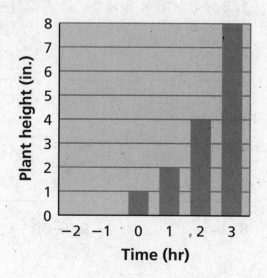

1. Draw and label a bar on the bar graph to show the height at hour −1 and hour −2. (*Hint:* The height doubles each hour.)

2. Use the graph and the pattern in the table to find the value of each exponential expression.

Time, x	Plant Height, 2^x
−3	$2^{-3} = \dfrac{1}{2^3} = \dfrac{1}{8}$
−2	
−1	
0	
1	
2	
3	

Think and Discuss

3. **Describe** the pattern in the bar graph.

4. **Describe** the pattern in the table.

Holt Mathematics

Review for Mastery

LESSON 4B *Look for a Pattern in Integer Exponents*

To rewrite a negative exponent,
move the power to the denominator $5^{-2} = \dfrac{1}{5^2}$
of a unit fraction.

Complete to rewrite each power with a positive exponent.

1. $7^{-3} = \dfrac{1}{}$ **2.** $9^{-5} = \dfrac{1}{}$ **3.** $13^{-4} = \dfrac{1}{}$

Complete each pattern.

4. $10^{-1} = \dfrac{1}{10} = 0.1$ **5.** $5^{-1} = \dfrac{1}{5}$

$10^{-2} = \dfrac{1}{10^2} = \dfrac{1}{100} = 0.01$ $5^{-2} = \dfrac{1}{5^2} = \dfrac{1}{5 \cdot 5} = \dfrac{1}{25}$

$10^{-3} = $ _____ $5^{-3} = $ _____

6. $3^{-1} = \dfrac{1}{3}$ **7.** $(-4)^{-1} = $ ____

$3^{-2} = \dfrac{1}{3^2} = \dfrac{1}{3 \cdot 3} = \dfrac{1}{9}$ $(-4)^{-2} = $ _____

$3^{-3} = $ _____ $(-4)^{-3} = $ _____

Evaluate.

8. $2^{-3} = \dfrac{1}{} = $ _____   **9.** $(-6)^{-2} = \dfrac{1}{} = $ _____

10. $4^{-2} = \dfrac{1}{} = $ _____   **11.** $(-3)^{-3} = \dfrac{1}{} = $ _____

12. $6^{-2} = $ _____   **13.** $(-2)^{-3} = $ _____

14. $6^{-3} = $ _____   **15.** $(-5)^{-2} = $ _____

16. $2^{-4} = $ _____   **17.** $(-9)^{-1} = $ _____

Name _____ Date _____ Class _____

Homework and Practice
Looking for a Pattern in Integer Exponents

Evaluate the powers of 10.

1. 10^{-6} **2.** 10^4 **3.** 10^{-3} **4.** 10^5

_____   _____   _____   _____

5. 10^{-1} **6.** 10^8 **7.** 10^{-5} **8.** 10^2

_____   _____   _____   _____

Evaluate.

9. $(-7)^{-3}$ **10.** $\dfrac{11^2}{11^5}$ **11.** $\dfrac{a^8}{a^{14}}$

_____   _____   _____

12. $(-8)^{-4}$ **13.** $6^{-3} \cdot 6^{-2}$ **14.** $\dfrac{5^9}{5^{13}}$

_____   _____   _____

15. $14^{-2} \cdot 14^5$ **16.** $\dfrac{19^7}{19^9}$ **17.** $\dfrac{(-15)}{(-15)^4}$

_____   _____   _____

18. $(-17)^{-3} \cdot (-17)^6$ **19.** $\dfrac{21^2}{21^4}$ **20.** $(20)^3 \cdot (20)^{-5}$

_____   _____   _____

Express the answer using powers of 10 and negative numbers.

21. 1 meter = $\dfrac{1}{1000}$ km = _____ km.

22. Find the volume of a cube with a side that measures 0.01 cm.
(Hint: $V = s^3$).

_____

Holt Mathematics

Georgia Performance Standards

M8N1.i

4C Properties of Exponents

You can use patterns to discover properties of exponents.

1. Complete the table.

Product of Powers	Write the Factors	Write As a Single Power
$3^2 \cdot 3^5$	$(3 \cdot 3) \cdot (3 \cdot 3 \cdot 3 \cdot 3 \cdot 3) =$ $3 \cdot 3 \cdot 3 \cdot 3 \cdot 3 \cdot 3 \cdot 3$	3^7
$4^3 \cdot 4^2$		
$7^4 \cdot 7^4$		
$5^2 \cdot 5^4$		

2. Look at the left-hand and right-hand columns of the table. What patterns do you notice?

3. Complete the table.

Product of Powers	Write the Factors	Write As a Single Power
$\dfrac{3^6}{3^2}$	$\dfrac{3 \cdot 3 \cdot 3 \cdot 3 \cdot 3 \cdot 3}{3 \cdot 3} = 3 \cdot 3 \cdot 3 \cdot 3$	3^4
$\dfrac{4^5}{4^3}$		
$\dfrac{5^4}{5^3}$		
$\dfrac{8^7}{8^3}$		

4. Look at the left-hand and right-hand columns of the table. What patterns do you notice?

Think and Discuss

5. **Explain** how you can use what you discovered to write $2^7 \cdot 2^{10}$ as a single power.

6. **Explain** how you can use what you discovered to write $\dfrac{2^{10}}{2^7}$ as a single power.

Holt Mathematics

Name _____ Date _____ Class _____

LESSON 4C Hands-On Lab
Use Tables to Explore the Properties of Exponents

You can use tables of numbers to see patterns in the value of exponents. These tables will help you see the properties of exponents and write a general form for them.

Activity

1. Complete the table.

$2^1 = 2$	$2^1 = 2$	$2^1 \times 2^1 = 4$	$2^2 = 4$
$2^1 = \underline{\ \ }$	$2^2 = 4$	$2^1 \times 2^2 = \underline{\ \ }$	$2^3 = 8$
$2^1 = 2$	$2^3 = \underline{\ \ }$	$2^1 \times 2^3 = \underline{\ \ }$	$2^4 = 16$
$2^1 = \underline{\ \ }$	$2^4 = 16$	$2^1 \times 2^4 = 32$	$2^5 = \underline{\ \ }$
$2^2 = 4$	$2^{\underline{\ }} = 4$	$2^2 \times 2^2 = 16$	$2^4 = \underline{\ \ }$
$2^2 = 4$	$2^3 = 8$	$2^2 \times 2^{\underline{\ }} = 32$	$\underline{\ }^5 = 32$
$2^2 = 4$	$2^4 = \underline{\ \ }$	$2^{\underline{\ }} \times 2^4 = 64$	$2^{\underline{\ }} = 64$
$2^{\underline{\ }} = 8$	$2^3 = 8$	$2^3 \times 2^3 = 64$	$2^6 = \underline{\ \ }$

Think and Discuss

1. What do all of the bases in the table have in common?

_____

2. How are the exponents in the third column combined in the fourth column?

_____

Copyright © by Holt, Rinehart and Winston. All rights reserved. 106 Holt Mathematics

LESSON
4C

Hands-On Lab

Use Tables to Explore the Properties of Exponents, continued

3. What pattern do you notice about the products in columns three and four?

_____

4. Use the observations from the table to complete this equation. This equation summarizes the property for multiplying exponents with the same base: $x^a \times x^b = x^?$.

_____

_____

Try This

1. Complete this table, which is similar to the one above but shows how exponents relate by division. Then complete the expression in the form

$x^a \div x^b = x^?$ that summarizes the division property.

$2^4 = 16$	$2^1 = 2$	$2^4 \div 2^1 = 8$	$2^3 = 8$
$2^4 = \_\_\_$	$2^2 = 4$	$2^4 \div 2^2 = \_\_\_$	$2^2 = 4$
$2^4 = 16$	$2^3 = \_\_$	$2^4 \div 2^3 = \_\_\_$	$2^1 = 2$
$2^3 = 8$	$2\_\_ = 2$	$2^3 \div 2^1 = 4$	$2^2 = \_\_\_$
$2^3 = \_\_\_$	$2^2 = 4$	$2^3 \div 2^2 = 2$	$2^1 = \_\_\_$
$2^2 = 4$	$2^1 = 2$	$2^2 \div 2\_\_ = 2$	$\_\_^1 = 2$

2. Determine which operations sign makes this property true: $(x^a)^b = x^{a\,?\,b}$. Use a table if necessary.

_____

LESSON 4C Review for Mastery
Properties of Exponents

To multiply powers with the same base, keep the base and add exponents.	To divide powers with the same base, keep the base and subtract exponents.	To raise a power to a power, keep the base and multiply exponents.
$x^a \cdot x^b = x^{a+b}$	$x^a \div x^b = x^{a-b}$	$(x^a)^b = x^{ab}$
$4^5 \cdot 4^2 = 4^{5+2} = 4^7$	$4^5 \div 4^2 = 4^{5-2} = 4^3$	$(4^5)^2 = 4^{5(2)} = 4^{10}$
$8^3 \cdot 8 = 8^{3+1} = 8^4$	$8^3 \div 8 = 8^{3-1} = 8^2$	

Complete to see why the rules for exponents work.

1. $4^5 \cdot 4^2 = (\_)\,(\_)\,(\_)\,(\_)(\_) \cdot (\_)(\_) = 4\text{---}$

2. $8^3 \cdot 8 = (\_)\,(\_)\,(\_) \cdot (\_) = 8\text{---}$

3. $4^5 \div 4^2 = \dfrac{4^5}{4^2} = \dfrac{4 \cdot 4 \cdot 4 \cdot 4 \cdot 4}{4 \cdot 4} = 4\text{---}$

4. $8^3 \div 8 = \dfrac{8^3}{8} = \dfrac{8 \cdot 8 \cdot 8}{8} = 8\text{---}$

5. $(4^2)^3 = 4^2 \cdot 4^2 \cdot 4^2 = 4^{2+2+2} = 4^{2(3)} = 4\text{---}$

Complete to write each product or quotient as one power.

6. $12^3 \cdot 12^2 = 12^{3+2} = 12\text{---}$

7. $9^4 \cdot 9^3 = 9\text{---} = 9\text{---}$

8. $\dfrac{7^6}{7^2} = 7^{6-2} = 7\text{---}$

9. $\dfrac{12^6}{12^4} = 12\text{---} = 12\text{---}$

Write each product or quotient as one power.

10. $10^4 \cdot 10^6 = $ _____

11. $5^5 \cdot 5 = $ _____

12. $4^5 \cdot 4 \cdot 4^3 = $ _____

13. $\dfrac{15^6}{15^2} = $ _____

14. $\dfrac{9^5}{9} = $ _____

15. $\dfrac{2^{10}}{2^2} = $ _____

Simplify.

16. $(5^3)^4 = 5^{3(4)} = $ _____

17. $(6^2)^4 = 6^{2(4)} = $ _____

18. $(2^5)^2 = $ _____

Holt Mathematics

Homework and Practice

LESSON 4C *Properties of Exponents*

Multiply. Write the product as one power.

1. $10^6 \times 10^9$ 2. $a^8 \times a^6$ 3. $15^6 \times 15^{12}$ 4. $11^{12} \times 11^7$

_____   _____   _____   _____

5. $(-w)^8 \times (-w)^{12}$ 6. $(-12)^{18} \times (-12)^{13}$ 7. $13^{10} \times 13^{15}$ 8. $w^{14} \times w^{12}$

_____   _____   _____   _____

Divide. Write the quotient as one power.

9. $\dfrac{a^{25}}{a^{18}}$ 10. $\dfrac{(-13)^{14}}{(-13)^9}$ 11. $\dfrac{14^{12}}{14^8}$ 12. $\dfrac{18^{11}}{18^5}$

_____   _____   _____   _____

13. $\dfrac{19^{15}}{19^4}$ 14. $\dfrac{21^{22}}{21^{20}}$ 15. $\dfrac{(-x)^{17}}{(-x)^7}$ 16. $\dfrac{25^8}{25^3}$

_____   _____   _____   _____

Write the product or quotient as one power.

17. $r^9 \times r^8$ 18. $\dfrac{16^{20}}{16^{10}}$ 19. $\dfrac{x^{15}}{x^9}$

_____   _____   _____

20. $(-17)^8 \times (-17)^7$ 21. $27^7 \times 27^6$ 22. $\dfrac{m^{16}}{m^{10}}$

_____   _____   _____

23. $(-b)^{21} \times (-b)^{14}$ 24. $\dfrac{26^{17}}{26^5}$ 25. $(-s)^{11} \times (-s)^4$

_____   _____   _____

26. Hampton has a baseball card collection of 5^6 cards. He organizes the cards into boxes that hold 5^4 each. How many boxes will Hampton need to hold the cards? Write the answer as one power.

_____

27. Write the expression for a number used as a factor seventeen times being multiplied by a number used as a factor fourteen times. Then write the product as one power.

_____

Holt Mathematics

EXPLORATION

4D Scientific Notation

Georgia Performance
Standards

M8N1.j

1. Complete the table of values for the powers of ten.

Exponent	Power
–6	$10^{-6} =$
–5	$10^{-5} =$
–4	$10^{-4} =$
–3	$10^{-3} =$
–2	$10^{-2} = \dfrac{1}{10^2} = \dfrac{1}{10 \times 10} = 0.01$
–1	$10^{-1} = \dfrac{1}{10^1} = \dfrac{1}{10} = 0.1$
0	$10^0 = 1$
1	$10^1 = 10$
2	$10^2 = 10 \times 10 = 100$
3	$10^3 =$
4	$10^4 =$
5	$10^5 =$
6	$10^6 =$

Think and Discuss

2. **Discuss** the pattern you see in the table of values for powers of ten.

3. **Explain** how you know that $10^{-9} = 0.000000001$.

Holt Mathematics

Technology Lab
LAB 4D *Scientific Notation*

Some numbers are so big that even calculators use scientific notation to display them. A scientific calculator displays numbers in standard form up to a certain number of digits. Beyond that limit, the calculator displays numbers in scientific notation. A scientific calculator makes it easy to multiply numbers in scientific notation.

Activity 1

Using a scientific or graphing calculator, you can determine the distance a ray of light travels in one day. The calculator will display the answer in scientific notation when it exceeds the display limit.

Light travels at a constant speed of 186,000 miles per second. To find out how far a ray of light travels in 1 minute, multiply 186,000 by 60 (1 minute = 60 seconds) to get 11,160,000.

To find out how far the light travels in an hour, multiply 11,160,000 by 60 (1 hour = 60 minutes) to get 669,600,000 miles.

Next, multiply 669,600,000 by 24 (24 hours = 1 day).

The calculator automatically converts the final answer to scientific notation. This number can be used for further calculations.

Holt Mathematics

Name _____ Date _____ Class _____

Activity 2

A scientific calculator allows you to easily multiply numbers written in scientific notation. Take the final answer from the previous activity (1.60704E10) and multiply that number by 8.96×10^3.

Enter the first number in scientific notation with the following

keystrokes: 1.60704 **2nd** **,**ᴱᴱ 10. Then press the multiplication button.

Enter the second number with the following keystrokes: 8.96 **2nd** **,**ᴱᴱ 3.
Then press "Enter" to obtain the product.

Think and Discuss

1. Which of the following products is displayed in scientific notation on your calculator?

   9,217,400,938 • 385,474,609 _____

   771,247,792 • 7.6312345 _____

   Were both of them displayed in scientific notation? Why or why not?

   _____

   _____

Try This

Perform each operation using a scientific calculator.

1. $(4.7 \cdot 10^9) \cdot (3.33 \cdot 10^6)$

   _____

2. $(9.92415 \cdot 10^3) \cdot (8.3 \cdot 10^{-7})$

   _____

3. $(4.3 \cdot 10^2) \div (6.3 \cdot 10^8)$

   _____

Holt Mathematics

Review for Mastery

LESSON 4D *Scientific Notation*

Standard Notation	Scientific Notation	
	$\begin{pmatrix} \text{1st factor is} \\ \text{between 1 and 10.} \end{pmatrix}$	$\begin{pmatrix} \text{2nd factor is an} \\ \text{integer power of 10.} \end{pmatrix}$
430,000	4.3×10^8	positive integer for large number
0.0000057	5.7×10^{-6}	negative integer for small number

To convert from scientific notation, look at the power of 10 to tell how many places and which way to move the decimal point.

Complete to write each in standard notation.

1. 4.12×10^6 **2.** 3.4×10^{-5}

Is the exponent positive or negative?   _____ _____

Move the decimal point right or left?
How many places?   _____ _____

Write the number in standard notation.   _____ _____

Write each number in standard notation.

3. 8×10^5 **4.** 7.1×10^{-4} **5.** 3.14×10^8

_____   _____   _____

To convert to scientific notation, determine the factor between 1 and 10. Then determine the power of 10 by counting from the decimal point in the first factor to the decimal point in the given number.

Complete to write each in scientific notation.

6. 32,000,000   **7.** 0.0000000712

What is the first factor?   _____ _____

From its location in the first factor, which way must the decimal move to its location in the given number? How many places?   _____ _____

Write the number in scientific notation.   _____ _____

Write each number in scientific notation.

8. 41,000,000   **9.** 0.0000000643   **10.** 1,370,000,000

_____   _____   _____

Holt Mathematics

Homework and Practice

LESSON 4D

Scientific Notation

Write each number in standard notation.

1. 6.12×10^2 2. 7.9×10^{-3} 3. 4.87×10^4 4. 9.3×10^{-2}

_____   _____   _____   _____

5. 8.06×10^3 6. 5.7×10^{-4} 7. 3.17×10^{-5} 8. 9.00613×10^{-2}

_____   _____   _____   _____

9. 9.85×10^{-5} 10. 6.004×10^7 11. 8.23×10^4 12. 1.48×10^{-6}

_____   _____   _____   _____

Write each number in scientific notation.

13. 108,000,000   14. 0.5943   15. 42   16. 0.0000673

_____   _____   _____   _____

17. 0.0056   18. 6004   19. 0.00852   20. 24,631,500

_____   _____   _____   _____

21. 89450   22. 0.005702   23. 8,005,000,000   24. 0.00012805

_____   _____   _____   _____

25. The mass of the Earth is 5,980,000,000,000,000,000,000,000 kilograms. Write this number in scientific notation.

_____

26. The mass of a dust particle is 7.53×10^{-10}. Write this number in standard notation.

_____

Holt Mathematics

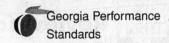

Georgia Performance Standards

M8N1.a, M8N1.b, M8N1.d, M8N1.e

4E Squares and Square Roots

The sequence shows the square numbers 1, 4, 9, and 16.

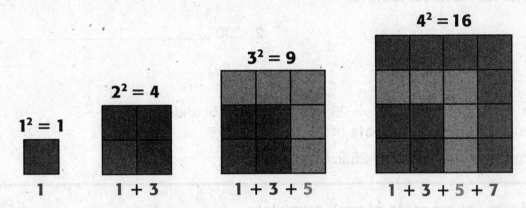

$1^2 = 1$ $2^2 = 4$ $3^2 = 9$ $4^2 = 16$

1   1 + 3   1 + 3 + 5   1 + 3 + 5 + 7

1. Draw a picture to show that $5^2 = 1 + 3 + 5 + 7 + 9$.

2. Add the odd numbers $1 + 3 + 5 + 7 + 9 + \cdots + 17 + 19$. What square number do you get?

3. The table starts with $11^2 = 1 + 3 + 5 + 7 + 9 + 11 + 13 + 15 + 17 + 19 + 21 = 121$. Complete the table by adding the next odd number to this sum.

11^2	12^2	13^2	14^2	15^2	16^2	17^2	18^2	19^2	20^2
121									

Think and Discuss

4. **Explain** how you can determine square numbers using sums of odd numbers.

5. **Demonstrate** that the value of 22^2 can be determined by adding odd numbers.

Holt Mathematics

Name _____ Date _____ Class _____

Review for Mastery
Squares and Square Roots

A **perfect square** has two identical factors.

$25 = 5 \times 5 = 5^2$ **or** $25 = (-5) \times (-5) = (-5)^2$ then 25 is a perfect square.

Tell if the number is a perfect square.
If yes, write its identical factors.

1. 121 _____ 2. 200 _____

3. 400 _____

Since $5^2 = 25$ and also $(-5)^2 = 25,$ $\sqrt{25} = 5$ and $-\sqrt{25} = -5$
both 5 and −5 are **square roots** of 25.

The **principal square root** of 25 is 5: $\sqrt{25} = 5$

Write the two square roots of each number.

4. $\sqrt{81} =$ _____ 5. $\sqrt{625} =$ _____ 6. $\sqrt{169} =$ _____

$-\sqrt{81} =$ _____ $-\sqrt{625} =$ _____ $-\sqrt{169} =$ _____

Write the principal square root of each number.

7. $\sqrt{144} =$ _____ 8. $\sqrt{6400} =$ _____ 9. $\sqrt{10,000} =$ _____

Use the principal square root when $5\sqrt{100} - 3$
evaluating an expression. For the $5(10) - 3$
order of operations, do square root $50 - 3$
first, as you would an exponent. 47

Complete to evaluate each expression.

10. $3\sqrt{144} - 20$ 11. $\sqrt{25 + 144} + 13$ 12. $\sqrt{\dfrac{100}{25}} + \dfrac{1}{2}$

$3 \times$ _____ $- 20$ _____ $+ 13$ $\dfrac{\sqrt{100}}{\sqrt{25}} + \dfrac{1}{2}$

_____ $- 20$ _____ $+ 13$ $\dfrac{\text{_____}}{5} + \dfrac{1}{2}$

_____   _____   _____ $+ \dfrac{1}{2}$

_____

Holt Mathematics

Name _____ Date _____ Class _____

Recall that the formula for the area of a
square is $A = s^2$. A power in which the
exponent is 2 is called a *square*.

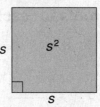

Use the model to help you find the square.

13. 5^2

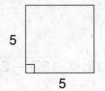

$A = s^2$

$A = \underline{\quad}^2$

$A = \underline{\quad} \cdot \underline{\quad}$

$A = \underline{\quad}$

14. 9^2

$A = s^2$

$A = (\underline{\quad})^2$

$A = \underline{\quad} \cdot \underline{\quad}$

$A = \underline{\quad}$

Find the square.

15. 13^2 **16.** 16^2 **17.** 11^2 **18.** 7^2

_____   _____   _____   _____

The numbers 36 and 81 are *perfect squares*. **Perfect squares** are
numbers that are the squares of whole numbers.

The square root of 36 is 6. $\sqrt{36} = 6$ because $6 \cdot 6 = 36$.

A table of square roots can help you estimate the square root of a
number that is not a perfect square.

Square Root	1	2	3	4	5	6	7	8	9	10
Perfect Squares	1	4	9	16	25	36	49	64	81	100

19. $\sqrt{44}$

Find the perfect square nearest 44.

44 is closest to _____.

Since $\sqrt{49} = $ _____,

$\sqrt{44}$ is closest to _____.

20. $\sqrt{87}$

Find the perfect square nearest 87.

87 is closest to _____.

Since $\sqrt{81} = $ _____,

$\sqrt{87}$ is closest to _____

Holt Mathematics

**LESSON
4E**
Homework and Practice
Squares and Square Roots

Find the two square roots for each number.

1. 16

2. 9

3. 64

4. 121

_____   _____   _____   _____

5. 36

6. 100

7. 225

8. 400

_____   _____   _____   _____

Evaluate each expression.

9. $\sqrt{27 + 37}$

10. $\sqrt{41 + 59}$

11. $\sqrt{122 - 41}$

12. $\sqrt{167 - 23}$

_____   _____   _____   _____

13. $3\sqrt{81} + 19$

14. $25 - \sqrt{25}$

15. $\sqrt{169} - \sqrt{36}$

16. $\sqrt{196} + 25$

_____   _____   _____   _____

17. $\dfrac{\sqrt{81}}{9}$

18. $-4.9\sqrt{64}$

19. $\dfrac{\sqrt{225}}{\sqrt{25}}$

20. $\dfrac{\sqrt{100}}{-2.5}$

_____   _____   _____   _____

21. Find the product of six and the sum of the square roots of 100 and 225.

_____

22. Find the difference between the square root of 361 and the square root of 289.

_____

23. If a replica of the ancient pyramids were built with a base area of 1,024 in.^{2}, what would be the length of each side?(Hint: $s = \sqrt{A}$)

_____

24. The maximum displacement speed of a boat is found using the formula:
Maximum Speed in km/h = 4.5 $\sqrt{}$ the waterline length of the boat in meters.
Find the maximum displacement speed of a boat that has a waterline length of 9 meters.

_____

Holt Mathematics

Name _____ Date _____ Class _____

Homework and Practice
LESSON 4E *Squares and Square Roots, continued*

Model each power using a square. Then evaluate the power.

25. 7^2 _____
26. $(2.6)^2$ _____
27. $(5.8)^2$ _____
28. 26^2 _____

29. 21^2 _____
30. $(1.7)^2$ _____
31. $(9.9)^2$ _____
32. 13^2 _____

Estimate each square root to the nearest whole number. Use a calculator to check the reasonableness of your answers.

33. $\sqrt{33}$ _____
34. $\sqrt{15}$ _____
35. $\sqrt{81}$ _____
36. $\sqrt{37}$ _____

37. $\sqrt{24}$ _____
38. $\sqrt{51}$ _____
39. $\sqrt{8}$ _____
40. $\sqrt{148}$ _____

41. $\sqrt{64}$ _____
42. $\sqrt{102}$ _____
43. $\sqrt{46}$ _____
44. $\sqrt{171}$ _____

45. $\sqrt{90}$ _____
46. $\sqrt{19}$ _____
47. $\sqrt{83}$ _____
48. $\sqrt{125}$ _____

49. $\sqrt{3}$ _____
50. $\sqrt{220}$ _____
51. $\sqrt{136}$ _____
52. $\sqrt{22}$ _____

53. $\sqrt{500}$ _____
54. $\sqrt{55}$ _____
55. $\sqrt{610}$ _____
56. $\sqrt{900}$ _____

57. The area of a square tetherball court is 260 ft². What is the approximate length of each side of the court? Find your answer to the nearest foot.

_____

58. The area of square watch face is 6 cm². What is the approximate length of each side of the watch face? Find your answer to the nearest tenth of a centimeter.

_____

59. Brian jogs one time around a square park with an area of 4 mi². How far does Brian jog?

_____

60. Steve wants to make a curtain to cover a square window with an area of 9 ft². How long should each side of the curtain be?

_____

Holt Mathematics

Georgia Performance
Standards

4F Estimating Square Roots M8N1.c, M8N1.f, M8N1.k

Knowing the square numbers can help you estimate square roots.

1. Complete the table of squares.

1^2	2^2	3^2	4^2	5^2	6^2	7^2	8^2	9^2	10^2
1									

11^2	12^2	13^2	14^2	15^2	16^2	17^2	18^2	19^2	20^2
121									

Use the table of squares above to help you estimate each square root to the nearest tenth. Use a calculator to check your estimates. Round to two decimal places.

	Square Root	Estimate	Calculator
2.	$\sqrt{10}$		
3.	$\sqrt{20}$		
4.	$\sqrt{200}$		
5.	$\sqrt{300}$		
6.	$\sqrt{57}$		
7.	$\sqrt{130}$		

Think and Discuss

8. Discuss your strategy for estimating square roots.

Holt Mathematics

Technology Lab

LAB 4F

Finding Square Roots

If you know the area of a square or circle and need to find the length of the side or the radius, you can find your answer by using square roots.

Activity

The area of a square is 289 cm^2. What is the length of a side?

$s = \sqrt{289}$

On your graphing calculator use the following keystrokes to find the square root:

[2nd] [$\sqrt{x^2}$] 289 [ENTER]

The length of a side is 17 cm.

The area (A) of a circle is 520 cm^2. What is the radius of the circle?

$$A = \pi r^2 \qquad r = \sqrt{\frac{A}{\pi}} = \sqrt{\frac{520}{\pi}} \approx \sqrt{165.52} \approx 12.87$$

On your calculator use the following keystrokes:

[2nd] [$\sqrt{x^2}$] 520 [÷] [2nd] [π] [A] [ENTER]

The radius is about 12.87 cm.

Think and Discuss

1. Enter [π] on your calculator. Is π a rational number? Explain why or why not.

   _____

2. Use your calculator to find the square root of pi. Is the number you see in your display the actual square root or an approximate square root? How do you know?

   _____

   _____

Holt Mathematics

Technology Lab

LAB 4F

Finding Square Roots, continued

Try This

1. Find the length (*s*) of a side of a square with an area *A* of 12.25 cm^2. Show the buttons you pressed on your calculator to find the answer.

   _____

   _____

   _____

2. Find the radius of a circle with an area of 144 cm^2. Show the buttons you pressed on your calculator to find the answer.

   _____

   _____

Holt Mathematics

Review for Mastery
Estimating Square Roots

To locate a square root between two integers, refer to the table.

Number	1	2	3	4	5	6	7	8	9	10
Square	1	4	9	16	25	36	49	64	81	100
Number	11	12	13	14	15	16	17	18	19	20
Square	121	144	169	196	225	256	289	324	361	400

Locate $\sqrt{260}$ between two integers.

260 is between the perfect squares 256 and 289:

$$256 < 260 < 289$$
$$\text{So:} \quad \sqrt{256} < \sqrt{260} < \sqrt{289}$$
$$\text{And:} \quad 16 < \sqrt{260} < 17$$

Use the table to complete the statements.

1. ____ < 39 < ____

   ____ < $\sqrt{39}$ < ____

   ____ < $\sqrt{39}$ < ____

2. ____ < 130 < ____

   ____ < $\sqrt{130}$ < ____

   ____ < $\sqrt{130}$ < ____

After locating a square root between two integers, you can determine which of the two integers the square root is closer to.

27 is between the perfect squares 25 and 36:

$$25 < 27 < 36$$
$$\text{So:} \quad \sqrt{25} < \sqrt{27} < \sqrt{36}$$
$$\text{And:} \quad 5 < \sqrt{27} < 6$$

The difference between 27 and 25 is 2;
the difference between 36 and 27 is 9.
So, $\sqrt{27}$, is closer to 5.

$$25 < 27 < 36$$
$$\quad\ \ 2 \qquad\ \ 9$$

Complete the statements.

3. 100 < 106 < 121

   ____ < $\sqrt{106}$ < ____

   ____ < $\sqrt{106}$ < ____

   106 − 100 = _____

   121 − 106 = _____

   $\sqrt{106}$ is closer to _____ than _____

4. _____ < 250 < _____

   _____ < $\sqrt{250}$ < _____

   _____ < $\sqrt{250}$ < _____

   250 − _____ = _____

   _____ − 250 = _____

   $\sqrt{250}$ is closer to _____ than _____

Holt Mathematics

Homework and Practice
Finding Square Roots

Each square root is between two integers. Name the integers.

1. $\sqrt{10}$ **2.** $\sqrt{24}$ **3.** $\sqrt{51}$ **4.** $\sqrt{39}$

_____   _____   _____   _____

5. $\sqrt{66}$ **6.** $\sqrt{30}$ **7.** $\sqrt{78}$ **8.** $\sqrt{87}$

_____   _____   _____   _____

Use a calculator to find each value. Round to the nearest tenth.

9. $\sqrt{18}$ **10.** $\sqrt{63}$ **11.** $\sqrt{19}$ **12.** $\sqrt{41}$

_____   _____   _____   _____

13. $\sqrt{53}$ **14.** $\sqrt{98}$ **15.** $\sqrt{54}$ **16.** $\sqrt{72}$

_____   _____   _____   _____

17. $\sqrt{83}$ **18.** $\sqrt{120}$ **19.** $\sqrt{200}$ **20.** $\sqrt{489}$

_____   _____   _____   _____

21. The distance a person can see at sea is measured in miles by using the formula $d = \sqrt{\dfrac{3}{2}h}$, where h is the height in ft above sea level. About how many miles can a person see that is 8 feet above sea level? Round the answer to the nearest tenth of a mile.

_____

22. The length of the hypotenuse of a right triangle is the square root of the sum of the squares of the measures of the other two legs of the triangle. Approximate the length of the hypotenuse of a right triangle if the legs have measures 12 and 15.

_____

23. At an accident scene, a police officer may determine the rate of speed, r, in mi/h, of the car by using the following formula $r = \sqrt{20\ell}$, where ℓ is length of the skid marks. How fast was a car going if the skid marks at the scene are 180 ft long?

_____

Holt Mathematics

Georgia Performance
Standards

4G The Real Numbers

M8N1.h

The Set of Real Numbers

Rational numbers can be written as fractions or as decimals that terminate or repeat.	*Irrational numbers* are decimals that do not terminate or repeat.
Examples: $\frac{1}{4}$ $5 = \frac{5}{1}$ $\sqrt{1.69} = 1.3$ $\frac{5}{3} = 1.\overline{6}$	Examples: $\sqrt{7} = 2.645751311\ldots$ $\pi = 3.141592653\ldots$

Classify each number as rational or irrational.

		Rational	Irrational
1.	$2\frac{1}{2}$		
2.	$\sqrt{24}$		
3.	$\sqrt{16}$		
4.	$7.\overline{7}$		
5.	$\sqrt{\frac{4}{9}}$		

Think and Discuss

6. Explain how to classify numbers as rational.

7. Explain how to classify numbers as irrational.

Holt Mathematics

LESSON 4G Hands-On Lab
Real Numbers

The square roots of numbers that are not perfect squares are impossible to express exactly, because they involve endless non-repeating decimals. They are definite quantities and can be used in calculations and in modeling figures.

Activity

Take a sheet of graph paper and turn it on its side. In the lower left corner, draw two squares side by side, each 5 units on a side. Label the first square ABDC and the second CDFE, as shown.

Take a compass and open it so that the point is on point B and the pencil is on point C, diagonally opposite. The opening of the compass is equal to the side of the square multiplied by the square root of two. With the compass at that opening, draw a square of that height and width. The new square should have an area twice that of the first square you drew.

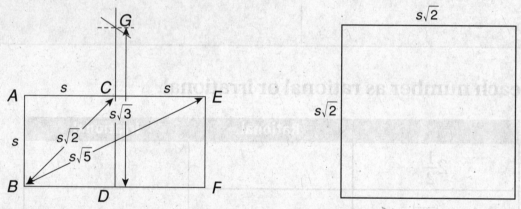

Between the first two squares you drew, extend a vertical line upwards from CD. Now put the compass on the point B and the pencil on point F. Keeping the point of the compass where it is, swing the pencil up to intersect the vertical line you just drew. Label the intersection point as point G. Now open the compass with its point on point D and the pencil on point F. The opening of the compass is equal to the side of the original square multiplied by the square root of three. Use that compass opening to draw a square of that side length. Its area should be three times that of the first square you drew.

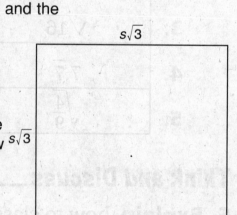

Holt Mathematics

Hands-On Lab
Real Numbers, continued

Think and Discuss

1. How do you know that the squares you constructed have two and three times the area, respectively, of the first square you drew?

   _____

   _____

   _____

2. Could you perform these operations just as well using a ruler and not a compass?

   _____

   _____

Try This

Using the points and lines you have already labeled, can you show how to use the compass to read off the correct length for a square that will be four times as large as your original square and another that will be five times as large?

_____

_____

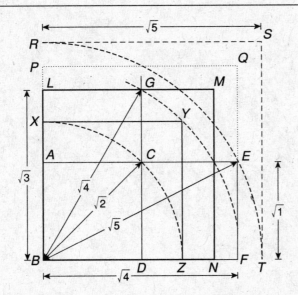

LESSON 4G

Technology Lab
The Real Numbers

Activity

You can use a calculator to verify the density property of real numbers.
To find a number between two given numbers, add the two numbers
together and divide by two.

Find a real number between

$1\frac{3}{4}$ and $3\frac{1}{4}$

On your calculator, enter the equivalent of $1\frac{3}{4}$ by pressing:

[3] [÷] [4] [+] [1]

And the equivalent of $3\frac{1}{4}$ by pressing:

[1] [÷] [4] [+] [3]

Add each fraction equivalent together and divide by 2.

[( ] [3] [÷] [4] [+] [1] [+] [1] [÷] [4] [+] [3] [ )] [÷]

[2] [ENTER]

LESSON 4G Technology Lab
The Real Numbers, continued

Think and Discuss

1. Why do each of the fractions need to be put into the calculator as a division problem first?

_____

Try This

Use the calculator to find a real number between the given numbers.

1. $1\frac{6}{8}$ and $2\frac{2}{8}$ 2. 1 and $2\frac{1}{3}$ 3. 1.4 and $3\frac{6}{10}$ 4. 2.45 and 3.55

_____   _____   _____   _____

     Holt Mathematics

Review for Mastery

LESSON 4G

The Real Numbers

The set of **rational numbers** contains all integers, all fractions, and decimals that end or repeat.

Irrational numbers can only be written as decimals that do not end or repeat.

Together, the rational numbers and the irrational numbers form the set of **real numbers.**

```
        Real Numbers
        /          \
Rational Numbers   Irrational Numbers
```

Square roots of numbers that are perfect squares are rational.

$$\sqrt{25} = 5$$

Square roots of numbers that are not perfect squares are irrational.

$$\sqrt{3} = 1.732050807\ldots$$

Tell if each number is rational or irrational.

1. $\sqrt{7}$ **2.** $\sqrt{81}$ **3.** $\sqrt{169}$ **4.** $\sqrt{101}$

_____   _____   _____   _____

The square of a nonzero number is positive. $3^2 = 9$ and $(-3)^2 = 9$
So, the square root of a negative number is not a real number.
    $\sqrt{-9}$ is not a real number.

Tell if each number is real or not real.

5. -8 **6.** $-\sqrt{8}$ **7.** $\sqrt{-8}$ **8.** $\sqrt{-25}$

_____   _____   _____   _____

Between any two real numbers, there is always another real number. One way to find a number between is to find the number halfway between.

To find a real number between $7\frac{1}{5}$ and $7\frac{2}{5}$,

divide their sum by 2: $7\frac{1}{5} + 7\frac{2}{5} = \left(14\frac{3}{5}\right) \div 2 = 7\frac{3}{10}$

Find a real number between each pair.

9. $8\frac{3}{7}$ and $8\frac{4}{7}$ **10.** -1.6 and -1.7 **11.** $-3\frac{7}{9}$ and $-3\frac{2}{9}$ **12.** $6\frac{1}{2}$ and $6\frac{3}{4}$

_____   _____   _____   _____

Holt Mathematics

Homework and Practice

LESSON 4G *The Real Numbers*

Write all names that apply to each number.

1. $\sqrt{\dfrac{36}{4}}$

2. $-\dfrac{3}{16}$

3. $\sqrt{0.81}$

_____

_____

_____

4. -81

5. $-7.23\overline{3}$

6. $\sqrt{95}$

_____

_____

_____

State if the number is rational, irrational, or not a real number.

7. $\sqrt{49}$

8. $-\sqrt{144}$

9. $\dfrac{9}{\sqrt{3}}$

10. $\dfrac{\sqrt{81}}{\sqrt{9}}$

_____

_____

_____

_____

11. $\dfrac{21}{0}$

12. $\dfrac{20}{8}$

13. $\sqrt{-100}$

14. 8.67

_____

_____

_____

_____

Find a real number between each pair of numbers.

15. $4\dfrac{2}{5}$ and $4\dfrac{3}{5}$

16. 7.25 and $\dfrac{15}{2}$

17. $\dfrac{5}{8}$ and $\dfrac{3}{4}$

_____

18. Give an example of a rational number between $-\sqrt{36}$ and $\sqrt{36}$

_____

19. Give an example of an irrational number less than 0.

_____

20. Give an example of a number that is not real.

_____

Holt Mathematics

EXPLORATION

4H The Pythagorean Theorem

Georgia Performance Standards

M8G2.a

The model shows a visual example of the Pythagorean Theorem.

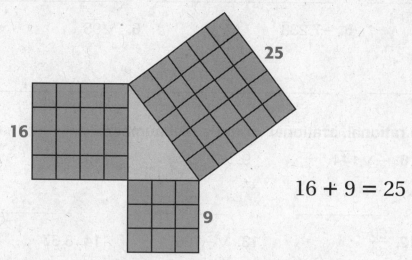

16 + 9 = 25

1. Find the lengths of the sides of the right triangle that is surrounded by the three squares.

2. What is the area of each square on each side of the triangle?

3. How does the length of each side of the triangle relate to the area of the corresponding square?

4. Can you form another example of the Pythagorean Theorem with the squares below?

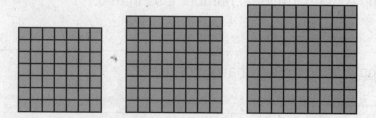

Think and Discuss _____

5. **Explain** how you found the answer for Problem 4.

Holt Mathematics

Name _____ Date _____ Class _____

Hands-On Lab
The Pythagorean Theorem

Activity

The Pythagorean Theorem states that in any right triangle, the sum of the squares of the lengths of the two legs is equal to the square of the length of the hypotenuse. In other words, $a^2 + b^2 = c^2$

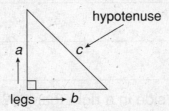

Demonstrate the validity of the Pythagorean Theorem by drawing a right triangle in the space below, labeling the sides as in the diagram above. Then measure the 2 legs and fill in the measurements to find the length of the hypotenuse. Use a centimeter ruler if possible. Round to the nearest hundredth.
$a^2 + b^2 = c^2$

_____ + _____ = c^2

Use the square-root key on your calculator ($\sqrt{}$) to find c: $c =$ _____

_____

Now measure the length of the hypotenuse: _____

_____

Holt Mathematics

Hands-On Lab

The Pythagorean Theorem, continued

Think and Discuss

1. How could you use the Pythagorean Theorem to find a side in a right triangle if you knew the measurements of the other 2 sides?

_____

_____

_____

2. Which side will always be the longest side in a right triangle?

_____

_____

Try This

Draw a right triangle. Measure the hypotenuse and one side. Use the Pythagorean Theorem to find the measurement of the third side. Round to the nearest hundredth.

$a^2 + b^2 = c^2$

$b^2 = c^2 - a^2$

$b^2 = $ _____ $-$ _____

$b = $

_____

To check your work, measure the length of the third side: _____

_____

Holt Mathematics

Name _____ Date _____ Class _____

Technology Lab

LAB 4H

Pythagorean Triples

Three positive integers *a*, *b*, and *c* that satisfy the equation
$a^2 + b^2 = c^2$ are called **Pythagorean Triples**. You know that
$3^2 + 4^2 = 5^2$. So, 3, 4, and 5 are Pythagorean triples.

Activity

You can generate Pythagorean triples *a*, *b*, and *c* by starting with
two different whole numbers *m* and *n*, where *m* is the larger number.
The Pythagorean triples will be as follows:

$a = m^2 - n^2$

$b = 2mn$

$c = m^2 + n^2$

Example: Using $m = 2$ and $n = 1$

$a = 2^2 - 1^2 = 4 - 1 = 3$

$b = 2(2)(1) = 4$

$c = 2^2 + 1^2 = 5$

Using a spreadsheet, enter the letters *m*, *n*, *a*, *b*, and *c*, respectively, in cells A1 to E1.

Then enter the formula for *a* as = **A2^2–B2^2** in cell C2.

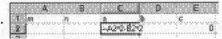

For *b*, enter = **2*A2*B2** in cell D2, and for *c*, enter
= **A2^2 + B2^2** in cell E2.

Highlight cells C2, D2, and E2, and click the
Copy button on the toolbar. Then select cells
C2, D2, and E2, and drag down to highlight
7 rows. Click the **Paste** button on the toolbar.

Next, enter 5 and 4 in cells A2 and B2, 5 and
3 in cells A3 and B3, and so forth until you
complete the seventh row for patterns given.

All integers *a*, *b*, and *c* shown in the last three
columns are Pythagorean triples.

Holt Mathematics

Technology Lab

LAB 4H

Pythagorean Triples, continued

Think and Discuss

1. Is order important in a Pythagorean triple? Why?

_____

_____

Try This

1. Using a spreadsheet, generate 30 Pythagorean triples.

_____

_____

Name _____ Date _____ Class _____

Review for Mastery
The Pythagorean Theorem

In a right triangle,
the sum of the areas of the squares on the legs
is equal to
the area of the square on the hypotenuse.

$$3^2 + 4^2 = 5^2$$
$$9 + 16 = 25$$

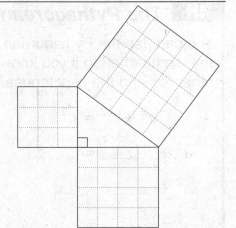

Given the squares that are on the legs of a right triangle, draw the square for the hypotenuse.

1. leg   leg   hypotenuse

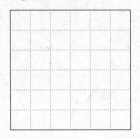

Without drawing the squares, you can find the length of a side.

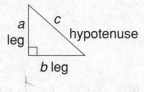

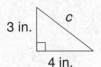

$$a^2 + b^2 = c^2$$
$$3^2 + 4^2 = c^2$$
$$9 + 16 = c^2$$
$$25 = c^2$$
$$c = 5 \text{ in.}$$

Complete to find the length of each hypotenuse.

2.

$$a^2 + b^2 = c^2$$
$$\underline{\hspace{1cm}} + \underline{\hspace{1cm}} = c^2$$
$$\underline{\hspace{1cm}} + \underline{\hspace{1cm}} = c^2$$
$$\underline{\hspace{1cm}} = c^2$$
$$c = \underline{\hspace{1cm}} \text{ ft}$$

3.
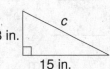

$$a^2 + b^2 = c^2$$
$$\underline{\hspace{1cm}} + \underline{\hspace{1cm}} = c^2$$
$$\underline{\hspace{1cm}} + \underline{\hspace{1cm}} = c^2$$
$$\underline{\hspace{1cm}} = c^2$$
$$c = \underline{\hspace{1cm}} \text{ in.}$$

Holt Mathematics

Name _____ Date _____ Class _____

Review for Mastery
The Pythagorean Theorem (continued)

You can use the Pythagorean Theorem to find the length of a leg if you know the length of the other leg and the hypotenuse.

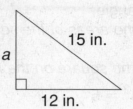

$a^2 + b^2 = c^2$

$a^2 + \underline{\hspace{1cm}} = \underline{\hspace{1cm}}$

$a^2 + \underline{\hspace{1cm}} = \underline{\hspace{1cm}}$

$- \underline{\hspace{1cm}} \quad - \underline{\hspace{1cm}}$

$a^2 = \underline{\hspace{1cm}}$

$a = \underline{\hspace{1cm}}$ in.

Complete to find the length of each leg.

4. $a^2 + b^2 = c^2$

   $\underline{\hspace{1cm}} + b^2 = \underline{\hspace{1cm}}$

   $\underline{\hspace{1cm}} + b^2 = \underline{\hspace{1cm}}$

   $- \underline{\hspace{1cm}} \quad - \underline{\hspace{1cm}}$

   $b^2 = \underline{\hspace{1cm}}$

   $b = \underline{\hspace{1cm}}$ in.

5. $a^2 + \underline{\hspace{1cm}} = \underline{\hspace{1cm}}$

   $a^2 + \underline{\hspace{1cm}} = \underline{\hspace{1cm}}$

   $- \underline{\hspace{1cm}} \quad - \underline{\hspace{1cm}}$

   $a^2 = \underline{\hspace{1cm}}$

   $a = \underline{\hspace{1cm}}$ cm

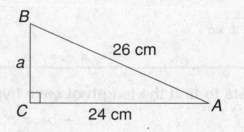

Holt Mathematics

Homework and Practice

LESSON 4H *The Pythagorean Theorem*

Find the length of the hypotenuse in each triangle.

1.

9

12

_____

2.

24

10

_____

3.

36

27

_____

4. Graph the triangle formed with coordinates (−7, 0), (−7, −6), (1, 0) and find the length of the hypotenuse.

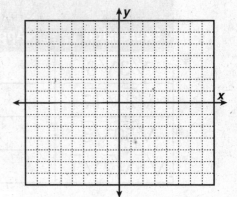

_____

Solve for the unknown side in each right triangle. Round the answers to the nearest hundredth.

5.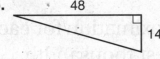

48

14

_____

6.

3.6

2.7

_____

7.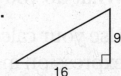

9

16

_____

8.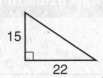

15

22

_____

9. 28

21

_____

10. 26

24

_____

11.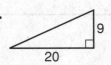

9

20

_____

12.

36

32

_____

13.

34

12

_____

14. Use the Pythagorean Theorem to find the height of the triangle at the right. Then use the height to find the area of the triangle.

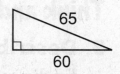

65

60

_____

Holt Mathematics

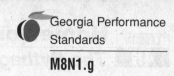
Georgia Performance
Standards

4I **Radical Expressions**   M8N1.g

You will need a calculator for this Exploration.

1. Use your calculator to find a decimal approximation for each expression in the table. Round to the nearest thousandth.

Expression	Decimal Approximation	Expression	Decimal Approximation
$\sqrt{3}\sqrt{6}$		$\sqrt{18}$	
$\sqrt{2}\sqrt{17}$		$\sqrt{34}$	
$\sqrt{50}\sqrt{3}$		$\sqrt{150}$	
$\sqrt{5}\sqrt{2}\sqrt{3}$		$\sqrt{30}$	

2. What do you notice in the table?

3. Use your calculator to find a decimal approximation for each expression in the table. Round to the nearest thousandth.

Expression	Decimal Approximation	Expression	Decimal Approximation
$\dfrac{\sqrt{10}}{\sqrt{2}}$		$\sqrt{5}$	
$\dfrac{\sqrt{38}}{\sqrt{19}}$		$\sqrt{2}$	
$\dfrac{\sqrt{30}}{\sqrt{5}}$		$\sqrt{6}$	

4. What do you notice in the table?

Think and Discuss

5. **Describe** any conjectures that you can make based on your findings.

Holt Mathematics

Review for Mastery

LESSON 4I

Multiplying and Dividing Expressions with Square Roots

Use the Product and Quotient Properties to multiply and divide radical expressions.

Product Property of Square Roots	Quotient Property of Square Roots
$\sqrt{ab} = \sqrt{a} \cdot \sqrt{b}$; where $a \geq 0$ and $b \geq 0$	$\sqrt{\dfrac{a}{b}} = \dfrac{\sqrt{a}}{\sqrt{b}}$; where $a \geq 0$ and $b \geq 0$

Multiply $\sqrt{6}\,\sqrt{10}$.

$\sqrt{6}\,\sqrt{10}$

$\sqrt{6 \cdot 10}$ *Product Property of Square Roots*

$\sqrt{60}$ *Multiply the factors in the radicand.*

$\sqrt{4 \cdot 15}$ *Factor 60 using a perfect square factor.*

$\sqrt{4} \cdot \sqrt{15}$ *Product Property of Square Roots*

$2\sqrt{15}$ *Simplify.*

A quotient with a square root in the denominator is not simplified. Rationalize the denominator by multiplying by a form of 1 to get a perfect square.

Simplify $\sqrt{\dfrac{10}{3}}$.

$\sqrt{\dfrac{10}{3}} = \dfrac{\sqrt{10}}{\sqrt{3}}$ *Quotient Property*

$\dfrac{\sqrt{10}}{\sqrt{3}}\left(\dfrac{\sqrt{3}}{\sqrt{3}}\right)$ *Multiply by form of 1.*

$\dfrac{\sqrt{30}}{\sqrt{9}}$ *Product Property*

$\dfrac{\sqrt{30}}{3}$ *Simplify.*

Multiply. Then simplify.

1. $\sqrt{3}\,\sqrt{12}$

2. $\sqrt{5}\,\sqrt{10}$

3. $\sqrt{8}\,\sqrt{11}$

Rationalize the denominator of each quotient. Then simplify.

4. $\dfrac{\sqrt{7}}{\sqrt{2}}$ $\left(\dfrac{\square}{\square}\right)$

5. $\dfrac{\sqrt{8}}{\sqrt{3}}$ $\left(\dfrac{\square}{\square}\right)$

6. $\dfrac{\sqrt{12}}{\sqrt{5}}$ $\left(\dfrac{\square}{\square}\right)$

Holt Mathematics

Name _____ Date _____ Class _____

Review for Mastery
Multiplying and Dividing Expressions with Square Roots (continued)

Terms can be multiplied and divided if they are both under the radicals OR if they are both outside the radicals.

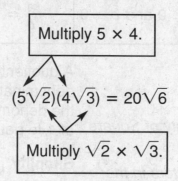

Multiply 5 × 4.

$(5\sqrt{2})(4\sqrt{3}) = 20\sqrt{6}$

Multiply $\sqrt{2} \times \sqrt{3}$.

Multiply $\sqrt{3}(6 + \sqrt{8})$. Write the product in simplest form.

$\sqrt{3}(6 + \sqrt{8})$	
$\sqrt{3}(6) + \sqrt{3}\sqrt{8}$	*Distribute.*
$6\sqrt{3} + \sqrt{24}$	*Multiply the factors in the radicand.*
$6\sqrt{3} + \sqrt{4 \cdot 6}$	*Factor 24 using a perfect square factor.*
$6\sqrt{3} + \sqrt{4}\sqrt{6}$	*Product Property of Square Roots*
$6\sqrt{3} + 2\sqrt{6}$	*Simplify.*

Use FOIL to multiply binomials with square roots.

Multiply $(3 + \sqrt{2})(4 + \sqrt{2})$.

$(3 + \sqrt{2})(4 + \sqrt{2})$	
$3(4) + 3\sqrt{2} + 4\sqrt{2} + \sqrt{2}\sqrt{2}$	*FOIL.*
$12 + 3\sqrt{2} + 4\sqrt{2} + \sqrt{4}$	*Multiply.*
$12 + 3\sqrt{2} + 4\sqrt{2} + 2$	*Simplify.*
$14 + 7\sqrt{2}$	*Add.*

Multiply. Write each product in simplest form.

7. $\sqrt{5}(4 + \sqrt{8})$

$\sqrt{5}\ \boxed{} + \sqrt{5}\ \boxed{}$

8. $\sqrt{2}(\sqrt{2} + \sqrt{14})$

_____   _____

9. $(6 + \sqrt{3})(5 - \sqrt{3})$

$(6)\ (\boxed{}) - (6)(\boxed{}) + \sqrt{3}(\boxed{}) - \sqrt{3}(\boxed{})$

10. $(5 + \sqrt{10})(8 + \sqrt{10})$

_____

Holt Mathematics

Homework and Practice

LESSON 4I

Multiplying and Dividing Expressions with Square Roots

Multiply. Write each product in simplest form.

1. $\sqrt{15} \cdot \sqrt{6}$

$\sqrt{15 \cdot 6}$

_____

2. $(3\sqrt{6})^2$

$3\sqrt{6} \cdot 3\sqrt{6}$

_____

3. $4\sqrt{7x} \cdot \sqrt{20x}$

$4 \cdot \sqrt{(7x)(20x)}$

_____

4. $\sqrt{12} \cdot \sqrt{5}$

_____

5. $(2\sqrt{7})^2$

_____

6. $-2\sqrt{5b} \cdot \sqrt{10b}$

_____

7. $3\sqrt{10y} \ \sqrt{6y}$

_____

8. $\sqrt{8}(\sqrt{12} - \sqrt{2})$

_____

9. $\sqrt{2x}(\sqrt{5} + \sqrt{2x})$

_____

10. $\sqrt{2}(\sqrt{7} - 5)$

_____

11. $\sqrt{10}(\sqrt{5m} - \sqrt{4})$

_____

12. $(4 + \sqrt{3})(2 - \sqrt{3})$

_____

13. $\sqrt{3}(\sqrt{8} - 6)$

_____

14. $\sqrt{5}(\sqrt{2} + \sqrt{8})$

_____

15. $(5 + \sqrt{2})(6 - \sqrt{2})$

_____

16. $\sqrt{5}(\sqrt{2} - \sqrt{6})$

_____

17. $(3 - \sqrt{2})(5 + \sqrt{2})$

_____

18. $(7 + \sqrt{3})(7 - \sqrt{3})$

_____

Simplify each quotient.

19. $\dfrac{\sqrt{2}}{\sqrt{6}}$

_____

20. $\dfrac{\sqrt{10}}{\sqrt{11}}$

_____

21. $\dfrac{\sqrt{13}}{\sqrt{50t}}$

_____

22. $\dfrac{\sqrt{7}}{\sqrt{15}}$

_____

23. $\dfrac{\sqrt{2}}{\sqrt{17}}$

_____

24. $\dfrac{\sqrt{32}}{\sqrt{48z}}$

_____

25. $\dfrac{\sqrt{3}}{\sqrt{3a}}$

_____

26. $\dfrac{\sqrt{8x}}{\sqrt{5}}$

_____

27. $\dfrac{\sqrt{75k}}{10\sqrt{2k}}$

_____

Holt Mathematics

EXPLORATION

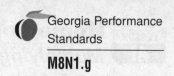
Georgia Performance
Standards
_____
M8N1.g

4J Radical Expressions

You will need a calculator for this Exploration.

1. Find a decimal approximation for each expression in the table. Round to the nearest thousandth.

Expression	Decimal Approximation	Expression	Decimal Approximation
$2\sqrt{3} + 3\sqrt{3}$		$5\sqrt{3}$	
$8\sqrt{2} - 5\sqrt{2}$		$3\sqrt{2}$	
$4\sqrt{7} + 11\sqrt{7}$		$15\sqrt{7}$	

2. What do you notice in the table?

3. Find a decimal approximation for each expression in the table. Round to the nearest thousandth.

Expression	Decimal Approximation	Expression	Decimal Approximation
$\sqrt{7} + \sqrt{3}$		$\sqrt{10}$	
$\sqrt{25} + \sqrt{9}$		$\sqrt{34}$	
$\sqrt{17} - \sqrt{5}$		$\sqrt{12}$	

Think and Discuss _____

4. **Describe** a conjecture you can make based on your findings in the first table.

5. **Discuss** whether $\sqrt{a} + \sqrt{b} = \sqrt{a + b}$ and whether $\sqrt{a} - \sqrt{b} = \sqrt{a - b}$.

Holt Mathematics

LESSON 4J — Review for Mastery
Adding and Subtracting Expressions with Square Roots

You can add and subtract radical expressions just like you add and subtract expressions with variables.

$$4\underline{x} + 2\underline{x} = 6x$$

These are like terms. Add.

$$2x + 4y$$

These are not like terms. Do not add.

Combine radicals only if they are like radicals.

$$4\underline{\sqrt{7}} + 2\underline{\sqrt{7}} = 6\sqrt{7}$$

These are like radicals. Add.

$$2\sqrt{5} + 4\sqrt{3}$$

These are not like radicals. Do not add.

Add $8\sqrt{10} + 5\sqrt{10}$.

$8\sqrt{10} + 5\sqrt{10}$ *These are like radicals.*

$\quad 13\sqrt{10}$

Subtract $10\sqrt{7x} - 12\sqrt{7x}$.

$10\sqrt{7x} - 12\sqrt{7x}$ *These are like radicals.*

$\quad -2\sqrt{7x}$

Add $4\sqrt{2} + 8\sqrt{3}$.

$4\sqrt{2} + 8\sqrt{3}$ *These are not like radicals. Do not add.*

Subtract $9\sqrt{5} - 4\sqrt{6}$.

$9\sqrt{5} - 4\sqrt{6}$ *These are not like radicals. Do not subtract.*

State whether the expressions can be added. If yes, find the sum.

1. $3\sqrt{2y} + 8\sqrt{2y}$

2. $2\sqrt{5} + 5\sqrt{2}$

_____

_____

3. $8 + \sqrt{8}$

4. $5\sqrt{11} - 6\sqrt{11}$

_____

_____

Add or subtract.

5. $4\sqrt{13} + 2\sqrt{13}$

6. $8\sqrt{2} - 3\sqrt{2}$

7. $5\sqrt{5} + 6\sqrt{5}$

8. $12\sqrt{3a} - 2\sqrt{3a}$

9. $7\sqrt{x} + \sqrt{x}$

10. $10\sqrt{6} - 3\sqrt{6}$

_____

_____

_____

Holt Mathematics

Name _____ Date _____ Class _____

Review for Mastery

Adding and Subtracting Expressions with Square Roots (continued)

Sometimes it is necessary to simplify expressions before adding or subtracting.

Simplify $\sqrt{50} + \sqrt{18}$.

$\sqrt{50} + \sqrt{18}$	
$\sqrt{25 \cdot 2} + \sqrt{9 \cdot 2}$	*Factor the radicands using perfect squares.*
$\sqrt{25} \cdot \sqrt{2} + \sqrt{9} \cdot \sqrt{2}$	*Product Property*
$5\sqrt{2} + 3\sqrt{2}$	*Simplify.*
$8\sqrt{2}$	*Combine like radicals.*

Simplify $\sqrt{45a} + \sqrt{80a} - \sqrt{20}$.

$\sqrt{9 \cdot 5a} + \sqrt{16 \cdot 5a} - \sqrt{4 \cdot 5}$	*Factor the radicands using perfect squares.*
$\sqrt{9} \cdot \sqrt{5a} + \sqrt{16} \cdot \sqrt{5a} - \sqrt{4} \cdot \sqrt{5}$	*Product Property*
$3\sqrt{5a} + 4\sqrt{5a} - 2\sqrt{5}$	*Simplify.*
$7\sqrt{5a} - 2\sqrt{5}$	*Combine like radicals.*
	Notice that $\sqrt{5a}$ and $\sqrt{5}$ are not like radicals.

Simplify each expression by filling in the boxes below.

11. $\sqrt{32} + \sqrt{2}$

$\sqrt{\boxed{} \cdot \boxed{}} + \sqrt{2}$

$\sqrt{\boxed{}}\, \sqrt{\boxed{}} + \sqrt{2}$

$\boxed{}\, \sqrt{\boxed{}} + \sqrt{2}$

$\boxed{}\, \sqrt{\boxed{}}$

12. $\sqrt{27} - \sqrt{3}$

$\sqrt{\boxed{} \cdot \boxed{}} + \sqrt{3}$

$\sqrt{\boxed{}}\, \sqrt{\boxed{}} + \sqrt{3}$

$\boxed{}\, \sqrt{\boxed{}} + \sqrt{3}$

$\boxed{}\, \sqrt{\boxed{}}$

13. $\sqrt{125} + \sqrt{5}$

$\sqrt{\boxed{} \cdot \boxed{}} + \sqrt{5}$

$\sqrt{\boxed{}}\, \sqrt{\boxed{}} + \sqrt{5}$

$\boxed{}\, \sqrt{\boxed{}} + \sqrt{5}$

$\boxed{}\, \sqrt{\boxed{}}$

Simplify.

14. $\sqrt{12} + \sqrt{300}$

15. $\sqrt{48} - \sqrt{27}$

16. $\sqrt{112} + \sqrt{14}$

_____

_____

_____

17. $\sqrt{75} + \sqrt{12} - \sqrt{27}$

18. $\sqrt{63x} + \sqrt{28x} - \sqrt{7x}$

19. $\sqrt{160y} + \sqrt{90y} - \sqrt{40y}$

_____

_____

_____

Holt Mathematics

Name _____ Date _____ Class _____

Homework and Practice

Adding and Subtracting Expressions with Square Roots

Add or subtract.

1. $9\sqrt{7} + 4\sqrt{7} = \underline{\quad} \sqrt{7}$

2. $-10\sqrt{5} + 2\sqrt{5} = \underline{\quad} \sqrt{5}$

3. $4\sqrt{y} + 6\sqrt{y} = \underline{\hspace{3cm}}$

4. $-2\sqrt{3b} + 10\sqrt{3b} = \underline{\hspace{3cm}}$

5. $6\sqrt{15} - \sqrt{15} + \sqrt{15} = \underline{\hspace{3cm}}$

6. $5\sqrt{2} - 3\sqrt{2x} - 4\sqrt{2} = \underline{\hspace{3cm}}$

Simplify each expression.

7. $\sqrt{108} + \sqrt{75}$

8. $\sqrt{63} + \sqrt{175} + \sqrt{112}$

9. $\sqrt{28x} + \sqrt{63x}$

_____ _____ _____

10. $\sqrt{45} + \sqrt{180}$

11. $\sqrt{52} - \sqrt{1300}$

12. $5\sqrt{98} - 3\sqrt{32}$

_____ _____ _____

13. $\sqrt{32} + \sqrt{128}$

14. $\sqrt{147} + 6\sqrt{3}$

15. $\sqrt{168} + \sqrt{42}$

_____ _____ _____

16. $5\sqrt{17} + 17\sqrt{5}$

17. $6\sqrt{3} + \sqrt{300}$

18. $-2\sqrt{3b} + \sqrt{27b}$

_____ _____ _____

19. $4\sqrt{2m} + 6\sqrt{3m} - 4\sqrt{2m}$ 20. $\sqrt{50m} + \sqrt{72m}$

21. $\sqrt{16z} + 2\sqrt{8z} - 3\sqrt{z}$

_____ _____ _____

22. $\sqrt{216t} + \sqrt{96t}$

23. $4\sqrt{52x} + \sqrt{117x} - 2\sqrt{13}$ 24. $3\sqrt{96k} + 2\sqrt{180}$

_____ _____ _____

25. Write the numbers $3\sqrt{8}$, $4\sqrt{2}$ and $\sqrt{50}$ in order from least to greatest.

_____

26. The map at right shows the path traveled by a delivery person on his afternoon route. Write the total distance traveled as a simplified radical expression.

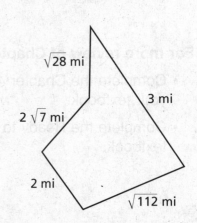

_____

Holt Mathematics

CHAPTER 4 Big Ideas

Answer these questions to summarize the important concepts from Chapter 4 in your own words.

1. Explain how to evaluate 3^6.

2. Explain the difference between 3.56×10^8 and 3.56×10^{-8}.

3. Explain why $\sqrt{81} = \pm 9$.

4. Explain $\sqrt{-25} \neq \pm 5$.

5. Explain how to estimate $\sqrt{60}$.

6. Explain why $0.\overline{3}$ is a rational number.

For more review of Chapter 4:

- Complete the Chapter 4 Study Guide and Review on pages 204–206 of your textbook.

- Complete the Ready to Go On quizzes on pages 180 and 200 of your textbook.

Holt Mathematics

Project
Ratios, Proportions, and Similarity: Miniature Nature

Career: Horticulturist

Chances are that a horticulturist helped create many of the varieties of plants at your local nursery. Horticulturists work in vegetable development, fruit growing, flower growing, and landscape design. Horticulturists who are also scientists work to develop new types of plants or ways to control plant diseases. The art of *bonsai*, or making miniature plants, began in China and became popular in Japan. Now bonsai is practiced all over the world.

In this chapter project...you will create a scale drawing of a tree. You will:

• Calculate the scale of different types of bonsai trees.

• Choose a tree you like and research its dimensions, such as average height, width, and size of leaves.

• Make a scale drawing of what your tree might look like as a bonsai. Apply your scale to the height of the tree, average width, and leaf size to make your scale drawing as accurate as possible. Include the scale on your drawing.

To get started, work through Growing Tiny Trees worksheet on the next page.

This chapter project reinforces your understanding of these Georgia Performance Standards:

M8P4.c Recognize and apply mathematical ideas in contexts outside of mathematics.

M8P5.a Create and use representations to organize, record, and communicate mathematical ideas.

go.hrw.com
Chapter Project Online
KEYWORD: MT7 Ch5

Holt Mathematics

Name _____ Date _____ Class _____

CHAPTER **5** | # Project Recording Sheet
Ratios, Proportions, and Similarity

Growing Tiny Trees

Do you like to grow things? Bonsai is something that everyone can do if they have patience and the desire for perfection. The bonsai grower uses both science and art as he or she creates a small model of a large tree.

Complete the table.

Scale = $\dfrac{\text{bonsai height in inches}}{\text{natural height in inches}}$

Tree	Natural Height (ft)	Natural Height (in.)	Bonsai Height (in.)	Approximate Scale
Chinese Elm	60	720	10	$\frac{1}{72}$
Brush Cherry	50	600	8	$\frac{1}{75}$
Juniper	10		6	
Fig	30		29	
Japanese Maple	12		28	
Pitch Pine	200		14	
Red Cedar	80		20	
Eastern Hemlock	80		18	

Project: Find a picture of a tree that you like. Find out how tall the tree is in nature. Construct a scale model or drawing of the tree. Label the scale. Compare your model or drawing with those of your classmates. How does the scale help you understand the natural tree?

_____

_____

Extension: What is the weight comparison between a bonsai tree and the natural-sized tree?

_____

Extension: Visit a nursery that specializes in bonsai and begin a project of your own.

Holt Mathematics

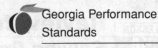
Georgia Performance
Standards
M8A1.a, M8A1.c

5A Solving Proportions

The grid shows three rectangles aligned by a diagonal line.

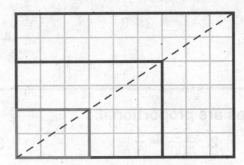

Complete the table. Use the grid to measure the length and width of each rectangle. Divide the length by the width and write this answer as a fraction in simplest form.

		Length	Width	$\frac{\text{Length}}{\text{Width}}$
1.	rectangle 1			
2.	rectangle 2			
3.	rectangle 3			

Think and Discuss

4. **Compare** the fractions you found in Problems 1–3.

5. **Explain** how you wrote each fraction in simplest form.

Holt Mathematics

Name _____ Date _____ Class _____

LESSON 5A Review for Mastery
Solving Proportions

In a proportion, the **cross products** are equal.

These ratios are proportional, since their cross products are equal.	These ratios are not proportional, since their cross products are not equal.
$\dfrac{7}{14} \overset{?}{=} \dfrac{8}{16}$	$\dfrac{4}{9} \overset{?}{=} \dfrac{2}{3}$
$7 \times 16 \overset{?}{=} 14 \times 8$	$4 \times 3 \overset{?}{=} 9 \times 2$
$112 = 112$	$12 \neq 18$

Complete to tell if the ratios are proportional.

1. $\dfrac{15}{45} \overset{?}{=} \dfrac{6}{18}$

$15 \times \underline{\hspace{1cm}} \overset{?}{=} 45 \times \underline{\hspace{1cm}}$

$\underline{\hspace{2cm}}$

The ratios $\underline{\hspace{1cm}}$ in proportion.

2. $\dfrac{75}{100} \overset{?}{=} \dfrac{4}{8}$

$\underline{\hspace{0.5cm}} \times \underline{\hspace{0.5cm}} \overset{?}{=} \underline{\hspace{0.5cm}} \times \underline{\hspace{0.5cm}}$

$\underline{\hspace{2cm}}$

The ratios $\underline{\hspace{1cm}}$ in proportion.

3. $\dfrac{7}{2} \overset{?}{=} \dfrac{21}{6}$

$\underline{\hspace{0.5cm}} \times \underline{\hspace{0.5cm}} \overset{?}{=} \underline{\hspace{0.5cm}} \times \underline{\hspace{0.5cm}}$

$\underline{\hspace{2cm}}$

The ratios $\underline{\hspace{1cm}}$ in proportion.

To solve for one member of a proportion, set the cross products equal.	To check the result, substitute and see if the ratios are equivalent.
$\dfrac{n}{32} = \dfrac{9}{16}$	$\dfrac{18}{32} \overset{?}{=} \dfrac{9}{16}$
$16n = 32 \times 9$	$\dfrac{18 \div 2}{32 \div 2} \overset{?}{=} \dfrac{9}{16}$
$\dfrac{16n}{16} = \dfrac{288}{16}$	$\dfrac{9}{16} = \dfrac{9}{16}$ ✔
$n = 18$	

Solve and check.

4. $\dfrac{8}{24} = \dfrac{2}{n}$

$8n = \underline{\hspace{2cm}}$

$\dfrac{8n}{\underline{\hspace{1cm}}} = \underline{\hspace{2cm}}$

$n = \underline{\hspace{2cm}}$

Check: $\dfrac{8}{24} = \dfrac{2}{n}$

$\dfrac{8}{24} \overset{?}{=} \dfrac{2}{\underline{\hspace{0.5cm}}}$

$\underline{\hspace{1cm}} \overset{?}{=} 2 \div \underline{\hspace{1cm}}$

$\underline{\hspace{2cm}} = \underline{\hspace{2cm}}$

Holt Mathematics

Homework and Practice

LESSON 5A *Solving Proportions*

Tell whether each pair of ratios are proportional.

1. $\dfrac{5}{6} \overset{?}{=} \dfrac{30}{36}$

2. $\dfrac{8}{20} \overset{?}{=} \dfrac{6}{14}$

3. $\dfrac{12}{27} \overset{?}{=} \dfrac{8}{18}$

4. $\dfrac{13}{15} \overset{?}{=} \dfrac{39}{45}$

_____   _____   _____   _____

5. $\dfrac{8}{16} \overset{?}{=} \dfrac{50}{100}$

6. $\dfrac{21}{49} \overset{?}{=} \dfrac{14}{36}$

7. $\dfrac{18}{24} \overset{?}{=} \dfrac{9}{15}$

8. $\dfrac{4}{18} \overset{?}{=} \dfrac{18}{81}$

_____   _____   _____   _____

9. $\dfrac{16}{10} \overset{?}{=} \dfrac{26}{20}$

10. $\dfrac{24}{14} \overset{?}{=} \dfrac{36}{21}$

11. $\dfrac{25}{16} \overset{?}{=} \dfrac{5}{4}$

12. $\dfrac{17}{11} \overset{?}{=} \dfrac{51}{33}$

_____   _____   _____   _____

Solve each proportion.

13. $\dfrac{4}{15} = \dfrac{a}{45}$

14. $\dfrac{16}{18} = \dfrac{8}{w}$

15. $\dfrac{m}{11} = \dfrac{32}{44}$

16. $\dfrac{12}{t} = \dfrac{4}{7}$

_____   _____   _____   _____

17. $\dfrac{9}{b} = \dfrac{27}{72}$

18. $\dfrac{x}{36} = \dfrac{21}{27}$

19. $\dfrac{6}{y} = \dfrac{18}{51}$

20. $\dfrac{10}{32} = \dfrac{15}{x}$

_____   _____   _____   _____

21. $\dfrac{45}{81} = \dfrac{n}{27}$

22. $\dfrac{28}{21} = \dfrac{44}{t}$

23. $\dfrac{d}{42} = \dfrac{49}{147}$

24. $\dfrac{17}{r} = \dfrac{102}{78}$

_____   _____   _____   _____

25. The Orlemann family planted 3 rows of corn this year and harvested 270 ears. How many rows should they plant if they want to harvest 360 ears of corn?

_____

26. Find the number of times a heart beats in 2 minutes if it beats 576 times in 8 minutes.

_____

27. David is making chocolate-chip cookies. Chocolate chips cost $1.79 for 12 ounces. David buys 60 ounces of chocolate chips for the cookies. How much did the chocolate chips cost?

Holt Mathematics

5B Indirect Measurement

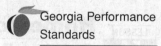

Georgia Performance Standards

M8A1.a, M8A1.c

Mr. Kelly's science class is tracking the motion of the sun during the year. To do so, they measure the shadow cast by a 120-foot building on four different days of the year. To check the measurements, the students also measure the shadow cast by a 36-inch stick. The table shows their findings.

Day	Height of Building	Length of Building's Shadow	Height of Stick	Length of Stick's Shadow
1	120 ft	20 ft	36 in.	6 in.
2	120 ft	30 ft	36 in.	9 in.
3	120 ft	40 ft	36 in.	12 in.
4	120 ft	80 ft	36 in.	24 in.

1. **a.** On Day 1, what was the ratio of the height of the building to the length of the building's shadow?

   b. What was the ratio of the height of the stick to the length of the stick's shadow?

   c. What do you notice about these ratios?

2. Does your observation about the ratios also hold for Day 2, Day 3, and Day 4?

Think and Discuss

3. **Describe** how you could find the length of the stick's shadow if you know that the length of the building's shadow is 60 ft.

4. **Explain** what must be true about the building's shadow on a day when the stick's shadow is 36 in.

Holt Mathematics

LESSON 5B Review for Mastery

Indirect Measurement

If two triangles are similar, you can set up and solve a proportion
to find a missing side length.

$\triangle ABC \sim \triangle DBE$

$\overline{AB}$ corresponds to $\overline{DB}$.

$\overline{BC}$ corresponds to $\overline{BE}$.

$$\frac{AB}{BC} = \frac{DB}{BE}$$

$$\frac{9}{6} = \frac{27}{x}$$ Find cross products.

$9x = 6(27)$ Simplify.

$$\frac{9x}{9} = \frac{162}{9}$$ Divide both sides by 9.

$x = 18$

The length of $\overline{EB}$ is 18 feet.

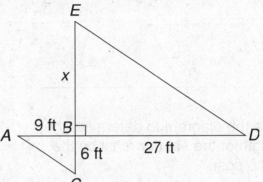

Each pair of triangles is similar. Find each missing length.

1.

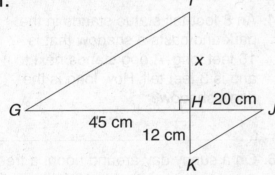

$$\frac{HK}{HJ} = \frac{HI}{HG}$$

$$\frac{12}{20} = \frac{x}{45}$$

$x = $ _____

$HI = $ _____

2.

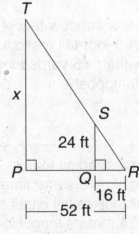

$$\frac{TP}{PR} = \frac{SQ}{QR}$$

$$\frac{x}{52} = \frac{24}{16}$$

$x = $ _____

$TP = $ _____

Holt Mathematics

LESSON 5B Homework and Practice
Indirect Measurement

1. Use the diagram to find the height of the building.

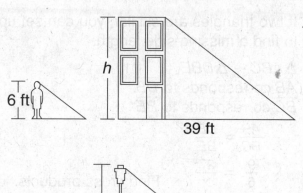

_____

2. Use the diagram to determine the length of the shadow cast by the lamp post.

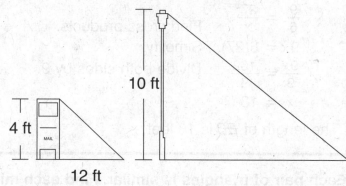

_____

3. A lamppost casts a shadow that is 15 yards long. A 3-foot-tall mailbox casts a shadow that is 5 yards long. How tall is the lamppost?

_____

4. An 8-foot-tall statue stands in the park and casts a shadow that is 16 feet long. A dog stands next to it and is 3 feet tall. How long is the dog's shadow?

_____

5. A building casts a shadow that is 420 meters long. At the same time, a person who is 2 meters tall casts a shadow that is 24 meters long. How tall is the building?

_____

6. On a sunny day around noon, a tree casts a shadow that is 12 feet long. At the same time, a person who is 6 feet tall standing beside the tree casts a shadow that is 2 feet long. How tall is the tree?

_____

Holt Mathematics

Name _____ Date _____ Class _____

Homework and Practice

Indirect Measurement (continued)

7. Use the diagram to determine the height of the sign.

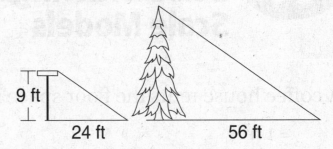

9 ft   24 ft   56 ft

_____

8. Use the diagram to determine the height of the tree.

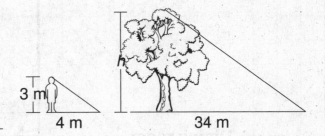

3 m   4 m   34 m

_____

9. A pole casts a shadow that is 21 feet long. A 3-feet-tall child standing next to the pole casts a shadow that is 9 feet long. How tall is the pole?

_____

10. Jeremy has two trophies next to each other sitting in the window of his room. His football trophy is 7 inches tall and his basketball trophy is 13 inches tall. As the light shines in, the basketball trophy's shadow measures 26 inches. How long is the football trophy's shadow?

_____

11. Vladimir wants to know the distance across a busy street. He can take measurements alongside the street, and in the field adjacent to the street. Explain how he can use indirect measurement to estimate the distance across the street. Include a diagram.

_____

_____

_____

Holt Mathematics

Georgia Performance
Standards

M8A1.a, M8A1.c

5C Scale Drawings and Scale Models

A coffee house rents the floor space modeled by the figure below.

$\square$ = 1 ft²

Kitchen

Dining room

Restrooms

Count the number of squares to answer each question.

1. What is the actual area of the dining room?

2. What is the actual area of the kitchen?

3. What is the actual area of the restrooms?

Think and Discuss

4. **Show** a possible arrangement of square tables in the dining area if the tabletops each measure 2 ft by 2 ft.

5. **Discuss** real-world situations in which scale drawings are used.

Holt Mathematics

Review for Mastery

LESSON 5C *Scale Drawings and Scale Models*

In a **scale drawing or a scale model,** all the dimensions of the actual object are reduced or enlarged proportionally.

A map is a scale drawing in which actual distance is reduced.

The towns of Ardon and Bacton are on a map with scale 1 cm = 15 km.

If the map distance between Ardon and Bacton is 4.5 cm, what is the actual distance?

$$\frac{\text{actual distance}}{\text{map distance}} = \frac{\text{actual distance}}{\text{map distance}}$$

$$\frac{15 \text{ km}}{1 \text{ cm}} = \frac{x \text{ km}}{4.5 \text{ cm}}$$

$$1(x) = 15(4.5)$$

$$x = 67.5 \text{ km} \longleftarrow \text{actual distance between Ardon and Bacton}$$

Bacton

Ardon

Complete to find each unknown measure.

1. A map scale is 1 in. = 75 mi. The map distance between two towns is 3.5 in. Find the actual distance *x* between the towns.

$$\frac{\text{actual distance}}{\text{map distance}} = \frac{\text{actual distance}}{\text{map distance}}$$

$$\frac{75 \text{ mi}}{\text{in.}} = \frac{x \text{ mi}}{\text{in.}}$$

$$x = \underline{\hspace{2cm}}$$

actual distance = _____

2. The actual distance between two towns is 175 km. If the distance between them on a map is 7 cm, what is the map scale?

$$\frac{x \text{ km}}{1 \text{ cm}} = \frac{\text{km}}{\text{cm}}$$

_____

$$x = \underline{\hspace{2cm}}$$

map scale: 1 cm = _____

3. An archway in a $\frac{1}{2}$ in. scale drawing is 4.5 in. tall. Find the actual height *x*.

$$\frac{\text{actual height}}{\text{scale height}} = \frac{\text{actual height}}{\text{scale height}}$$

$$\frac{1 \text{ ft}}{0.5 \text{ in.}} = \frac{\text{ft}}{\text{in.}}$$

_____

_____

actual height = _____

4. Under a 7:1 magnification, this letter F appears to be 84 points high. Find the actual height *x*.

$$\frac{\text{actual height}}{\text{scale height}} = \frac{\text{actual height}}{\text{scale height}}$$

$$\frac{1}{7} = \frac{points}{points}$$

_____

_____

actual height = _____

Holt Mathematics

LESSON 5C Homework and Practice
Scale Drawings

The scale of a drawing is $\frac{1}{4}$ in. = 12 ft. Find the actual measurement.

1. 8 in.   **2.** 11 in.   **3.** 16 in.   **4.** 18 in.

_____   _____   _____   _____

5. 22 in.   **6.** 27 in.   **7.** 21.5 in.   **8.** 38.5 in.

_____   _____   _____   _____

The scale is 2 cm = 15 m. Find the length each measurement would be on a scale drawing.

9. 180 m   **10.** 585 m   **11.** 330 m   **12.** 420 m

_____   _____   _____   _____

13. 225 m   **14.** 622.5 m   **15.** 547.5 m   **16.** 682.5 m

_____   _____   _____   _____

17. On a map the distance between Charleston and Mt. Pleasant is 3.2 cm. The scale is 1 cm = 25 mi. What is the actual distance in miles between these two towns?

_____

18. Blueprints of a building are drawn with a scale of 1 cm = 25 ft. If the base of the building is a square with a perimeter 700 feet, what is the length of one side of the base of the building on the scale drawing?

_____

19. If the scale drawing of a room has measurements of 8 cm by 4.5 cm and the scale of the drawing is 1 cm = 8 ft, what are the actual measurements of the room?

_____

Holt Mathemtics

Homework and Practice
LESSON 5C *Scale Models*

Tell whether each scale reduces, enlarges, or preserves the size of the actual object.

20. 1 in.:15 in.

21. 3 ft:1 yd.

22. 1 cm:1 in.

_____

_____

_____

23. 40 cm:10 in.

24. 1,760 yd:1 mi

25. 1 mi:1 km

_____

_____

_____

Change both measurements to the same unit of measure, and find the scale factor.

26. 2-in. model of a 5-ft desk

27. 4-ft model of a 120-yd field

_____

_____

28. 30-cm model of a 7.5-m wall

29. 50-in. model of a 7,000-ft volcano

_____

_____

30. The museum has a 2-ft model of a 10-yard shark. What is the scale factor of the model?

_____

31. Marina made a scale model of her yard. Her yard is 40 ft × 28 ft 9 in. Her drawing is 16 in. × 11.5 in. What scale factor did she use?

_____

32. A 17 in. model of a 2002 Buick Rendezvous is made with a scale factor of $\frac{1}{11}$. Estimate the actual length of a 2002 Buick Rendezvous.

_____

33. A miniature fireplace for a dollhouse is 4.5 in. by 6.75 in. If the scale factor is $\frac{1}{12}$, what size fireplace does the miniature represent?

Holt Mathemtics

Big Ideas

Answer these questions to summarize the important concepts from Chapter 5 in your own words.

1. Explain how to find two ratios equivalent to $\frac{12}{6}$.

2. Explain how to solve the proportion $\frac{40}{15} = \frac{30}{x}$ using equivalent fractions.

3. The length of an object on a scale drawing is 5 in., and its actual length is 50 ft. Explain how to find the scale.

For more review of Chapter 5:

- Complete the Chapter 5 Study Guide and Review on pages 262–264 of your textbook.

- Complete the Ready to Go On quizzes on pages 234 and 258 of your textbook.

Holt Mathematics

Project

Percents: Home Run Derby

Career: Sports Statistician

Statisticians are mathematicians who work with data, creating statistics, graphs, and tables that describe and explain the real world. Sports statisticians combine their love of sports with their ability to use mathematics. Statistics not only explain what has happened, but can help you predict what may happen in the future.

In this chapter project... you will create a fantasy team of current baseball players. You will:

- Calculate the homerun statistics for four historic baseball players.

- Choose four current baseball players and research their home run statistics.

- Compare your team to your classmates' teams and decide who has the best overall team of home run hitters.

To get started, work through the Home Run Derby worksheet on the next page.

This chapter project reinforces your understanding of these Georgia Performance Standards:

M8P1.a Build new mathematical knowledge through problem solving.

M8P4.c Recognize and apply mathematical ideas in contexts outside of mathematics.

---

go.hrw.com
Chapter Project Online
KEYWORD: MT7 Ch6

Holt Mathematics

Name _____ Date _____ Class _____

Project Recording Sheet
Percents

Home Run Derby

One of the reasons that people like baseball is that they can spend hours looking at the statistics to compare players and teams. Statistics allow us to see what has happened in the past and try to predict what will happen in the future. Use the data below to compare four great players.

Player	Seasons Played	At-Bats	Hits	Home Runs
Joe DiMaggio	13	6821	2214	361
Mickey Mantle	18	8102	2415	536
Ted Williams	19	7706	2654	521
Willie Mays	22	10881	3283	660

Use the data given above to complete the table.

Player	Average Number of Home Runs per Season	Percentage of Home Runs out of Hits
Joe DiMaggio	$\frac{361}{13} \approx 28$	$\frac{361}{2214} \times 100 \approx 16\%$
Mickey Mantle		
Ted Williams		
Willie Mays		

1. Who has the highest percent of home runs out of hits? _____

2. Who has the lowest average of home runs per season? _____

3. If Mickey Mantle had played for 22 seasons instead of 18, with the same average number of home runs per season, would he have beat Willie Mays total number of home runs? Explain.

_____

_____

_____

Holt Mathematics

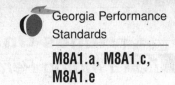

Georgia Performance
Standards

M8A1.a, M8A1.c,
M8A1.e

6A Finding Percents

The circle graph shows results from a mock election in which
40 students were polled.

Percent of Votes Received by Each Candidate

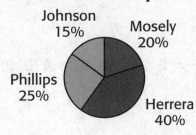

Johnson
15%

Mosely
20%

Phillips
25%

Herrera
40%

**Complete the table to find the number of votes each
candidate received.**

	Candidate	Percent of Votes	Number of Votes
	Mosely	20%	$0.20 \cdot 40 = 8$
1.	Herrera	40%	
2.	Phillips	25%	
3.	Johnson	15%	

Think and Discuss

4. **Discuss** whether there is a clear winner in the election.

5. **Tell** which two candidates combined received the same
   total votes as another candidate. Did they also get the same
   percent of the votes as the other candidate?

Holt Mathematics

Name _____ Date _____ Class _____

Hands-On Lab
Finding Percents

Use with Lesson 6-3

A percent equation is a linear equation and can be drawn as a line graph.

Activity 1

The whole is 50. Write the percent equation using y (percent) and x (part).

$$y = \frac{100}{50} \cdot x = \frac{2}{1} \cdot x$$

Draw a line graph with a slope $= \frac{2}{1} = 2$ and the point A (0, 0) and B (50, 100).

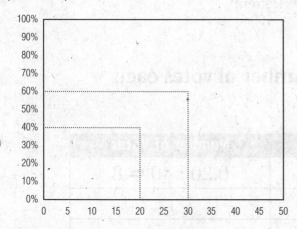

1. What percent of 50 is 30?
   Draw a vertical line from 30 to the graphed line. Then draw a line to the y-axis. The corresponding value on the y-axis is 60: 30 is 60% of 50.

2. What percent of 50 is 20?
   The corresponding value on the y-axis is 40: 20 is 40% of 50.

Activity 2

Draw a line graph for a whole of 30.

$$y = \frac{100}{30} \cdot x = \frac{10}{3} \cdot x$$

The slope $= \frac{10}{3}$.

Holt Mathematics

LESSON 6A Hands-On Lab
Finding Percents, continued

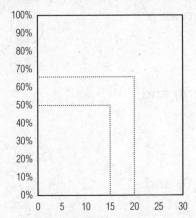

1. What percent of 30 is 15? The corresponding value on the *y*-axis is 50%.

2. What percent of 30 is 20? The corresponding value on the *y*-axis is about 67%.

Think and Discuss

1. How does the line change when the whole increases? Explain.

_____

_____

Try This

1. What is the slope for a whole of 150? For a point *C* with an *x*-coordinate of 90, what is the *y*-coordinate?

_____

2. Draw a line graph using the data above.

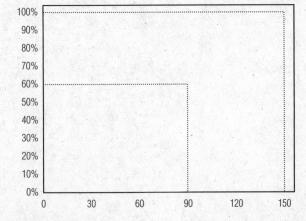

167
Holt Mathematics

Name _____ Date _____ Class _____

Technology Lab
Finding Percents

The percent equation is a linear equation and can be drawn as a line graph.

Activity 1

The whole is 50. Write the percent equation using *y* (percent) and *x* (part).

$$y = \frac{100}{50} \cdot x = \frac{2}{1} \cdot x$$

Draw a line graph with a slope $= \frac{2}{1} = 2$ and the point *A*(0, 0) and *B*(50, 100).

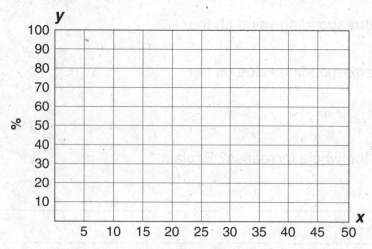

1. What percent of 50 is 30?

Draw a vertical line from 30 on the *x*-axis to the graph of the line. Then draw a horizontal line to the *y*-axis. The corresponding value on the *y*-axis is 60: 30 is 60% of 50.

2. What percent of 50 is 20?
The corresponding value on the y-axis is 40: 20 is 40% of 50.

Holt Mathematics

Technology Lab
Finding Percents, continued

Activity 2

Draw a line graph of the percent equation for a whole of 30.

$$y = \frac{100}{30} \cdot x = \frac{10}{3} \cdot x.$$

The slope is $\frac{10}{3}$.

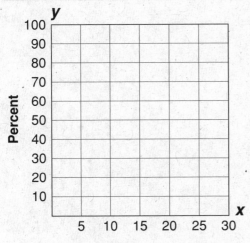

1. What percent of 30 is 15? The corresponding value on the y-axis is 50%.

2. What percent of 30 is 20? The corresponding value on the y-axis is about 67%.

Think and Discuss

1. How does the line change, when the whole increases? Explain.

_____

_____

_____

_____

Technology Lab

Finding Percents, continued

Try This

1. What is the slope of the percent equation for a whole of 150?
   For a point *C* with an *x*-coordinate of 90, what is the *y*-coordinate?

_____

_____

2. Draw a line graph using the data above.

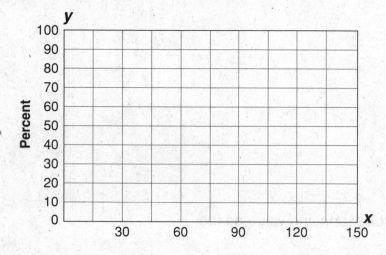

Name _____ Date _____ Class _____

LESSON 6A Review for Mastery
Finding Percents

Since a percent is a ratio, problems involving percent can be solved by using a proportion.

There are different possibilities for an unknown quantity in this proportion.

Possibility 1: Find the *symbol number*.

What percent of 80 is 16?

$$\frac{\text{symbol number}}{100} = \frac{\textit{is} \text{ number}}{\textit{of} \text{ number}}$$

$$\frac{x}{100} = \frac{16}{80}$$

$$80 \cdot x = 16 \cdot 100$$

$$\frac{80x}{80} = \frac{1600}{80}$$

$$x = 20 \qquad \text{So, 16 is 20\% of 80.}$$

$$\boxed{\frac{\text{symbol number}}{100} = \frac{\textit{is} \text{ number}}{\textit{of} \text{ number}}}$$

Find what percent one number is of another.

1. What percent of 64 is 16?

$$\frac{x}{100} = \underline{\hspace{1.5cm}}$$

$$\underline{\hspace{1.5cm}} \cdot x = \underline{\hspace{1.5cm}} \cdot \underline{\hspace{1.5cm}}$$

$$\frac{x}{\underline{\hspace{1cm}}} = \underline{\hspace{1.5cm}}$$

$$x = \underline{\hspace{1.5cm}}$$

So, 16 is _____ of 64.

2. What percent of 200 is 150?

$$\frac{x}{\underline{\hspace{1cm}}} = \underline{\hspace{1.5cm}}$$

$$\underline{\hspace{1.5cm}} \cdot x = \underline{\hspace{1.5cm}} \cdot \underline{\hspace{1.5cm}}$$

$$\frac{x}{\underline{\hspace{1cm}}} = \underline{\hspace{1.5cm}}$$

$$x = \underline{\hspace{1.5cm}}$$

So, 150 is _____ of 200.

3. What percent of 4 is 6?

$$\frac{x}{\underline{\hspace{1cm}}} = \underline{\hspace{1.5cm}}$$

$$\underline{\hspace{1.5cm}} \cdot x = \underline{\hspace{1.5cm}} \cdot \underline{\hspace{1.5cm}}$$

$$\frac{x}{\underline{\hspace{1cm}}} = \underline{\hspace{1.5cm}}$$

$$x = \underline{\hspace{1.5cm}}$$

So, 6 is _____ of 4.

4. About what percent of 115 is 40?

$$\frac{\underline{\hspace{1cm}}}{100} = \underline{\hspace{1.5cm}}$$

$$\underline{\hspace{1.5cm}} \cdot x = \underline{\hspace{1.5cm}} \cdot \underline{\hspace{1.5cm}}$$

$$\frac{x}{\underline{\hspace{1cm}}} = \underline{\hspace{1.5cm}}$$

$$x = \underline{\hspace{1.5cm}}$$

So, 40 is about _____ of 115.

Holt Mathematics

Review for Mastery

LESSON
6A *Finding Percents (continued)*

Possibility 2: Find the *is* number.

What is 20% of 80?

$$\frac{\text{symbol number}}{100} = \frac{is\ \text{number}}{of\ \text{number}}$$

$$\frac{20}{100} = \frac{x}{80}$$

$$100 \cdot x = 20 \cdot 80$$

$$\frac{100x}{100} = \frac{1600}{100}$$

$$x = 16 \qquad \text{So, 20\% of 80 is 16.}$$

Find the indicated percent of each number.

5. What is 30% of 150?

$$\frac{\quad}{100} = \frac{x}{\quad}$$

$$\underline{\quad} \cdot x = \underline{\quad} \cdot \underline{\quad}$$

$$\frac{x}{\underline{\quad}} = \frac{\underline{\quad}}{\underline{\quad}}$$

$$x = \underline{\quad}$$

So, 30% of 150 is _____.

6. What is 75% of 205?

$$\frac{\quad}{100} = \frac{x}{\quad}$$

$$\underline{\quad} \cdot x = \underline{\quad} \cdot \underline{\quad}$$

$$\frac{x}{\underline{\quad}} = \frac{\underline{\quad}}{\underline{\quad}}$$

$$x = \underline{\quad}$$

So, 75% of 205 is _____.

7. What is 125% of 300?

$$\frac{\quad}{100} = \frac{x}{\quad}$$

$$\underline{\quad} \cdot x = \underline{\quad} \cdot \underline{\quad}$$

$$\frac{x}{\underline{\quad}} = \frac{\underline{\quad}}{\underline{\quad}}$$

$$x = \underline{\quad}$$

So, 125% of 300 is _____.

8. What is $66\frac{2}{3}$% of 81?

$$\frac{66\frac{2}{3}}{100} = \frac{x}{\quad}$$

$$\underline{\quad} \cdot x = 66\frac{2}{3} \cdot \underline{\quad}$$

$$\underline{\quad} \cdot x = \frac{200}{3} \cdot \underline{\quad}$$

$$\underline{\quad} \cdot x = \underline{\quad}$$

$$\frac{x}{\underline{\quad}} = \frac{\underline{\quad}}{\underline{\quad}}$$

$$x = \underline{\quad}$$

Holt Mathematics

Homework and Practice

LESSON 6A

Finding Percents

Find each percent.

1. What percent of 60 is 45?

_____

2. 45 is what percent of 90?

_____

3. What percent of 45 is 18?

_____

4. What percent of 75 is 15?

_____

5. 21 is what percent of 84?

_____

6. 51 is what percent of 85?

_____

7. What percent of 60 is 27?

_____

8. What percent of 90 is 27?

_____

9. 18 is what percent of 60?

_____

10. 24.2 is what percent of 110?

_____

11. What percent of 42 is 35?

_____

12. What percent of 64 is 24?

_____

13. What percent of 78 is 27.3?

_____

14. 105 is what percent of 60?

_____

15. An airplane completed 900 miles of a 1200-mile flight.
What percent of the trip remains to be completed?

_____

16. Cloe had 36 of the 45 questions on the math test correct.
What percent of problems did Cloe have correct?

_____

17. Lincoln received $55 for his birthday. He puts $22 of it in his
savings account. What percent of the money did Lincoln deposit
in his savings account?

_____

18. Chico bought a jacket for $42. The cost of the jacket including tax,
was $44.31. What was the percent of sales tax on the purchase?

_____

Holt Mathematics

6B Finding a Number When the Percent is Known

Georgia Performance Standards
M8A1.a, M8A1.c, M8A1.e

A CD player is on sale for $15 off the original price. According to the advertisement, this is a 25% discount. You can use what you know about percents to figure out the original price of the CD player.

Think: 25% is $\frac{1}{4}$, so $15 must be $\frac{1}{4}$ of the original price.

You can model the situation as shown.

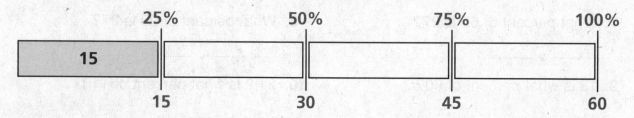

The original price is $60.

Draw a model to find the original price for each of the following.

1. Amount of discount: $8; percent of discount: 20%
2. Amount of discount: $12; percent of discount: $33\frac{1}{3}$%
3. Amount of discount: $17; percent of discount: 50%

Think and Discuss

4. **Explain** how you could find the value of a number given that 7 is 10% of the number.

5. **Describe** what must be true about a number if you know that 45 is 100% of the number.

Holt Mathematics

Name _____ Date _____ Class _____

6B

Review for Mastery
Finding a Number When the Percent Is Known

Since a percent is a ratio, problems
involving percent can be solved by
using a proportion.

$\dfrac{\text{symbol number}}{100}$	$=$	$\dfrac{\textit{is} \text{ number}}{\textit{of} \text{ number}}$

To find a number when the percent is
known, the variable appears in the *of*
position in the proportion

16 is 20% of what number?

$$\frac{20}{100} = \frac{16}{x}$$

$$20 \cdot x = 16 \cdot 100$$

$$\frac{20x}{20} = \frac{1600}{20}$$

$$x = 80$$

So, 16 is 20% of 80.

Find each number whose percentage is given.

1. 18 is 75% of what number?

$$\frac{}{100} = \frac{}{x}$$

$$\underline{\hspace{1cm}} \cdot x = \underline{\hspace{1cm}} \cdot \underline{\hspace{1cm}}$$

$$\frac{x}{\underline{\hspace{1cm}}} = \underline{\hspace{1cm}}$$

$$x = \underline{\hspace{1cm}}$$

So, 18 is 75% of _____.

2. 96 is 40% of what number?

$$\frac{}{100} = \frac{}{x}$$

$$\underline{\hspace{1cm}} \cdot x = \underline{\hspace{1cm}} \cdot \underline{\hspace{1cm}}$$

$$\frac{x}{\underline{\hspace{1cm}}} = \underline{\hspace{1cm}}$$

$$x = \underline{\hspace{1cm}}$$

So, 96 is 40% of _____.

3. 7 is 125% of what number

$$\frac{}{100} = \frac{7}{x}$$

$$\underline{\hspace{1cm}} \cdot x = \underline{\hspace{1cm}} \cdot \underline{\hspace{1cm}}$$

$$\frac{x}{\underline{\hspace{1cm}}} = \underline{\hspace{1cm}}$$

$$x = \underline{\hspace{1cm}}$$

So, 7 is 125% of _____.

4. 40 is about 30% of what number?

$$\frac{}{100} = \frac{}{\underline{\hspace{1cm}}}$$

$$\underline{\hspace{1cm}} \cdot x = \underline{\hspace{1cm}} \cdot \underline{\hspace{1cm}}$$

$$\frac{x}{\underline{\hspace{1cm}}} = \underline{\hspace{1cm}}$$

$$x = \underline{\hspace{1cm}}$$

So, 40 is about 30% of _____.

Copyright © by Holt, Rinehart and Winston.
All rights reserved.

Holt Mathematics

LESSON 6B Homework and Practice
Finding a Number When the Percent Is Known

Find each number.

1. 25% of what number is 12?

   _____

2. 27 is 54% of what number?

   _____

3. 51 is 60% of what number?

   _____

4. 32% of what number is 8?

   _____

5. 80% of what number is 16?

   _____

6. 76 is 95% of what number?

   _____

7. 27 is 18% of what number?

   _____

8. 24% of what number is 72?

   _____

9. 104 is 65% of what number?

   _____

10. 12 is 3% of what number?

    _____

11. 5% of what number is 12.2?

    _____

12. 16% of what number is 4.8?

    _____

13. 90 is $66\frac{2}{3}$% of what number?

    _____

14. 40.5 is 150% of what number?

    _____

15. Meredith bought a bicycle that cost $385.89. In addition, she had to pay 7% sales tax on her purchase. What was the amount of sales tax Meredith paid? Round the answer to the nearest cent.

    _____

16. Wilson answered 92% of a 25 question test correctly. How many questions did he answer correctly?

    _____

17. Rodriquez had $84.60 of his salary withheld for taxes. This was 15% of his gross pay. What is his gross pay?

    _____

18. A car dealer receives an order of 340 new cars. Thirty percent of the cars are silver in color. How many of the cars received by the dealership are silver?

    _____

Holt Mathematics

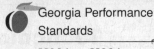

6C Applications of Percents

You often need to calculate percents when making a purchase.

Use a calculator to find the tax on each item and the total cost of the item including the tax.

	Item	Cost	Tax Rate	Tax	Total Cost = Cost + Tax
1.	CD	$13.95	8%		
2.	DVD	$24.99	8%		
3.	Headphones	$29.95	8%		

Use a calculator to find the total cost of each item.

	Item	Cost	Tax Rate	Total Cost = 1.08 · Cost
4.	CD	$13.95	8%	
5.	DVD	$24.99	8%	
6.	Headphones	$29.95	8%	

Think and Discuss

7. **Explain** how you calculated the tax on each item in Problems 1–3.

8. **Explain** why the total cost is the same whether you use the formula *total cost* = *cost* + *tax* or the formula *total cost* = 1.08 · *cost*.

Holt Mathematics

Name _____ Date _____ Class _____

Technology Lab
Applications of Percents

Use with Lesson 6-6

Percentages are important in financial transactions. Whenever you make a purchase, you may have to add a sales tax to the price of the item. When you get a discount on an item, you need to deduct a certain percentage from the price of the item.

Activity 1
The sales tax is 8.25% in Texas. If you want to buy a bicycle that is priced at $220, how much will you pay?

1. First, find the amount of the tax (T) you pay on the bicycle. Use your calculator to compute the following:

$$T = \frac{8.25}{100} \cdot 220 = 18.15$$

You may also use the keystrokes
in the order given.   8.25 ☒× 220 ☒%

2. Then add this amount to the price of the bicycle to find the final amount (A):

$$A = 220 + 18.15 = 238.15$$

You may also use the following
keystrokes in the order given.   220 ☒+ 8.25 ☒%

If you have an algebraic calculator, you can input
$220 + 0.0825 \times 220 = 238.15$.

Activity 2
The merchant gives you a 15% discount on the $220 bicycle and you live in a state without a sales tax.

How much do you have to pay?

You may also use the following keystrokes
in the order given.   220 ☒− 15 ☒%

The bicycle costs $187.

Holt Mathematics

LESSON 6C Technology Lab
Applications of Percents, continued

Think and Discuss

1. A department store in a state without sales tax has advertised its annual sale: 50% off of every item. When you get to the store, an additional 25% discount is offered. You also have a discount coupon for 25%. You buy a coat with an original price tag of $160. Does the coat cost anything? Why or why not?

_____

_____

_____

Try This

1. Use your calculator to complete the following receipt from a department store:

Receipt	
11/5/03	
Coat	110.00
− 15% discount	_____
Shirt	22.00
Belt	17.00
Sub Total	_____
+ 6% sales tax	
Total	_____

LESSON 6C Review for Mastery

Applications of Percents

Salespeople often earn a **commission,** a percent of their total sales.

Find the commission on a real-estate sale of $125,000
if the commission rate is 4%.

Write the percent as a decimal and multiply.

> **commission rate × amount of sale = amount of commission**
> $0.04 × \$125,000 \qquad = \$5000$

If, in addition to the commission, the salesperson earns a
salary of $1000, what is the total pay?

> **commission+ salary = total pay**
> $\$5000 + \$1000 = \$6000$

Complete to find each total monthly pay.

1. total monthly sales = $170,000; commission rate = 3%; salary = $1500

   amount of commission = 0.03 × $_____ = $_____

   total pay = $_____ + $1500 = $_____

2. total monthly sales = $16,000; commission rate = 5.5%; salary = $1750

   amount of commission = _____ × $_____ = $_____

   total pay = $_____ + $_____ = $_____

A **tax** is a charge, usually a percentage, generally imposed by a government.

Sales tax is the tax on the sale of an item or service.

If the sales tax rate is 7%, find the tax on a sale of $9.49.

Write the tax rate as a decimal and multiply.

> **tax rate × amount of sale = amount of tax**
> $0.07 \qquad × \$9.49 \qquad\qquad = \$0.6643 ≈ \$0.66$

Complete to find each amount of sales tax.

3. item price = $5.19; sales tax rate = 6%

   amount of sales tax = 0.06 × $_____ = $_____ ≈ $_____

4. item price = $250; sales tax rate = 6.75%

   amount of sales tax = _____ × $_____ = $_____ ≈ $_____

Holt Mathematics

Name _____ Date _____ Class _____

Review for Mastery

6C *Applications of Percents (continued)*

Use a proportion to find what percent of a person's income goes to a specific expense.

Heather earned $3,200 last month. She paid $448 for transportation. To find the percent of her earnings that she put towards transportation, write a proportion.

Think: What percent of 3200 is 448?

$$\frac{n}{100} = \frac{448}{3200}$$ ◄— Set up a proportion.

Think: $\frac{part}{whole} = \frac{part}{whole}$

$3200n = 448 \times 100$ ◄— Find cross products.

$3200n = 44{,}800$ ◄— Simplify.

$\frac{3200n}{3200} = \frac{44{,}800}{3200}$ ◄— Divide both sides by 3200.

$n = 14$ ◄— Simplify.

Heather put 14% of her earnings towards transportation.

Complete each proportion to find the percent of earnings.

5. Wayne earned $3,100 last month. He paid $837 for food. What percent of his earnings went to food?

$$\frac{n}{100} = \frac{\rule{1cm}{0.4pt}}{3100}$$

$3100n = \rule{1cm}{0.4pt} \times 100$

$3100n = \rule{1cm}{0.4pt}$

$\frac{3100n}{3100} = \rule{1cm}{0.4pt}$

$n = \rule{1cm}{0.4pt}$

_____ of Wayne's earnings went to food.

6. Leah earned $1,900 last month. She paid $304 for utilities. What percent of her earnings went to utilities?

$$\frac{n}{100} = \frac{304}{\rule{1cm}{0.4pt}}$$

$\rule{1cm}{0.4pt} \times n = \rule{1cm}{0.4pt} \times 100$

$\rule{1cm}{0.4pt} = \rule{1cm}{0.4pt}$

$\rule{1cm}{0.4pt} = \rule{1cm}{0.4pt}$

$n = \rule{1cm}{0.4pt}$

_____ of Leah's earnings went to utilities.

Holt Mathematics

LESSON
6C
Homework and Practice
Applications of Percents

Complete the table to find the amount of sales tax for each sale amount to the nearest cent.

1.

	6% sales tax	7% sales tax	5.5% sales tax
$53.50			
$80.50			
$219.95			
$2,640.00			

Complete the table to find the commission for each sale amount to the nearest cent.

2.

	5% commission	8% commission	7.5% commission
$365.00			
$2,140.00			
$16,300.00			
$94,750.00			

3. Mr. Darney bought a house for $58,000. He made a down payment of 20% and got a loan for the rest. What was the amount of his loan?

_____

4. Elijah buys three pens for $1.89 each and a notebook for $3.95. The sales tax rate is 6%. What is Elijah's total cost? Round the answer to the nearest cent.

_____

5. Seth is a real estate agent. He receives 8% commission on the selling price of any home he sells. If the last house he sold had a selling price of $145,900, what was Seth's commission?

_____

Holt Mathematics

Georgia Performance Standards

M8A1.a, M8A1.c, M8A1.e

6D Simple Interest

Simple interest is the amount earned on money deposited in some savings accounts.

The interest your account earns is calculated using the formula $I = Prt$. For example, if you start a savings account with $100.00 (**principal P**) and your savings account pays 5% (**interest rate r**), the interest (I) you will have earned at the end of 1 year (**time t**) will be $0.05 \cdot 100 = \$5$. Your total balance at the end of 1 year will be $\$100.00 + \$5.00 = \$105.00$.

Complete the table.

	Savings	Interest Rate	Interest	Total Balance
	$100	5%	$0.05 \cdot 100 = \$5$	$100 + 5 = \$105$
1.	$200	6%		
2.	$300		$24	
3.	$500			$550

Think and Discuss

4. **Describe** your strategies for completing the table.

5. **Explain** how to use the formula $I = Prt$ when you need to find an interest rate.

Holt Mathematics

Review for Mastery
6D Simple Interest

Interest is money paid on an investment.
A borrower pays the interest. An investor earns the interest.

Simple interest, *I*, is earned when
an amount of money, the *principal P*,
is borrowed or invested at a *rate of interest r*
for a *period of time t*.

Interest = Principal · Rate · Time
$I = P \cdot r \cdot t$

Situation 1: Find *I* given *P*, *r*, and *t*.

Calculate the simple interest on a loan of $3500
for a period of 6 months at a yearly rate of 5%.

Write the interest rate as a decimal.   5% = 0.05
Write the time period in terms of years.   6 months = 0.5 year
$I = P \cdot r \cdot t$
$I = 3500 \cdot 0.05 \cdot 0.5 = \$87.50$ ⟵ interest earned

Find the interest in each case.

1. principal *P* = $5000; time *t* = 2 years; interest rate *r* = 6%

   $I = P \cdot r \cdot t =$ _____ · 0.06 · _____ = $_____

2. principal *P* = $2500; time *t* = 3 months; interest rate *r* = 8%

   $I = P \cdot r \cdot t =$ _____ · _____ · _____ = $_____

Situation 2: Find *t* given *I*, *P*, and *r*.

An investment of $3000 at a yearly rate
of 6.5% earned $390 in interest. Find
the period of time for which the money
was invested.

The investment was for 2 years.

$I = P \cdot r \cdot t$
$390 = 3000 \cdot 0.065 \cdot t$
$390 = 195t$
$\dfrac{390}{195} = \dfrac{195t}{195}$
$2 = t$

Find the time in each case.

3. *I* = $1120; *P* = $4000; *r* = 7%
   $I = P \cdot r \cdot t$

   $1120 =$ _____ · 0.07 · *t*

   $1120 =$ _____ *t*

   $\dfrac{\text{_____}}{\text{_____}} = \dfrac{t}{\text{_____}}$

   _____ years = *t*

4. *I* = $812.50; *P* = $5000; *r* = 6.5%
   $I = P \cdot r \cdot t$

   $812.50 =$ _____ · _____ · *t*

   $812.50 =$ _____ *t*

   $\dfrac{\text{_____}}{\text{_____}} = \dfrac{t}{\text{_____}}$

   _____ years = *t*

Holt Mathematics

Review for Mastery

Simple Interest

Situation 3: Find *r* given *I*, *P*, and *t*.

$2500 was invested for 3 years and earned $450 in interest. Find the rate of interest.

$I = P \cdot r \cdot t$

$450 = 2500 \cdot r \cdot 3$

$450 = 7500r$

$$\frac{450}{7500} = \frac{7500r}{7500}$$

The interest rate was 6%.

$0.06 = r$

Find the interest rate in each case.

5. *I* = $1200; *P* = $6000; *t* = 4 years

$I = P \cdot r \cdot t$

$1200 = $ _____ $\cdot r \cdot 4$

$1200 = $ _____ r

$$\frac{}{} = \frac{r}{}$$

_____ $= r$

The interest rate was _____ %.

6. *I* = $325; *P* = $2000; *t* = 2.5 years

$I = P \cdot r \cdot t$

$325 = $ _____ $\cdot r \cdot$ _____

$325 = $ _____ r

$$\frac{}{} = \frac{r}{}$$

_____ $= r$

The interest rate was _____ %.

The total amount *A* of money in an account after interest has been earned, is the sum of the principal *P* and the interest *I*.

> **Amount = Principal + Interest**
> $A = P + I$

Find the amount of money in the account after $3500 has been invested for 3 years at a yearly rate of 6%.

First, find the interest earned.

$I = P \cdot r \cdot t$

$I = 3500 \cdot 0.06 \cdot 3 = 630 ⟵ interest earned

Then, add the interest to the principal. $3500 + 630 = 4130$

So, the total amount in the account after 3 years is $4130.

Find the total amount in the account.

7. principal *P* = $4500; time *t* = 2.5 years; interest rate *r* = 5.5%

$I = P \cdot r \cdot t = $ _____ $\cdot$ _____ $\cdot$ _____ $= $$ _____

Total Amount $= P + I = 4500 + $ _____ $= $ _____

So, after 2.5 years, the total amount in the account was $ _____ .

Holt Mathematics

Name _____ Date _____ Class _____

Homework and Practice
Simple Interest

Find the missing value.

1. principal = $175
   rate = 4%
   time = 5 years
   interest = ?

   _____

2. principal = ?
   rate = 6%
   time = 6 years
   interest = $81

   _____

3. principal = $210
   rate = 5%
   time = ? years
   interest = $31.50

   _____

4. principal = $125
   rate = ?%
   time = 4 years
   interest = $35

   _____

5. principal = ?
   rate = $5\frac{1}{4}$%
   time = 2 years
   interest = $126

   _____

6. principal = ?
   rate = 6.5%
   time = 3 years
   interest = $165.75

   _____

7. Scott deposits $1,000 in an account that earns 5% simple
   interest. What will the account be worth after two years?

   _____

8. A bank pays 5.5% simple interest per year. Find the total amount
   at the end of one year on a principal of $3,000.

   _____

9. Mr. Womer borrowed $1,100 to start his own business. National
   Bank charged him 15% interest per year. Mr. Womer paid $330 in
   interest. For what period of time did he borrow the money?

   _____

10. Ms. Lang borrows $2,300 for 30 months at 13% interest per year.
    How much interest will Ms. Lang pay? What is the total amount
    she will repay?

    _____

Holt Mathematics

Big Ideas

Answer these questions to summarize the important concepts from Chapter 6 in your own words.

1. Explain how to convert $\frac{3}{8}$ to a percent.

2. Explain how to solve "34 is 25% of what number?".

3. Explain how to find the percent increase or decrease from 200 to 145.

4. Explain how to find the interest and total amount of $400 at 7.5% per year for 8 years.

For more review of Chapter 6:

- Complete the Chapter 6 Study Guide and Review on pages 312–314 of your textbook.

- Complete the Ready to Go On quizzes on pages 292 and 308 of your textbook.

Holt Mathematics

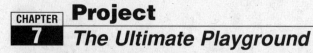

Project
The Ultimate Playground

Career: Playground Equipment Designer

Playground equipment must be attractive, safe, fun, and appropriate for the ages of children who will use it. Years ago, designers used pencils, T-squares, and slide rules to create their designs. Designers now use computers, 3-D programs, and virtual reality to design playgrounds.

In this chapter project...you will design your own playground. You will:

- Identify the different geometric shapes in playground equipment.

- Choose the equipment you would put on your playground.

- Create drawings or models of your equipment and compare your playground with those designed by your classmates.

To get started, work through The Ultimate Playground worksheet on the next page.

This chapter project reinforces your understanding of these Georgia Performance Standards:

M8P3.d Use the language of mathematics to express mathematical ideas precisely.

M8P4.c Recognize and apply mathematical ideas in contexts outside of mathematics.

---

go.hrw.com
Chapter Project Online
KEYWORD: MT7 Ch7

Holt Mathematics

Name _____ Date _____ Class _____

Project Recording Sheet

CHAPTER 7 *Foundations of Geometry*

The Ultimate Playground

Do you remember the playground equipment you played on when you were younger? Which kinds did you enjoy? Were some kinds scary? Are all of those pieces of equipment still around? Some kinds of old playground equipment are now considered too dangerous. Below is a list of some popular equipment. How many do you know about?

- Monkey bars
- Merry-go-round
- Climbing wall
- Swing
- Chin-up bar
- Bridge
- Teeter-totter
- Balance beam
- Tunnel
- Slide
- Spring toy
- Rope ladder
- Fire pole
- Ladder
- Rings
- Tire swing
- Trapeze
- Glider
- Track ride
- Platform

Copy and complete the chart below to describe the equipment you are familiar with. The first row is an example.

Equipment	Fun/Not fun	Dangerous/ Not dangerous	Angles and Lines	Activity
Swing	*Fun (if they are tall)*	*Less dangerous with soft seats*	*Parallel lines, right angles*	*Individual swinging*

Use your chart to create a description of the kind of equipment that you prefer.

Create a model of what you think is a perfect piece of playground equipment. Use toothpicks, drinking straws, pipe cleaners, and other materials. Compare your model with those of your classmates. Answer these questions to analyze your findings.

What similarities and differences do you find?

_____

_____

What geometric shapes are most common? Most unusual?

_____

_____

What kind of activity is the most common?

_____

_____

Why do you think the results turned out the way that they did?

_____

Holt Mathematics

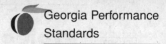

Georgia Performance Standards

M8G1.a, M8G1.b

7A Parallel and Perpendicular Lines

A carpenter cuts boards at different angles.

The board below is cut at a 45° angle.

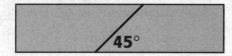

1. Label the angles formed by the cut.

2. Which angles are **congruent,** or have the same measure?

3. Which angles are **supplementary,** or have measures that add to 180°?

The board below is cut at a 30° angle.

4. Label the angles formed by the cut.

5. Which angles are congruent?

6. Which angles are supplementary?

Think and Discuss

7. **Describe** the top and bottom edges of the boards above. What kinds of lines do they form?

8. **Describe** the angles formed after cutting the board at a 90° angle.

Holt Mathematics

LESSON 7A Hands-On Lab 1
Explore Parallel Lines and Transversals

Parallel lines are lines in the same plane that never cross. When two parallel lines are intersected by a third line, the angles formed have special relationships. This third line is called a *transversal*.

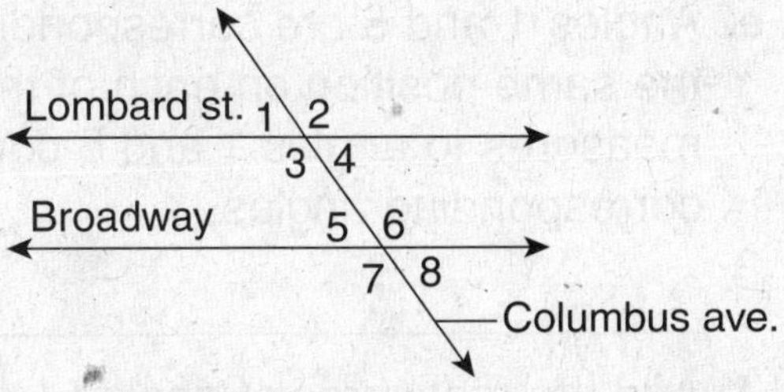

In San Francisco, California, many streets are parallel such as Lombard St. and Broadway.

Columbus Ave. is a transversal that runs diagonal across them. The eight angles that are formed are labeled on the diagram below.

Activity

1. Measure angles 1-8 in the diagram above. Write these measures in your table.

Angle Number	Angle Measure
1	
2	
3	
4	
5	
6	
7	
8	

2. Use the table you completed and the corresponding diagram for the following problems.

a. Angles inside the parallel lines are *interior angles.* Name them.

_____

b. Angles outside the parallel lines are *exterior angles.* Name them.

_____

c. Angles 3 and 6 and angles 4 and 5 are *alternate interior angles.* What do you notice about angles 3 and 6? What do you notice about angles 4 and 5?

_____

d. Angles 2 and 7 and angles 1 and 8 are *alternate exterior angles.* How do the measures of each pair of alternate exterior angles compare?

_____

Holt Mathematics

Hands-On Lab 1
Explore Parallel Lines and Transversals (continued)

e. Angles 1 and 5 are corresponding angles because they are in the same position on each of the parallel lines. How do the measures to angles 1 and 5 compare? Name another set of corresponding angles.

_____

f. Add the measures of angles 1 and 2. Now add the measures of angles 3 and 8. What can you say about the relationship of the angles in each of these sets? Name two other angles that have the same relationship.

_____

Think and Discuss

1. $\overleftrightarrow{FG}$ and $\overleftrightarrow{LO}$ are parallel. Tell what you know about the angles that are labeled 1 through 8.

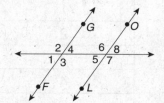

_____

2. If angle 2 measures 125, what are the measures of angles 1, 3, 4, 5, 6, 7, and 8?

_____

3. If a transversal intersects two parallel lines and one of the angles formed measures 90°, discuss the relationship between all the angles.

_____

Try This

Use a protractor to measure one angle in each diagram. Then find the measures of all the other angles without using a protractor. Tell how to find each angle measure.

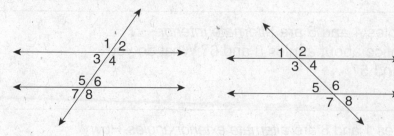

_____

_____

Holt Mathematics

Name _____ Date _____ Class _____

Hands-On Lab 2
Parallel and Perpendicular Lines

Activity

1. Parallel lines are two lines in a plane that never meet.
   Perpendicular lines intersect at 90° angles.

   Prove the two lines below are parallel by measuring using a
   transversal and a protractor.

   How did you prove the lines are parallel?

   _____

   _____

   _____

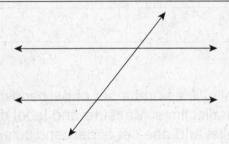

2. Prove that these lines are perpendicular using a protractor. Then
   explain your proof.

   _____

   _____

   _____

Holt Mathematics

Hands-On Lab

LESSON 7A
Parallel and Perpendicular Lines (continued)

Think and Discuss

1. If an angle measured 38° in a line intersecting 2 parallel lines, how many other angles would you expect to be 38° angles?

_____

_____

2. If a transversal intersects 2 parallel lines and you know one angle is 72°, why do you know every other angle?

_____

_____

_____

Try This

In the space below, draw a set of parallel lines and a set of perpendicular lines. Draw a transversal intersecting the parallel lines. Measure and label the angles that prove that one set of lines is parallel and one set is perpendicular.

_____

Parallel Lines

Perpendicular Lines

Holt Mathematics

Name _____ Date _____ Class _____

Parallel Lines

Parallel lines never meet.

When parallel lines are cut by a **transversal**, 8 angles are formed, 4 acute and 4 obtuse.

The acute angles are all congruent.

The obtuse angles are all congruent.

Any acute angle is supplementary to any obtuse angle.

Perpendicular Lines

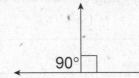

Perpendicular lines form right angles.

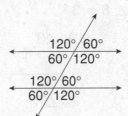

In each diagram, parallel lines are cut by a transversal. Name the angles that are congruent to the indicated angle.

1.

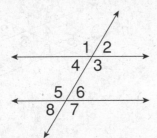

The angles congruent to ∠1 are:

_____

2.

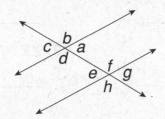

The angles congruent to ∠a are:

_____

3.

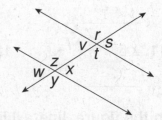

The angles congruent to ∠z are:

_____

In each diagram, parallel lines are cut by a transversal and the measure of one angle is given. Write the measures of the remaining angles on the diagram.

4.

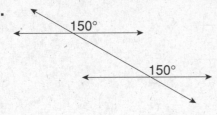

5.

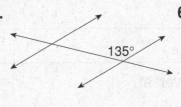

6.

Holt Mathematics

Name _____ Date _____ Class _____

1. Measure the angles formed by the transversal and the parallel lines. Which angles seem to be congruent?

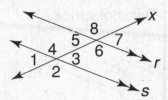

_____

_____

In the figure, line *x* || line *y*. Find the measure of each indicated angle, if the $m \angle 8 = 34°$.

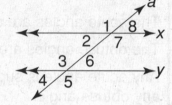

2. ∠2   **3.** ∠3   **4.** ∠4

_____   _____   _____

5. ∠6   **6.** ∠7   **7.** ∠1

_____   _____   _____

In the figure, line *m* || line *n*. Find the measure of each angle, if $m \angle 1 = 131°$.

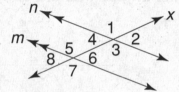

8. ∠2   **9.** ∠3   **10.** ∠4

_____   _____   _____

11. ∠5   **12.** ∠6   **13.** ∠7

_____   _____   _____

In the figure, line *a* || line *b*.

14. Name all angles congruent to ∠5.

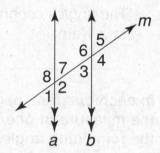

_____

15. Name all angles congruent to ∠4.

_____

16. Name three pairs of angles with sums of 180°.

_____

_____

17. Which line is the transversal?

_____

Holt Mathematics

Georgia Performance
Standards

M8G1.c

7B Segments Cut by Parallel Lines

When three parallel lines are cut by two or more transversals, the segments formed have a special relationship. In the diagram, $\overleftrightarrow{AD} \parallel \overleftrightarrow{BE} \parallel \overleftrightarrow{CF}$.

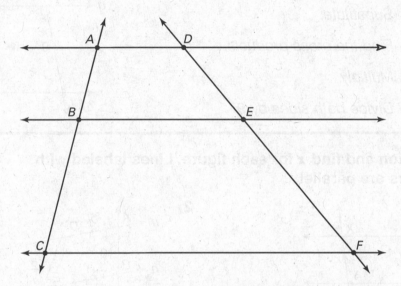

1. Use a centimeter ruler to measure $\overline{AB}$, $\overline{BC}$, $\overline{DE}$, and $\overline{EF}$.

2. Calculate the rations $\frac{AB}{BC}$ and $\frac{DE}{EF}$. How do the two ratios compare?

3. Use your results from Question 2 to fill in the blank in this statement:

   When parallel lines are cut by two transversals, the corresponding segments are _____.

Think and Discuss

4. **Discuss** what would happen if two parallel transversals cut three parallel lines. How would the segments be related?

Holt Mathematics

Name _____ Date _____ Class _____

Review for Mastery
Segments Cut by Parallel Lines

When three parallel lines are cut by two transversals, the lengths of
the segments formed are proportional.

**Line *p* ∥ line *q* ∥ line *r*. Write a
proportion based on the figure and
find *x*.**

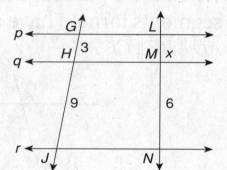

$\dfrac{GH}{HJ} = \dfrac{LM}{MN}$ The segments are proportional.

$\dfrac{3}{9} = \dfrac{x}{6}$ Substitute.

$3 \cdot 6 = 9x$ Find the cross products.

$18 = 9x$ Multiply.

$x = 2$ Divide both sides by 9.

**Write a proportion and find *x* for each figure. Lines labeled with
lowercase letters are parallel.**

1.

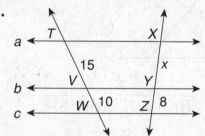

$\dfrac{\square}{\square} = \dfrac{\square}{\square}$ *x* = _____

2.

$\dfrac{\square}{\square} = \dfrac{\square}{\square}$ *x* = _____

3.

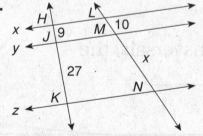

$\dfrac{\square}{\square} = \dfrac{\square}{\square}$ *x* = _____

4.

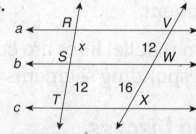

$\dfrac{\square}{\square} = \dfrac{\square}{\square}$ *x* = _____

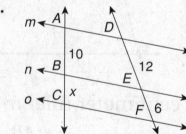

Holt Mathematics

Homework and Practice

**LESSON
7B** *Relations and Functions*

**Write a proportion and find *x* for each figure. Lines labeled with
lowercase letters are parallel.**

1.

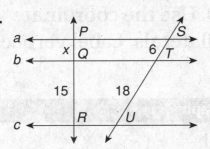

$$\frac{\square}{\square} = \frac{\square}{\square}$$ $x =$ _____

2.

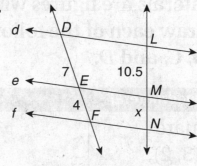

$$\frac{\square}{\square} = \frac{\square}{\square}$$ $x =$ _____

3.

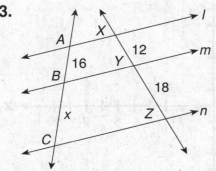

$$\frac{\square}{\square} = \frac{\square}{\square}$$ $x =$ _____

4.

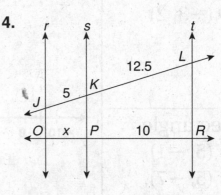

$$\frac{\square}{\square} = \frac{\square}{\square}$$ $x =$ _____

5. There are other proportional relationships
among the segments on transversals that
cut parallel lines. In the figure at right:

$$\frac{x}{y} = \frac{w}{z}$$

Use these relationships to write proportions
and the missing value in the figure below.

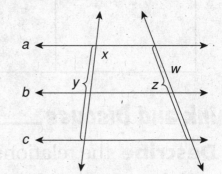

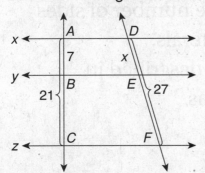

    $x =$ _____

Holt Mathematics

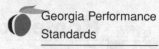

Georgia Performance
Standards

M8G1.a, M8A4.b

7C Coordinate Geometry

Quadrilaterals are figures with four sides. Use the coordinate
grid to draw each of the following quadrilaterals. Label vertices
with *A, B, C,* and *D.*

Quadrilateral	Graph
1. Square *A* (3, 2), *B* (3, 8), *C* (−3, 8), *D* (−3, 2)	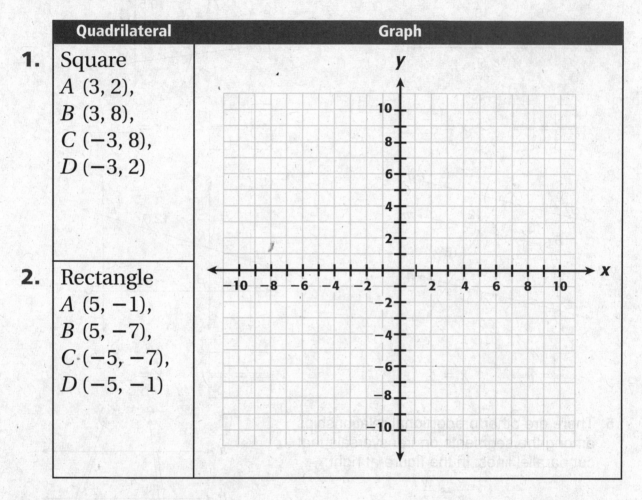
2. Rectangle *A* (5, −1), *B* (5, −7), *C* (−5, −7), *D* (−5, −1)	

Think and Discuss

3. Describe the relationship between the number of sides
and the number of vertices of quadrilaterals.

4. Discuss whether the relationship you described in
Problem **3** is also true for other polygons.

Holt Mathematics

LESSON 7C Review for Mastery
Coordinate Geometry

Possible Values for Slope

Slope is Positive	Slope is Negative	Slope = 0	Slope is Undefined
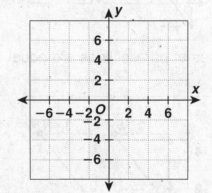			
Line slants up. Forms acute angle with the positive direction of *x*-axis.	*Line slants down.* Forms obtuse angle with positive direction of *x*-axis.	*Horizonal Line* Parallel to *x*-axis.	*Vertical Line* Perpendicular to *x*-axis

Plot the given points. Describe the slope of the line that joins them.

1. (−2, 2) and (2, 5)

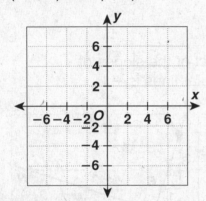

slope is: _____

2. (−2, −5) and (−2, 2)

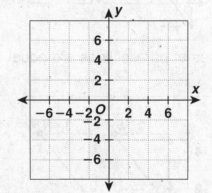

slope is: _____

3. (1, 2) and (5, −2)

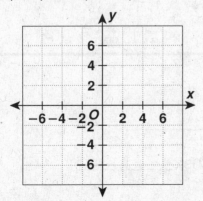

slope is: _____

4. (−2, −2) and (4, −2)

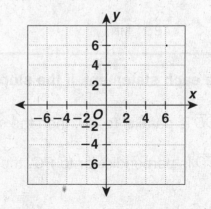

slope is: _____

Holt Mathematics

Name _____ Date _____ Class _____

Review for Mastery

Coordinate Geometry (continued)

To find the slope of a line, use a
direction ratio such as $\frac{up}{right}$.

direction ratio from A to $B = \frac{up\ 5}{right\ 3}$

slope of $\overleftrightarrow{AB} = \frac{5}{3}$

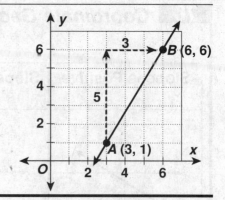

Complete to find the slope of each line.

5.

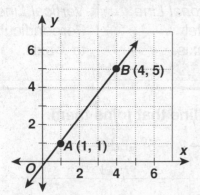

From A to B, do you go up
or down? How many units? _____

Do you go right or left?
How many units? _____

slope of $\overleftrightarrow{AB} =$ _____

The slopes of parallel lines are equal.

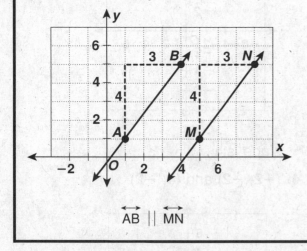

$\overleftrightarrow{AB} \parallel \overleftrightarrow{MN}$

The product of the slopes of
perpendicular lines is −1.

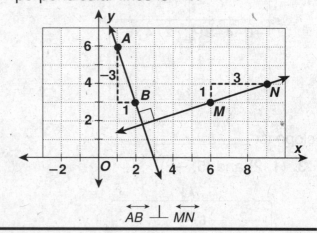

$\overleftrightarrow{AB} \perp \overleftrightarrow{MN}$

Complete each statement. If the slope of $\overleftrightarrow{CD} = -\frac{2}{3}$

6. and $\overleftrightarrow{CD}$ is parallel to $\overleftrightarrow{XY}$, then the slope of $\overleftrightarrow{XY}$ is: _____

7. and $\overleftrightarrow{CD}$ is perpendicular to $\overleftrightarrow{PQ}$, then the slope of $\overleftrightarrow{PQ}$ is: _____

Holt Mathematics

LESSON
7C Homework and Practice
Coordinate Geometry

Determine if the slope of each line is positive, negative, 0, or undefined. Then find the slope of each line.

1. $\overleftrightarrow{AD}$

2. $\overleftrightarrow{BC}$

_____   _____

3. $\overleftrightarrow{MW}$

4. $\overleftrightarrow{TD}$

_____   _____

5. $\overleftrightarrow{SV}$

6. $\overleftrightarrow{RS}$

_____   _____

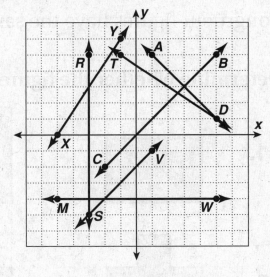

7. Which lines are parallel?

_____

8. Which lines are perpendicular?

_____

_____

Graph the quadrilaterals with the given vertices. Write all the names that apply to each quadrilateral.

9. $(-3, 2)$, $(-6, -4)$, $(4, 2)$, $(6, -4)$

_____

10. $(2, 6)$, $(6, -5)$, $(2, -5)$, $(6, 6)$

_____

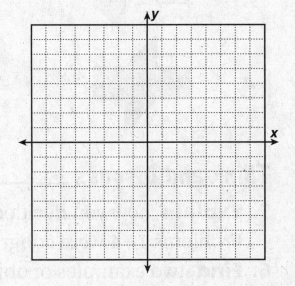

Holt Mathematics

Georgia Performance Standards

M8G1.d

7D Congruence

Congruent figures have the same size and shape.

Determine whether the figures in each pair are congruent.

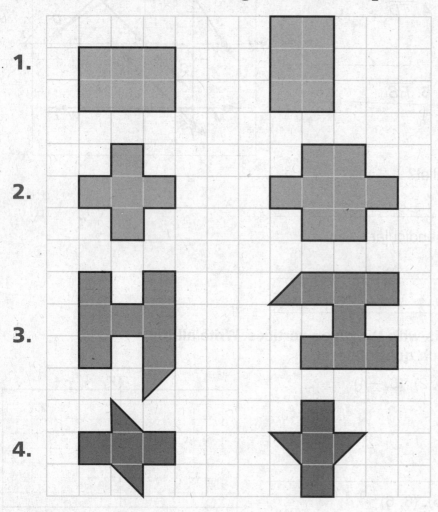

1.

2.

3.

4.

Think and Discuss

5. **Explain** how you decided whether the figures in Problems **1–4** were congruent or not.

6. **Find** two examples of objects that are congruent. What makes the two objects congruent?

Holt Mathematics

Hands-On Lab

LESSON 7D
Congruence

Activity

When two polygons are congruent, all their corresponding sides and angles are congruent.

In the space below, construct a polygon congruent to this polygon but in a different position on the page. Label the angles with different letters, and write in the degrees of each angle:

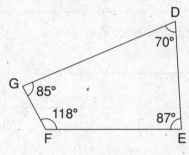

Write a congruence statement for the pair of polygons. In a congruence statement, the vertices in the second polygon are written in the order of correspondence. For example, you might write $\angle A \cong \angle G$, $\angle \cong \angle H$, and so on.

_____

_____

_____

_____

Holt Mathematics

Name ______________________ Date ____________ Class ____________

LESSON 7D

Hands-On Lab

Congruence, continued

Think and Discuss

1. How can you tell if two polygons are congruent?

____

____

____

2. If two polygons are dilations, are they congruent?

____

____

Try This

In the space below, draw 2 congruent polygons in different positions. Write in the lengths of the sides and measurements of the angles. Write a congruence statement to prove the polygons are congruent.

____

____

____

____

Name _____ Date _____ Class _____

Review for Mastery
Congruence

Congruent polygons have
the same size and shape.

Corresponding angles are congruent.

$\angle J \cong \angle J'$ $\angle K \cong \angle K'$ $\angle L \cong \angle L'$

(Read J' as J prime.)

Corresponding sides are congruent.

$\overline{JK} \cong \overline{J'K'}$ $\overline{KL} \cong \overline{K'L'}$ $\overline{LJ} \cong \overline{L'J'}$

In a congruence statement, the vertices
of the second polygon are written in
order of correspondence with the first polygon.

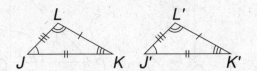

$\triangle JKL \cong \triangle J'K'L'$

Use the markings in each diagram.
Complete to write each congruence statement.

1.

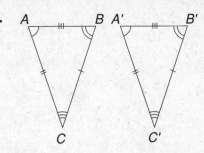

$\angle A \cong$ _____, $\angle B \cong$ _____,

$\angle C \cong$ _____, $\overline{AB} \cong$ _____,

$\overline{BC} \cong$ _____, $\overline{AC} \cong$ _____,

$\triangle ABC \cong$ _____

2.

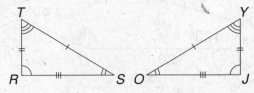

$\angle R \cong$ _____, $\angle S \cong$ _____,

$\angle T \cong$ _____, $\overline{RS} \cong$ _____,

$\overline{RT} \cong$ _____, $\overline{TS} \cong$ _____,

$\triangle RST \cong$ _____

3.

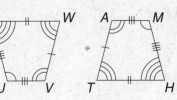

$\angle U \cong$ _____, $\angle V \cong$ _____, $\angle W \cong$ _____, $\angle X \cong$ _____,

$\overline{UV} \cong$ _____, $\overline{VW} \cong$ _____, $\overline{WX} \cong$ _____, $\overline{XU} \cong$ _____

quad. $UVWX \cong$ _____

Holt Mathematics

LESSON 7D **Review for Mastery**

Congruence (continued)

Congruence relations can be used to find unknown values.

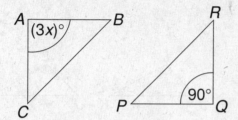

$$\angle A \cong \angle Q$$
$$3x = 90$$
$$\frac{3x}{3} = \frac{90}{3}$$
$$x = 30$$

$$\triangle ABC \cong \triangle QPR$$

Using the congruence relationship, complete to find each unknown value.

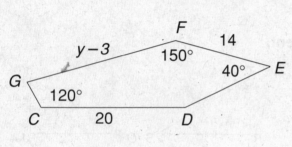

4. $\overline{GF} \cong \overline{RA}$

$y - 3 =$ _____

_____   _____

$y =$ _____

6. $\angle A \cong$ _____

$\dfrac{z}{2} =$ _____

_____ $\times \dfrac{z}{2} =$ _____ $\times$ _____

$z =$ _____

5. $\angle C \cong$ _____

_____ $= 2t$

_____ $= \dfrac{2t}{}$

_____ $= t$

7. $\overline{AZ} \cong$ _____

$3x + 2 =$ _____

_____   _____

$3x =$ _____

$\dfrac{3x}{} =$ _____

$x =$ _____

Holt Mathematics

Homework and Practice

LESSON 7D

Congruence

Write a congruence statement for each pair of polygons.

1.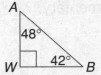

_____

2.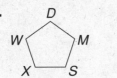

_____

3.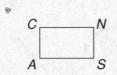

_____

4.

_____

Find the value of the variable if triangle *ABC* is congruent to triangle *XYZ*.

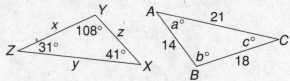

5. Find *a*.   6. Find *b*.

_____   _____

7. Find *c*.   8. Find *x*.

_____   _____

9. Find *y*.   10. Find *z*.

_____   _____

Holt Mathematics

Answer these questions to summarize the important concepts from Chapter 7 in your own words.

1. Explain the difference between complementary angles and supplementary angles.

2. If $\angle 1$ is 50°, explain how to find m$\angle 5$.

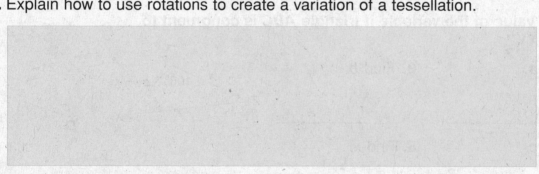

3. If the measures of two angles in a triangle are 43° and 74°, explain how to find the measure of the third angle.

4. Explain how to use rotations to create a variation of a tessellation.

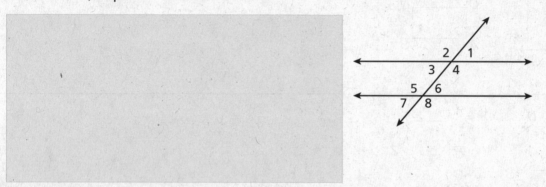

For more review of Chapter 7:

- Complete the Chapter 7 Study Guide and Review on pages 376–378 of your textbook.

- Complete the Ready to Go On quizzes on pages 352 and 372 of your textbook.

Holt Mathematics

Project
Perimeter, Area, and Volume: Solid Guessing

Career: Surgeon

Today, some surgeons perform specialized operations known as laser surgery. With many laser surgeries, surgeons cannot actually see the three-dimensional area where they are operating; instead, they must rely on what they can see in two-dimensional images projected onto a screen to guide them.

In this chapter project...you will try to identify three-dimensional shapes by seeing their shadows. You will:

• Explore what various solid figures look like from the front, side, and top.

• Identify mystery solids from what their front, side, and top views look like.

• Choose or create your own solid and see if your classmates can identify it from only the front, side and, top views.

To get started, work through the Mystery Solids worksheet on the next page.

This chapter project reinforces your understanding of these Georgia Performance Standards:

M8P1.a Build new mathematical knowledge through problem solving.

M8P5.b Select, apply, and translate among mathematical representations to solve problems.

---

go.hrw.com
Chapter Project Online
KEYWORD: MT7 Ch8

Holt Mathematics

CHAPTER 8

Project Recording Sheet
Perimeter, Area, and Volume

Mystery Solids

There are many opportunities to identify three-dimensional objects by looking at their surfaces. Have you ever been able to recognize a bird, a car, a tool or even a person by seeing the shadow? What are the aspects of the object that make recognition possible? Use this worksheet to enhance your skills.

Here are four more mystery geometric solids. Figure out what they are and check your decisions by using an overhead projector, flashlight or other light source to produce shadows of the surfaces.

Mystery Solid	Front View	Side View	Top View
	Triangle	Triangle	Square
	Square	Square	Square
	Rectangle	Rectangle	Triangle
	Rectangle	Rectangle	Rectangle

Create some mystery solids. Draw the various surface views. Exchange your mystery solids with classmates. Check your answers with the light sources when possible.

Mystery Solid	Front View	Side View	Top View

Make some shadow drawings of common objects. Take turns identifying the objects with your classmates.

Shadow	Mystery Object

Holt Mathematics

EXPLORATION

8A Perimeter and Area of Rectangles and Parallelograms

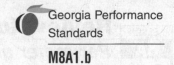

Georgia Performance Standards

M8A1.b

Recall that the area of a rectangle is the product of its length times its width, or the product of its base times its height, *bh*. You can use this fact to develop the formula for the area of a parallelogram.

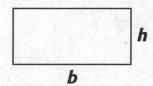

1. Draw a parallelogram on a sheet of graph paper. Label the base and height as shown.

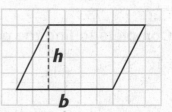

2. Cut out the parallelogram.

3. Now cut a right triangle off the end of the parallelogram as shown.

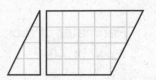

4. Arrange the two pieces to form a rectangle.

5. What are the base and height of the rectangle you made? What is the rectangle's area?

6. How is the area of the parallelogram related to the area of the rectangle?

Think and Discuss

7. **Explain** how to write a formula for the area of a parallelogram with base *b* and height *h*.

8. **Describe** how you can use your formula to find the area of this parallelogram.

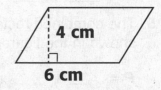

4 cm

6 cm

Holt Mathematics

LESSON 8A Review for Mastery
Perimeter and Area of Rectangles and Parallelograms

Perimeter = distance around a figure.
To find the perimeter of a figure, add the lengths of all its sides.

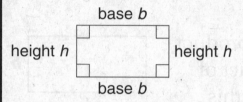

base b

height h height h

base b

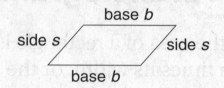

base b

side s side s

base b

Perimeter of Rectangle	**Perimeter of Parallelogram**
$= b + h + b + h$	$= b + s + b + s$
$= 2b + 2h$	$= 2b + 2s$

Complete to find the perimeter of each figure.

1.
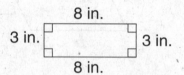

8 in.

3 in.   3 in.

8 in.

Perimeter of rectangle
$= 2b + 2h$

$= 2(\underline{\ \ \ }) + 2(\underline{\ \ \ })$

$= \underline{\ \ \ } + \underline{\ \ \ }$

$= \underline{\ \ \ }$ in.

2.
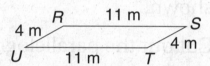

R 11 m S

4 m   4 m

U 11 m T

Perimeter of parallelogram
$= 2b + 2s$

$= 2(\underline{\ \ \ }) + 2(\underline{\ \ \ })$

$= \underline{\ \ \ } + \underline{\ \ \ }$

$= \underline{\ \ \ }$ m

Find the perimeter of each.

3. Large rectangle

$P = \underline{\ \ \ } + \underline{\ \ \ } + \underline{\ \ \ } + \underline{\ \ \ } = \underline{\ \ \ }$

4. Small rectangle

$P = \underline{\ \ \ } + \underline{\ \ \ } + \underline{\ \ \ } + \underline{\ \ \ } = \underline{\ \ \ }$

5. The combined rectangles as shown in the figure.

$P = \underline{\ \ \ } + \underline{\ \ \ } + \underline{\ \ \ } + \underline{\ \ \ } + \underline{\ \ \ } + \underline{\ \ \ } = \underline{\ \ \ }$

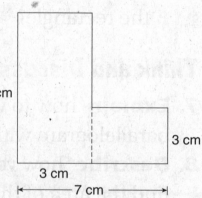

8 cm

3 cm

3 cm

7 cm

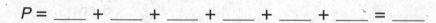

Holt Mathematics

LESSON 8A — Review for Mastery
Perimeter and Area of Rectangles and Parallelograms (cont.)

Area = number of square units contained inside a figure.

The rectangle contains 12 square units.

Area of rectangle = 4 × 3 = 12 units^2

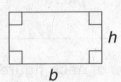

3

4

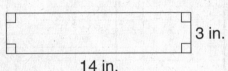

h

b

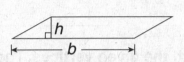

h

b

Area of Rectangle = $b \times h$ **Area of Parallelogram = $b \times h$**

Complete to find the area of each figure.

6.

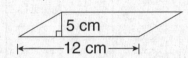

3 in.

14 in.

Area of rectangle
= $b \times h$

= _____ × _____ = _____ in^2

7.

5 cm

|←————— 12 cm —————→|

Area of parallelogram *WXYZ*
= $b \times h$

= _____ × _____ = _____ cm^2

8. In the rectangle graphed on the coordinate plane:

base = _____ units

height = _____ units.

Area of rectangle
= base × height

= _____ × _____

= _____ units^2

Name _____ Date _____ Class _____

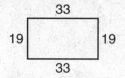
Homework and Practice

Perimeter and Area of Rectangles and Parallelograms

Find the perimeter of each figure.

1.
```
      33
   ┌──────┐
19 │      │ 19
   └──────┘
      33
```
_____

2.
```
      24
    ┌────┐
 17 /    / 17
   └────┘
      24
```
_____

3.
```
       16.25
     ┌──────┐
19.5 │      │ 19.5
     └──────┘
       16.25
```
_____

Graph each figure with the given vertices. Then find the area of each figure.

4. (−4, 3), (−7, −3), (4, −3), (7, 3)

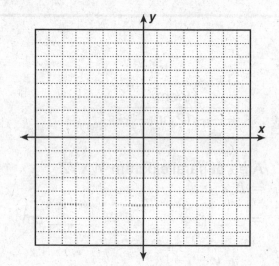

_____

5. (−7, 7), (−7, −7), (7, −7), (7, 7)

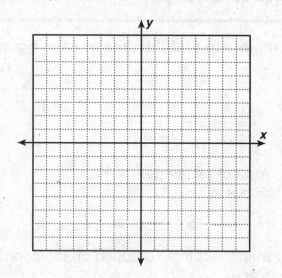

_____

6. Mrs. Delfina is having new carpet installed in a room and hall in her home. The diagram at the right shows the dimensions of the area. If the carpet costs $1.95 a square foot, how much will it cost Mrs. Delfina to carpet the area?

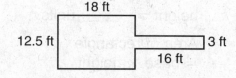

_____

Holt Mathematics

EXPLORATION

8B Perimeter and Area of Triangles and Trapezoids

Georgia Performance Standards

M8A1.a, M8A1.b, M8A1.c, M8A1.e, M8G2.a

You can use what you know about the area of a parallelogram to develop the formula for the area of a triangle.

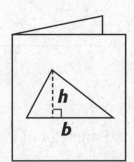

1. Fold a sheet of paper in half.

2. Draw a triangle on the folded paper. Label the base, b, and height, h, as shown.

3. Cut out the triangle through both layers of paper. This will create a pair of congruent triangles.

4. Arrange the two triangles to form a parallelogram.

5. What are the base and height of the parallelogram you made? What is the parallelogram's area?

6. How is the area of one of the triangles related to the area of the parallelogram?

Think and Discuss

7. **Explain** how to write a formula for the area of a triangle with base b and height h.

8. **Describe** how you can use your formula to find the area of this triangle.

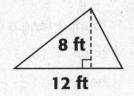

217

Holt Mathematics

Name _____ Date _____ Class _____

LESSON 8B Review for Mastery
Perimeter and Area of Triangles and Trapezoids

To find the perimeter of a figure, add the lengths of all its sides.

Complete to find the perimeter of each figure.

1.
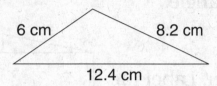

Perimeter of triangle

= _____ + _____ + _____

= _____ cm

2.
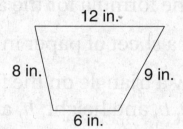

Perimeter of trapezoid

= _____ + _____ + _____ + _____

= _____ in.

Area of Triangle = $\frac{1}{2}bh$

The area of a triangle is one-half the product of a base length *b* and the height *h* drawn to that base.

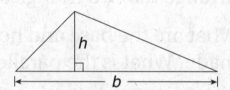

Complete to find the area of each triangle.

3. Area of triangle

$= \frac{1}{2}bh$

$= \frac{1}{2} \times$ _____ $\times$ _____

$= \frac{1}{2} \times$ _____ $=$ _____ in^2

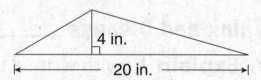

4. In the triangle graphed on the coordinate plane:

base = 10 − 3 = _____ units

height = 4 − (−2) = _____ units.

Area of triangle

$= \frac{1}{2} \times$ base $\times$ height

$= \frac{1}{2} \times$ _____ $\times$ _____

$= \frac{1}{2} \times$ _____ $=$ _____ units^2

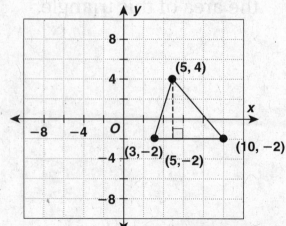

Holt Mathematics

Review for Mastery
LESSON 8B
Perimeter and Area of Triangles and Trapezoids (continued)

Area of Trapezoid $= \frac{1}{2}h(b_1 + b_2)$
The area of a trapezoid is one-half the
height h times the sum of the
base lengths b_1 and b_2.

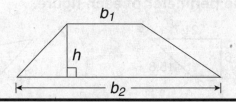

Complete to find the area of each trapezoid.

5.

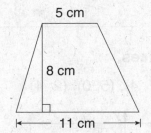

5 cm

8 cm

11 cm

Area of trapezoid

$= \frac{1}{2}h(b_1 + b_2)$

$= \frac{1}{2} \times$ _____ $\times ($ _____ $+$ _____ $)$

$=$ _____ $\times ($ _____ $) =$ _____ cm^2

6.

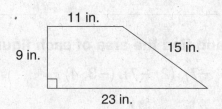

11 in.

9 in.   15 in.

23 in.

Area of trapezoid

$= \frac{1}{2}h(b_1 + b_2)$

$= \frac{1}{2} \times$ _____ $\times ($ _____ $+$ _____ $)$

$=$ _____ $\times ($ _____ $) =$ _____ in^2

7. In the trapezoid graphed on coordinate plane:

base$_1$ = 8 − 4 = _____ units

base$_2$ = 11 − 2 = _____ units

height = 6 − 2 = _____ units.

Area of trapezoid

$= \frac{1}{2} \times$ height $\times ($ base$_1$ + base$_2)$

$= \frac{1}{2} \times$ _____ $\times ($ _____ $+$ _____ $)$

$=$ _____ $\times ($ _____ $)$

$=$ _____ units^2

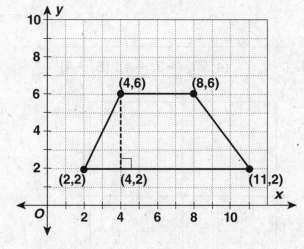

Holt Mathematics

Name _____ Date _____ Class _____

Homework and Practice
Perimeter and Area of Triangles and Trapezoids

Find the perimeter of each figure.

1.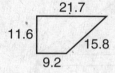

2.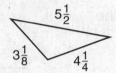

3.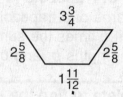

_____   _____   _____

Graph and find the area of each figure with the given vertices.

4. $(-6, -7), (2, -7), (-3, 4)$

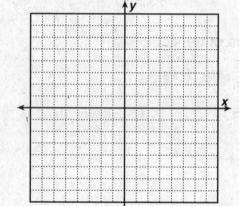

5. $(-5, 0), (-1, 4), (5, 0), (2, 4)$

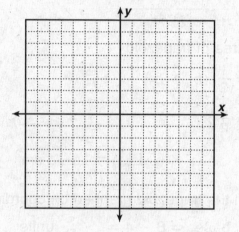

_____   _____

6. $(-1, 7), (4, 7), (-3, -4), (6, -4)$

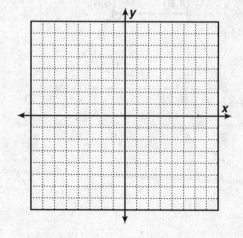

7. $(-6, 2), (6, 2), (6, -4)$

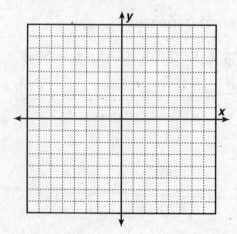

_____   _____

Holt Mathematics

Georgia Performance
Standards

M8A1.b

8C Circles

First estimate the area of each circle by counting squares. Then square each circle's radius. Then compare each estimated area with the square of the radius by computing $\frac{A}{r^2}$.

		Radius	Estimated Area	r^2	$\frac{A}{r^2}$
1.		$r = 1$			
2.		$r = 2$			
3.		$r = 3$			
4.		$r = 4$			

Think and Discuss

5. **Discuss** how you can make a generalization about how to estimate the area of a circle if you know the radius.

Holt Mathematics

Name _____ Date _____ Class _____

Review for Mastery

Circles

A **radius** connects the **center** of a **circle** to any point on the circle.

A **diameter** passes through the center and connects two points on the circle.

diameter d = twice radius r

$$d = 2r$$

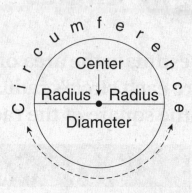

Circumference is the distance around a circle.

(The symbol $\approx$ means *is approximately equal to*.)

Circumference $C \approx$ 3(diameter d)
$$C = \pi d$$

Circumference $C \approx$ 6(radius r)
$$C = 2\pi r$$

For a circle with diameter = 8 in.
$$C = \pi d$$
$$C = \pi(8)$$
$$C = 8\pi \text{ in.}$$
$\pi \approx 3.14 \quad C \approx 8(3.14) \approx 25.12 \text{ in.}$

For a circle with radius = 8 in.
$$C = 2\pi r$$
$$C = 2\pi(8)$$
$$C = 16\pi \text{ in.}$$
$\pi \approx 3.14 \quad C \approx 16(3.14) \approx 50.24 \text{ in.}$

Find the circumference of each circle, exactly in terms of π and approximately when $\pi = 3.14$.

1. diameter = 15 ft
$$C = \pi d$$

$$C = \pi(\underline{\hspace{1cm}}) = \underline{\hspace{1cm}} \text{ ft}$$

$$C \approx 3.14(\underline{\hspace{1cm}}) \approx \underline{\hspace{1cm}} \text{ ft}$$

2. radius = 4 m
$$C = 2\pi r$$

$$C = 2\pi(\underline{\hspace{1cm}}) = \underline{\hspace{1cm}} \text{ m}$$

$$C \approx \underline{\hspace{1cm}}(3.14) \approx \underline{\hspace{1cm}} \text{ m}$$

Area $A \approx$ 3(the square of radius r)

$$A = \pi r^2$$

For a circle with radius = 5 in.: $A = \pi r^2 = \pi(5^2) = 25\pi \text{ in}^2$
$$A \approx 25(3.14) \approx 78.5 \text{ in}^2$$

Find the area of each circle, exactly in terms of π and approximately when $\pi = 3.14$.

3. radius = 9 ft
$$A = \pi r^2$$

$$A = \pi(\underline{\hspace{1cm}}) = \underline{\hspace{1cm}} \text{ ft}^2$$

$$A \approx \underline{\hspace{1cm}}(3.14) \approx \underline{\hspace{1cm}} \text{ ft}^2$$

4. diameter = 10 m, radius = _____ m
$$A = \pi r^2$$

$$A = \pi(\underline{\hspace{1cm}}) = \underline{\hspace{1cm}} \text{ m}^2$$

$$A \approx \underline{\hspace{1cm}}(3.14) \approx \underline{\hspace{1cm}} \text{ m}^2$$

Holt Mathematics

CHAPTER **8C** Homework and Practice
Circles

Find the circumference of each circle, both in terms of π and to the nearest tenth of a unit. Use 3.14 for π.

1. circle with diameter 12 cm
_____

2. circle with radius 11 in.
_____

3. circle with radius 17 ft
_____

4. circle with diameter 28 yd
_____

5. circle with radius 10.8 in.
_____

6. circle with diameter 23.6 m
_____

Find the area of each circle, both in terms of π and to the nearest tenth of a unit. Use 3.14 for π.

7. circle with diameter 12 yd
_____

8. circle with radius 16 cm
_____

9. circle with radius 30 ft
_____

10. circle with diameter 38 m
_____

11. circle with radius 8.9 m
_____

12. circle with diameter 56 m
_____

13. Graph a circle with center (0, 0) that passes through (0, −5). Find the area and circumference, both in terms of π and to the nearest tenth of a unit. Use 3.14 for π.

_____
_____

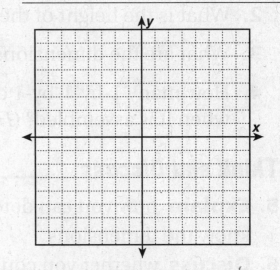

14. If a circle has an area of 7,850 yd², what is the diameter of the circle? Use 3.14 for π.

_____

Holt Mathematics

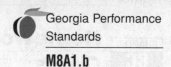

Georgia Performance Standards

M8A1.b

8D Volume of Prisms and Cylinders

The drawing below represents a box that has been unfolded and laid flat. The darker rectangles represent the bottom and the lid of the box. The lighter rectangles represent the sides of the box.

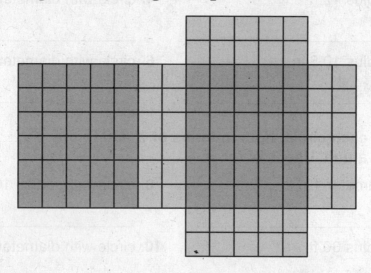

1. What are the dimensions of the bottom and the lid of the box?

2. What is the height of the box when it is assembled?

3. What are the dimensions of each side of the box?

4. How many 1-by-1-by-1 cubes will it take to fill the box when it is assembled? (*Hint:* This is the *volume* of the box.)

Think and Discuss

5. **Explain** how you can determine the volume of a box if you know the dimensions.

6. **Discuss** whether you could figure out the height of a box if you know the volume and the dimensions of the base.

Holt Mathematics

Name _____ Date _____ Class _____

LESSON 8D Review for Mastery
Volume of Prisms and Cylinders

Volume = number of cubic units
inside a solid figure

To find the volume of this solid figure:

Count the number of cubic centimeters
in one "slice" of the figure.
$4 \times 3 = 12$

Multiply by the number of "slices." $12 \times 6 = 72 \text{ cm}^3$

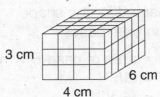
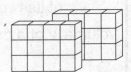

3 cm
6 cm
4 cm

Complete to find the volume of each solid figure.

1.

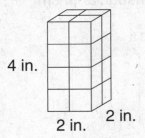

4 in.

2 in.   2 in.

number in^3 in a slice

= _____ × _____ = _____

number of slices = _____

volume = _____ in^3

2.

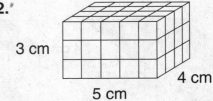

3 cm

4 cm
5 cm

number cm^3 in a slice

= _____ = _____

number of slices = _____

volume = _____ cm^3

3.

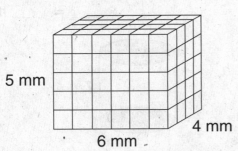

5 mm

6 mm   4 mm

number mm^3 in a slice

= _____ = _____

number of slices = _____

volume = _____ mm^3

Holt Mathematics

LESSON 8D Review for Mastery
Volume of Prisms and Cylinders (continued)

Prism: solid figure named for the shape of its two congruent bases

Volume V of a prism = area of base B × height h

$V = Bh$
$V = (6 \times 4)5$
$V = 24(5)$
$V = 120 \text{ in}^3$

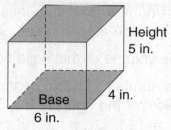

Height
5 in.

Base
6 in.

4 in.

Rectangular Prism

Complete to find the volume of each prism.

4. rectangular prism

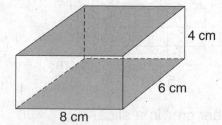

4 cm

6 cm

8 cm

base is a rectangle
$V = Bh$

$V = (\underline{} \times \underline{}) \times \underline{}$

$= \underline{} \text{ cm}^3$

5. cube

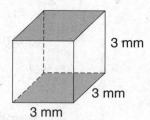

3 mm

3 mm

3 mm

base is a _____
$V = Bh$

$V = (\underline{} \times \underline{}) \times \underline{}$

$= \underline{} \text{ mm}^3$

6. triangular prism

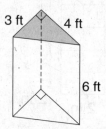

3 ft   4 ft

6 ft

base is a _____
$V = \frac{1}{2} Bh$

$V = \frac{1}{2}(\underline{} \times \underline{})$

$\times \underline{} = \underline{} \text{ ft}^3$

Cylinder: solid figure with a circular base

Volume V of a cylinder = area of base B × height h

$V = Bh$
$V = (\pi \times 4^2)7 = (16\pi)7$
$V = 112\pi$
$V \approx 112(3.14) \approx 351.7 \text{ units}^3$

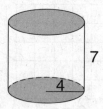

7

4

Complete to find the volume of the cylinder.

7.

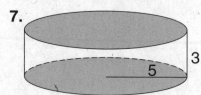

3

5

$V = Bh$

$V = (\pi \times \underline{}) \times \underline{}$

$V = \underline{} \approx \underline{} \text{ units}^3$

Holt Mathematics

Name _____ Date _____ Class _____

Find the volume to the nearest tenth of a unit. Use 3.14 for π.

1.

8 ft
8 ft
8 ft

_____

2.
10 cm
15 cm

_____

3.
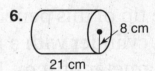
7 yd
8 yd
20 yd

_____

4.
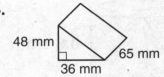
48 mm
65 mm
36 mm

_____

5.
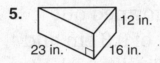
12 in.
23 in.   16 in.

_____

6.
8 cm
21 cm

_____

7.
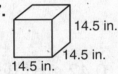
14.5 in.
14.5 in.
14.5 in.

_____

8.
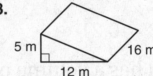
5 m   16 m
12 m

_____

9.
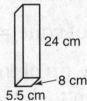
24 cm
8 cm
5.5 cm

_____

10. A cylinder has a radius of 8 cm and a height of 20 cm. Explain whether tripling the height will triple the volume of the cylinder.

_____

_____

11. Find the height of a cylinder if the volume is 2,512 in.^{3} and the radius is 10 in. Use 3.14 for π.

_____

_____

12. What is the volume of a can of peanuts with a height of 5 in. and a lid that is 4 in. wide? Use 3.14 for π. Round the answer to the nearest tenth of an inch.

_____

_____

Holt Mathematics

8E Volume of Pyramids and Cones

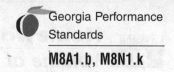

Georgia Performance
Standards

M8A1.b, M8N1.k

The tip of a sharpened pencil is shaped like a cone. How much of the pencil is lost after the tip is formed? To answer this question, you should know that the volume of a cone is $\frac{1}{3}$ the volume of the cylinder from which it was formed.

The tip of this pencil was formed out of a cylinder with a height of 0.8 cm and a diameter of 1cm. The cylinder had a volume of approximately 0.63 cm³.

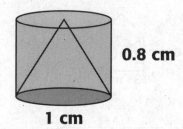

0.8 cm

1 cm

volume of cone = $\frac{1}{3}$ · volume of cylinder

volume of cone = $\frac{1}{3}$ · 0.63 = 0.21

Since the tip of the pencil has a volume of 0.21 cm³, 0.42 cm³ was lost when the tip of the pencil was formed.

Find the volume of each cone.

	Volume of Cylinder	Volume of Cone = $\frac{1}{3}$ · Volume of Cylinder
1.	66.9 in³	
2.	99 cm³	
3.	108 in³	

Think and Discuss

4. Name familiar objects that are shaped like a cone.

5. Explain how to estimate the volume of one of the cone-shaped objects you named in Problem **4.**

Holt Mathematics

Review for Mastery

LESSON 8E

Volume of Pyramids and Cones

Pyramid: solid figure named for the shape of its base, which is a polygon; all other faces are triangles

Pentagonal Pyramid

This rectangular pyramid and rectangular prism have congruent bases and congruent heights.

Volume of Pyramid = $\frac{1}{3}$ Volume of Prism

$$V = \frac{1}{3} Bh$$

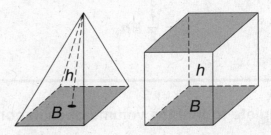

Complete to find the volume of each pyramid.

1. square pyramid

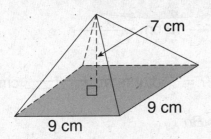

7 cm

9 cm

9 cm

base is a _____

$V = \frac{1}{3} Bh$

$V = \frac{1}{3}$ (area of square) $\times h$

$V = \frac{1}{3}$ (___ $\times$ ___) $\times$ ___

$V = \frac{1}{3}$ (___) $\times$ ___

$V = $ _____ cm^3

2. rectangular pyramid

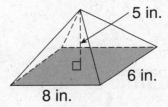

5 in.

6 in.

8 in.

base is a _____

$V = \frac{1}{3} Bh$

$V = \frac{1}{3}$ (area of rectangle) $\times h$

$V = \frac{1}{3}$ (___ $\times$ ___) $\times$ ___

$V = \frac{1}{3}$ (___) $\times$ ___

$V = $ _____ in^3

Holt Mathematics

Review for Mastery

LESSON 8E Volume of Pyramids and Cones (continued)

Cone: solid figure with a circular base

This cone and cylinder have congruent bases and congruent heights.

Volume of Cone = $\frac{1}{3}$ Volume of Cylinder

$$V = \frac{1}{3} Bh$$

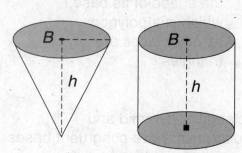

Complete to find the volume of each cone.

3.

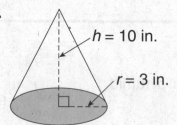

$h = 10$ in.

$r = 3$ in.

radius r of base = _____ in.

$V = \frac{1}{3} Bh$

$V = \frac{1}{3} (\pi r^2)h$

$V = \frac{1}{3} (\pi \times \text{\_\_\_\_}) \times \text{\_\_\_\_}$

$V = \frac{1}{3} (\text{\_\_\_\_}) \times \text{\_\_\_\_}$

$V = \text{\_\_\_\_} \times \text{\_\_\_\_}$

$V = \text{\_\_\_\_}$

$V \approx \text{\_\_\_\_} \times 3.14$

$V \approx \text{_____}$ in^3

4.

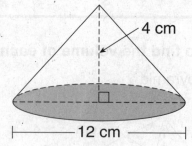

4 cm

12 cm

radius $r = \frac{1}{2}$ diameter = _____ cm

$V = \frac{1}{3} Bh$

$V = \frac{1}{3} (\pi r^2)h$

$V = \frac{1}{3} (\pi \times \text{\_\_\_\_}) \times \text{\_\_\_\_}$

$V = \frac{1}{3} (\text{\_\_\_\_}) \times \text{\_\_\_\_}$

$V = \text{\_\_\_\_} \times \text{\_\_\_\_}$

$V = \text{\_\_\_\_}$

$V \approx \text{\_\_\_\_} \times 3.14$

$V \approx \text{_____}$ cm^3

Holt Mathematics

Name _____ Date _____ Class _____

Homework and Practice
Volume of Pyramids and Cones

Find the volume of each figure to the nearest tenth of a unit.
Use 3.14 for π.

1.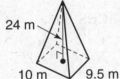

8 in.

6 in.

_____

2.

4 m

6 m   6 m

_____

3.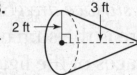

3 ft

2 ft

_____

4.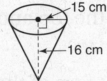

24 m

10 m   9.5 m

_____

5.

15 cm

16 cm

_____

6.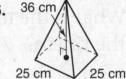

36 cm

25 cm   25 cm

_____

7. A funnel has a diameter of 8 in. and is 21 in. deep. What is
the volume of the funnel to the nearest tenth of a unit? Use
3.14 for π

_____

8. The radius of a cone is 13 ft and its height is 27 ft. Find the
volume of the cone to the nearest tenth. Use 3.14 for π.

_____

9. Find the volume of a rectangular pyramid if the height is 35 cm
and the base sides are 21 cm and 28 cm.

_____

10. The base of a regular pyramid has an area of 135 in.^{2}. The
height of the pyramid is 8.5 in. Find the volume.

_____

Holt Mathematics

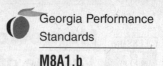Georgia Performance
Standards
M8A1.b

8F Surface Area of Prisms and Cylinders

The *surface area* of a three-dimensional
figure is the sum of the areas of all the
surfaces of the figure. Follow these steps
to find the surface area of the prism.

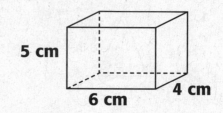

5 cm

6 cm   4 cm

1. Find the area of the bottom face of the prism.

2. What is the total area of the top and bottom faces of
   the prism?

3. Find the area of the front face of the prism.

4. What is the total area of the front and back faces of
   the prism?

5. Find the area of one of the side faces of the prism.

6. What is the total area of both side faces of the prism?

7. Add the areas in Steps 2, 4, and 6 to find the surface area.

Think and Discuss

8. **Explain** how you can find the surface area of a rectangular
   prism.

9. **Describe** a shortcut you can use to find the surface area of
   a cube.

Holt Mathematics

Review for Mastery

LESSON 8F

Surface Area of Prisms and Cylinders

Find the number of tiles needed to cover the faces of the prism.
Unfold the prism to get a better look at its six faces.

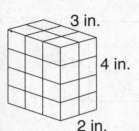

3 in.

4 in.

2 in.

top	2

2	3	2	3
left	front	right	back
4 4	4	4	4
2	3	2	3

4

bottom	2

Face	Area	in²
top	3 × 2	6
bottom	3 × 2	6
front	3 × 4	12
back	3 × 4	12
left	2 × 4	8
right	2 × 4	8
	total =	52 tiles

Surface Area S = the sum of the areas of the faces of the prism
$\qquad$ = top + bottom + front + back + left + right
$\qquad$ = area of bases + area of lateral faces
$\qquad$ = 2B + perimeter of the base × height of prism

$S = 2B + Ph$
$S = 2(3 \times 2) + (3 + 2 + 3 + 2) \times 4$
$S = 12 \qquad + \qquad (10) \qquad \times 4$
$S = 12 \qquad + \qquad\qquad 40$
$S = 52$ in²

---

1. Complete to find the number of square units needed to cover all the faces of the rectangular prism.

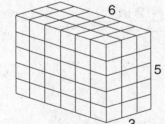

6

5

3

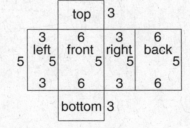

top	3

3	6	3	6
left	front	right	back
5 5	5	5	5
3	6	3	6

bottom	3

Face	Area	in²
top	_____	_____
bottom	_____	_____
front	_____	_____
back	_____	_____
left	_____	_____
right	_____	_____
	total =	_____

2. Complete to find the surface area of the prism.

$S = 2B + Ph$

$S = 2(\underline{\qquad}) + (\underline{\qquad\qquad}) \times \underline{\quad}$

$S = 2(\underline{\qquad}) + (\underline{\qquad\qquad}) \times \underline{\quad}$

$S = \underline{\qquad} + \underline{\qquad\qquad} = \underline{\qquad}$ in²

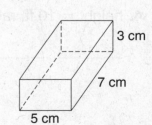

3 cm

7 cm

5 cm

Holt Mathematics

LESSON 8F Review for Mastery
Surface Area of Prisms and Cylinders (continued)

An unfolded cylinder results
in two circles and a lateral
surface drawn as a rectangle.

The base of the rectangle equals
the circumference of the circular base.

The height of the rectangle equals
the height of the cylinder.

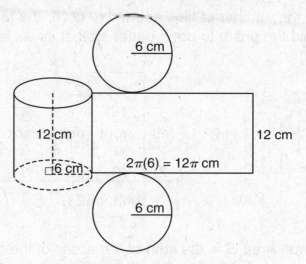

Surface Area S = area of 2 circular bases + area of lateral surface (rectangle)

$$= \quad 2(\pi r^2) \quad + \text{circumference} \times \text{height}$$
$$= \quad 2\pi r^2 \quad + \quad 2\pi r \times h$$
$$S = 2\pi r^2 + 2\pi rh$$
$$S = 2\pi(6^2) + 2\pi(6)(12)$$
$$S = 72\pi + 144\pi = 216\pi \text{ cm}^2$$
$$S \approx 216(3.14) \approx 678.24 \text{ cm}^2$$

3. Complete to find the surface area of the cylinder.

$$S = 2\pi r^2 + 2\pi rh$$
$$S = 2\pi(\text{_____}) + 2\pi \times \text{\_\_\_\_\_} \times \text{\_\_\_\_\_}$$
$$S = \text{_____}\pi + \text{_____}\pi$$
$$S = \text{_____}\pi$$
$$S \approx \text{_____}(3.14)$$
$$S \approx \text{_____}\text{in}^2$$

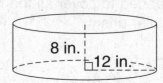

**Find the surface area of each cylinder. Round to the nearest
whole number.**

4. height = 10 ft, radius = 5 ft

_____

5. height = 2.5 cm, diameter = 8 cm

_____

Holt Mathematics

Name _____ Date _____ Class _____

Homework and Practice

Surface Area of Prisms and Cylinders

Find the surface area of each figure to the nearest of a tenth unit. Use 3.14 for π.

1.

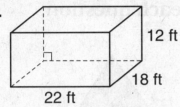

12 ft
18 ft
22 ft

_____

2.

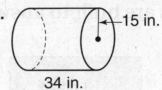

15 in.
34 in.

_____

3.

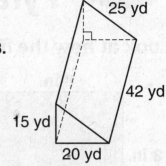

25 yd
42 yd
15 yd
20 yd

_____

4.

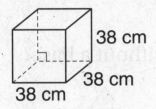

38 cm
38 cm
38 cm

_____

5.

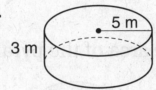

5 m
3 m

_____

6.

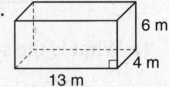

6 m
4 m
13 m

_____

7.

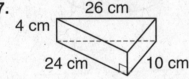

26 cm
4 cm
24 cm   10 cm

_____

8.

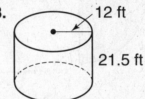

12 ft
21.5 ft

_____

9.

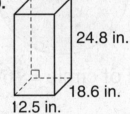

24.8 in.
18.6 in.
12.5 in.

_____

10. Find the surface area to the nearest tenth of a unit of a cylinder 84.5 m tall that has a diameter of 50 m. Use 3.14 for π.

_____

11. Find the surface area to the nearest tenth of a unit of a rectangular prism with height 24 cm and sides 18 cm and 14 cm.

_____

12. A recipe calls for a 9 × 13 × 2 in. baking dish to have the inside of the baking dish coated before adding the recipe contents. What is the surface area of the baking dish that will be coated?

_____

Holt Mathematics

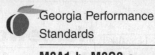
Georgia Performance
Standards
M8A1.b, M8G2.a

8G Surface Area of Pyramids and Cones

Look at how the figures are built to answer each question.

8 in.

8 in.

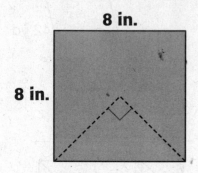
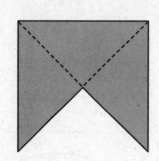
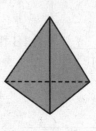

1. What is the surface area of the pyramid without a base?

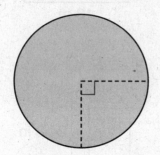

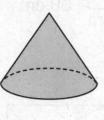

Area of circle $= 16\pi$ in^2

2. What is the surface area of the cone without a base?

Think and Discuss_____

3. Explain what you would need to do to find the surface area of the pyramid and cone including the base.

Holt Mathematics

Name _____ Date _____ Class _____

Review for Mastery
Surface Area of Pyramids and Cones

Regular Pyramid:
base is a regular polygon; lateral faces are congruent triangles

When a square pyramid is unfolded, there are 5 faces: a square and 4 congruent triangles.

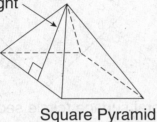

Slant height
ℓ

Square Pyramid

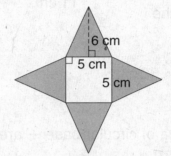

6 cm
5 cm
5 cm

Surface Area S = the sum of the areas of the faces of the pyramid
= area of base + area of lateral faces

Surface Area S = area of square + 4(area of triangle)

$\quad = \quad B \quad + \frac{1}{2}$ perimeter P of base × slant height ℓ of prism

$S = B + \frac{1}{2}P\ell$

$S = (5 \times 5) + \frac{1}{2} \times (5 \times 4) \times 6$

$S = 25 \quad + \quad 60$

$S = 85 \text{ cm}^2$

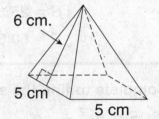

6 cm.
5 cm
5 cm

1. Find the surface area of the square pyramid.

S = area of square + 4(area of triangle)

$S = $ _____ + _____

$S = $ _____ + _____

$S = $ _____ in^2

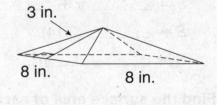

3 in.
8 in.   8 in.

2. Complete to find the surface area of the square pyramid.

$S = B + \frac{1}{2}P\ell$

$S = $ _____ $+ \frac{1}{2}$ _____ × _____

$S = $ _____ + _____

$S = $ _____ ft^2

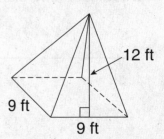

12 ft
9 ft
9 ft

Holt Mathematics

Name _____ Date _____ Class _____

Review for Mastery
Surface Area of Pyramids and Cones *(continued)*

An unfolded cone results in a circle and a lateral surface drawn as a sector of a circle.

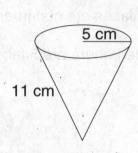

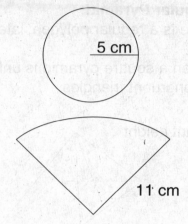

The slant height of the cone is the radius of the circle sector.

Surface Area S = area of circular base + area of lateral surface (circle sector)

$$= \pi r^2 + \frac{1}{2} \text{ circumference of base} \times \text{slant height}$$

$$= \pi r^2 + \frac{1}{2}(2\pi r) \times \ell$$

$$S = \pi r^2 + \pi r\ell$$

$$S = \pi(5^2) + \pi(5)(11)$$

$$S = 25\pi + 55\pi = 80\pi \text{ cm}^2$$

$$S \approx 80(3.14) \approx 251.2 \text{ cm}^2$$

Complete to find the surface area of the cone.

3. $S = \pi r^2 + \pi r\ell$

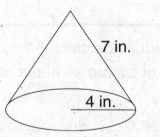

$S = \pi(\text{_____}) + \pi \times \text{\_\_\_\_\_} \times \text{\_\_\_\_\_}$

$S = \text{_____} \pi + \text{_____} \pi = \text{_____} \pi$

$S \approx \text{_____} (3.14)$

$S \approx \text{_____} \text{ in}^2$

Find the surface area of each cone. Round to the nearest whole number.

4. radius = 3 ft, slant height = 5 ft

5. diameter = 8.6 cm, slant height = 10 cm

_____   _____

Holt Mathematics

Homework and Practice

LESSON 8G *Surface Area of Pyramids and Cones*

Find the surface area of each figure to the nearest of a tenth unit. Use 3.14 for π.

1.

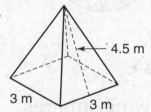

20 cm
40 cm

_____

2.

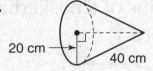

28 in.
19 in.
19 in.

_____

3.

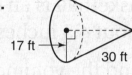

17 ft
30 ft

_____

4.

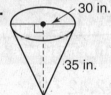

4.5 m
3 m
3 m

_____

5.

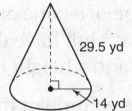

29.5 yd
14 yd

_____

6.

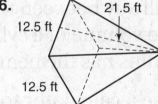

21.5 ft
12.5 ft
12.5 ft

_____

7.

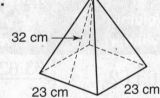

30 in.
35 in.

_____

8.

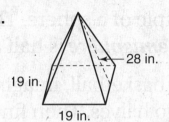

32 cm
23 cm   23 cm

_____

9.

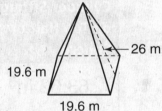

26 m
19.6 m
19.6 m

_____

10. Find the length of the slant height of a square pyramid if the one side of the base is 26 cm and the surface area is 2,236 cm^2.

_____

11. Find the surface area of a regular square pyramid with a slant height of 27 in. and a base perimeter of 96 in.

_____

12. Find the length of the slant height of a cone with a radius of 40 ft and a surface area of 9,420 ft^2. Use 3.14 for π.

_____

Holt Mathematics

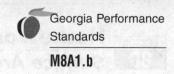

Georgia Performance
Standards

M8A1.b

8H Spheres

A basketball is an example of a sphere. The radius of a basketball is about 4.5 inches. A *hemisphere* is half a sphere.

To find the volume of a basketball, imagine the ball is sliced into two halves. Then find the volume of one half and multiply times 2.

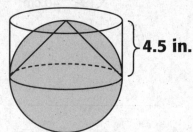

4.5 in.

The volume of a hemisphere is exactly halfway between the volume of a cone and the volume of a cylinder that both have the same radius *r* as the hemisphere and a height equal to *r*.

Use a calculator to find the volume of the following spheres.

	Volume of Cylinder Sitting on Top Half of Sphere	Volume of Cone = $\frac{1}{3}$ · Volume of Cylinder	Volume of Hemisphere = Halfway Between Vol. of Cylinder and Vol. of Cone	Volume of Sphere = Volume of Hemisphere · 2
1.	63.62 in³	$\frac{1}{3}$ · 63.62 = 21.21 in³	$\frac{63.62 + 21.21}{2}$ = 42.42 in³	42.42 · 2 = 84.84 in³
2.	70 in³			
3.	27 in³			
4.	123 in³			

Think and Discuss

5. **Describe** how you could find the volume of the solid at right. The height of the dome is the same as the height of the cylinder, which is equal to the radius of the base.

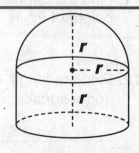

r
r
r

Holt Mathematics

LESSON **Review for Mastery**

8H *Spheres*

Sphere: the set of points in space
at a fixed distance (its *radius r*)
from a fixed point (its *center*)

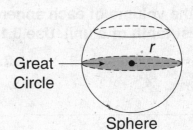

Great
Circle

Sphere

Volume V of Sphere $= \frac{4}{3}\pi r^3$

For a sphere of radius = 9 cm,

$V = \frac{4}{3}\pi r^3$

$V = \frac{4}{3}\pi \times 9^3 = \frac{4}{3}\pi \times 729 = \frac{4 \times \cancel{729}^{243}}{\cancel{3}}\pi = 972\pi \text{ cm}^3$

$V \approx 972(3.14) \approx 3052.08 \text{ cm}^3$

Complete to find the volume of the sphere.

1. $V = \frac{4}{3}\pi r^3$

$V = \frac{4}{3}\pi \times \underline{\hspace{1cm}} = \frac{4}{3}\pi \times \underline{\hspace{1cm}}$

$V = \underline{\hspace{1cm}}\pi \text{ in}^3$

$V \approx \underline{\hspace{1cm}}(3.14) \approx \underline{\hspace{2cm}} \text{ in}^3$

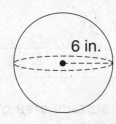

6 in.

Surface Area S of Sphere $= 4\pi r^2$

For a sphere of radius = 9 in.,

$S = 4\pi r^2$

$S = 4\pi \times 9^2 = 4\pi \times 81 = 324\pi \text{ in}^2$

$S \approx 324(3.14) \approx 1017.36 \text{ in}^2$

Complete to find the surface area of the sphere.

2. $S = 4\pi r^2$

$S = 4\pi \times \underline{\hspace{1cm}} = 4\pi \times \underline{\hspace{1cm}}$

$S = \underline{\hspace{1cm}}\pi \text{ ft}^2$

$S \approx \underline{\hspace{1cm}}(3.14) \approx \underline{\hspace{2cm}} \text{ ft}^2$

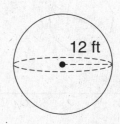

12 ft

Holt Mathematics

Name _____ Date _____ Class _____

Homework and Practice
Spheres

Find the volume of each sphere, both in terms of π and to the nearest tenth of a unit. Use 3.14 for π.

1. $r = 12$ yd

2. $r = 27$ ft

3. $d = 36$ m

_____

_____

_____

4. $d = 48$ ft

5. $r = 4.5$ m

6. $r = 7.5$ cm

_____

_____

_____

7. $r = 33$ cm

8. $d = 32.02$ ft

9. $d = 60$ m

_____

_____

_____

Find the surface area of each sphere, in terms of π and to the nearest tenth of a unit.

10. 5.6 in.

11. 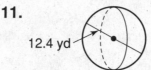 12.4 yd

12. 25 cm

_____

_____

_____

13. 36 ft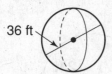

14. 14.1 cm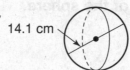

15. 21.5 in.

_____

_____

_____

16. Estimate to the nearest tenth of a square inch the surface area of a baseball with a 3 in. diameter. Use 3.14 for π.

_____

Holt Mathematics

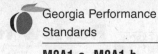
Georgia Performance
Standards

M8A1.a, M8A1.b,
M8A1.c, M8A1.d

8I Scaling Three-Dimensional Figures

A rectangular box has a volume of 2 cubic units. If one of its dimensions is doubled, the volume of the box is doubled. If all three dimensions are doubled, the volume is 8 times the volume of the original box.

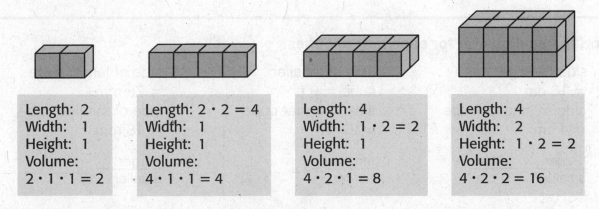

Length: 2
Width: 1
Height: 1
Volume:
$2 \cdot 1 \cdot 1 = 2$

Length: $2 \cdot 2 = 4$
Width: 1
Height: 1
Volume:
$4 \cdot 1 \cdot 1 = 4$

Length: 4
Width: $1 \cdot 2 = 2$
Height: 1
Volume:
$4 \cdot 2 \cdot 1 = 8$

Length: 4
Width: 2
Height: $1 \cdot 2 = 2$
Volume:
$4 \cdot 2 \cdot 2 = 16$

A box has a length of 3 in., a width of 2 in., and a height of 1 in. Multiply the dimensions of the box by each scale factor. Then find the volume.

	Scale Factor	Length (ℓ)	Width (w)	Height (h)	Volume $\ell \cdot w \cdot h$
	2	$3 \cdot 2 = 6$ in.	$2 \cdot 2 = 4$ in.	$1 \cdot 2 = 2$ in.	$6 \cdot 4 \cdot 2 = 48$ in^3
1.	3				
2.	4				
3.	5				

Think and Discuss

4. Discuss how each scale factor affects the volume of the rectangular box.

5. Predict what would happen to the volume if you were to multiply each dimension of the box by a scale factor of 0.5.

Holt Mathematics

Name _____ Date _____ Class _____

Review for Mastery
Scaling Three-Dimensional Figures

Any two cubes are similar.

The sides of this larger cube are
3 times as long as the sides of
this smaller cube.

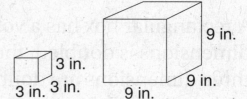

$$\frac{\text{side of larger cube}}{\text{side of smaller cube}} = \frac{9 \text{ in.}}{3 \text{ in.}} = \frac{3}{1} = 3$$

The scale factor is 3.

Find the scale factor for each pair of cubes.

1. side of larger cube
= 16 cm
side of smaller cube
= 4 cm

$$\frac{\text{larger}}{\text{smaller}} = \frac{16 \text{ cm}}{4 \text{ cm}}$$

= _____

scale factor = _____

2. side of smaller
cube = 9 ft
side of larger cube
= 27 ft

$$\frac{\text{smaller}}{\text{larger}} = $$ _____

= _____

scale factor = _____

3. side of larger cube
= 78 mm
side of smaller cube
= 18 mm

$$\frac{\text{larger}}{\text{smaller}} = $$ _____

= _____

scale factor = _____

The ratio of the surface areas *S* of two cubes is the
square of the scale factor.

The scale factor for these two cubes is 3.

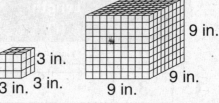

$$\frac{\text{side of larger cube}}{\text{side of smaller cube}} = \frac{9 \text{ in.}}{3 \text{ in.}} = \frac{3}{1} = 3$$

$$\frac{S \text{ larger}}{S \text{ smaller}} = \frac{6(\text{area one face})}{6(\text{area one face})} = \frac{\cancel{6}(\cancel{9} \times \cancel{9})}{\cancel{6}(\cancel{3} \times \cancel{3})} = \left(\frac{3}{1}\right)^2 = 9$$

Find the scale factor for each pair of cubes.
Then find the ratio of the surface areas.

4. side of smaller cube = 16 in.

side of larger cube = 64 in.

$$\frac{\text{smaller}}{\text{larger}} = $$ _____

scale factor = _____

ratio of surface areas

$$= (\text{scale factor})^2 = \frac{(\quad)}{}$$ _____ =

Holt Mathematics

Name _____ Date _____ Class _____

The ratio of the volumes V of two cubes is the cube of the scale factor.

The scale factor for these two cubes is 3.

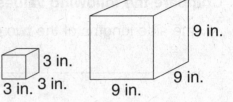

9 in.

3 in.

3 in. 3 in.

9 in.

9 in.

$$\frac{\text{side of larger cube}}{\text{side of smaller cube}} = \frac{9 \text{ in.}}{3 \text{ in.}} = \frac{3}{1} = 3$$

$$\frac{V \text{ larger}}{V \text{ smaller}} = \frac{\ell \times w \times h}{\ell \times w \times h} = \frac{\overset{3}{\cancel{9}} \times \overset{3}{\cancel{9}} \times \overset{3}{\cancel{9}}}{\underset{1}{\cancel{3}} \times \underset{1}{\cancel{3}} \times \underset{1}{\cancel{3}}} = \left(\frac{3}{1}\right)^3 = 27$$

**Find the scale factor for each pair of cubes.
Then find the ratio of the volumes.**

5. side of larger cube = 100 in.
side of smaller cube = 25 in.

$$\frac{\text{larger}}{\text{smaller}} = \frac{100 \text{ in.}}{25 \text{ in.}} = \underline{\hspace{2cm}}$$

scale factor = _____

ratio of volumes

$= (\text{scale factor})^3 = (\underline{\hspace{1cm}})^3 = \underline{\hspace{1cm}}$

6. side of smaller cube = 6 m
side of larger cube = 36 m

$$\frac{\text{smaller}}{\text{larger}} = \frac{\underline{\hspace{1.5cm}} =}{\underline{\hspace{2cm}}}$$

scale factor = _____

ratio of volumes

$= (\text{scale factor})^3 = \dfrac{(\quad)^3 =}{\underline{\hspace{3cm}}}$

As with the cube, the measures of other similar solids
are related in the same ways to their scale factors.

Find the indicated ratios for these similar cylinders.

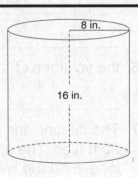

8 in.

16 in.

2 in.

4 in.

7. $\dfrac{\text{height of larger cylinder}}{\text{height of smaller cylinder}} = \dfrac{\underline{\hspace{1.5cm}} =}{\underline{\hspace{3cm}}}$

8. $\dfrac{\text{radius of larger cylinder}}{\text{radius of smaller cylinder}} = \dfrac{\underline{\hspace{1.5cm}} =}{\underline{\hspace{3cm}}}$

9. scale factor = _____

10. $\dfrac{\text{area of circular base of larger cylinder}}{\text{area of circular base of smaller cylinder}} = \dfrac{\pi \cdot (\text{larger radius})^2}{\pi \cdot (\text{smaller radius})^2} = \dfrac{\pi \cdot (\quad)^2}{\pi \cdot (\quad)^2}$

$= \dfrac{\dfrac{\pi}{\pi}}{\underline{\hspace{2cm}}} = \underline{\hspace{1.5cm}} = \underline{\hspace{1cm}} = (\text{scale factor})^2$

Holt Mathematics

LESSON 8-1 Homework and Practice
Scaling 3-Dimensional Figures

**A 15-in. cube is built from small cubes, each 1 in. on a side.
Compare the following values.**

1. the side lengths of the two cubes

_____

_____

2. the surface area of the two cubes

_____

_____

3. the volumes of the two cubes

_____

_____

**A 20-in. cube is built from small cubes, each 1 in. on a side.
Compare the following values.**

4. the side lengths of the two cubes

_____

_____

5. the surface area of the two cubes

_____

_____

6. the volumes of the two cubes

_____

_____

7. The dimensions of a warehouse are 180 ft long, 225 ft wide, and
90 ft high. The scale model used to build the warehouse is 15 in.
long. Find the width and height of the model of the warehouse.

_____

8. A 4-cm × 3-cm × 5-cm solid figure is built with centimeter
cubes. If each dimension is doubled, how many cubes are used
to build the larger solid?

_____

Holt Mathematics

Big Ideas

Answer these questions to summarize the important concepts from Chapter 8 in your own words.

1. Explain how to find the area of a trapezoid with bases 3 inches and 7 inches, and height 6 inches.

2. Explain how to find the circumference of a circle with radius 6 meters.

3. Explain how to find the volume of a cone with radius 3 feet and height 8 feet.

4. Explain how to find the surface area of a cylinder with diameter 6 inches and height 7 inches.

For more review of Chapter 8:

- Complete the Chapter 8 Study Guide and Review on pages 450–452 of your textbook.

- Complete the Ready to Go On quizzes on pages 404 and 444 of your textbook.

Holt Mathematics

Project

Data and Statistics: Poor Pizza

Career: Quality Assurance Specialist

How do manufacturers know that their products are well made? It is the job of the quality assurance specialist. QA specialists design tests and procedures that allow the companies to determine how good their products are. Because checking every product or procedure may not be possible, QA specialists use sampling to predict the margin of error.

In this chapter project...you will pretend to run a frozen pizza company and determine the quality of your pizzas. You will:

• Learn about sampling and error rates.

• Divide your class into two teams: the pizza makers and the quality assurance specialists.

• The pizza makers should decide how many errors there will be per 100 pizzas and not tell the QA specialists. The pizza makers should then write "good" or "waste" on slips of paper and seal them in envelopes.

• The QA specialists should then take a sampling of the envelopes and try to guess the error rate per 100 pizzas.

To get started, work through the Making Quality Products worksheet on the next page.

This chapter project reinforces your understanding of these Georgia Performance Standards:

M8P1.c Apply and adapt a variety of appropriate strategies to solve problems.

M8P4.c Recognize and apply mathematics in contexts outside of mathematics.

---

go.hrw.com
Chapter Project Online
KEYWORD: MT7 Ch9

Holt Mathematics

Project Recording Sheet

CHAPTER 9

Data and Statistics

Making Quality Products

The type of product being made often determines how many errors occur during the production process. To judge efficiency, you need to compare companies that produce the same kind of product.

Frozen Pizza Companies	Errors per Sample (100 pizzas)												
	1	2	3	4	5	6	7	8	9	10	11	12	13
Taste of New York	2	6	1	7	4	2	3	3	4	9	1	8	4
Momma Mildred's	7	6	12	7	15	14	13	5	18	15	7	16	11
Speedworks	4	8	8	6	4	9	7	3	5	8	7	9	3
Pizza Pizzazz	3	2	4	5	2	1	0	7	5	4	6	8	2

Calculate the mean, median, and mode for each company.

Company	Mean	Median	Mode
Taste of New York			
Momma Mildred's			
Speedworks			
Pizza Pizzazz			

Make a bar graph showing the average number of bad pizzas per hundred produced by each company.

_____

Rank the companies from best to worst.

_____

If each waste pizza costs the companies $1.50 and each company produces 10,000 pizzas a year, how much does each lose in that time? How does that loss affect the price they must charge for a pizza?

_____

_____

Holt Mathematics

Georgia Performance
Standards

M8D4.b

9A Scatter Plots

1. The table shows the numbers of pages in some paperback books and the books' prices. Plot the data on the graph provided.

Pages	Price ($)
300	2.25
200	1.75
130	1.65
450	3.00
180	1.75
75	1.25
250	2.50

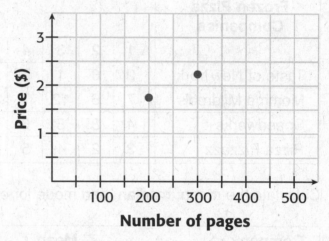

2. The table shows the number of hours some people spent outside and spent watching TV in one day. Plot the data on the graph provided.

TV hours	Outside hours
2.0	1.5
0.5	3.5
1.5	1.5
1.0	2.5
2.5	0.5
1.5	2.0
2.0	0.5

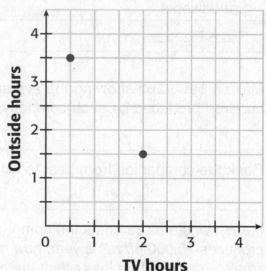

Think and Discuss

3. **Explain** what the shape of a graph tells you about the data being displayed.

Holt Mathematics

LESSON 9A Hands-On Lab
Scatter Plots

Activity

Scatter plots are used to show relationships between two variables. The data displayed on the graph may resemble a line. If the slope of the line is positive, there is a positive correlation between the two sets of data; if the slope of the line is negative, a negative correlation would exist. If the plot on the graph is scattered in such a way that it does not approximate a line, there is no correlation between the sets of data.

Using the data in the table, determine if studying longer will affect the grades on students' math exams.

Hours Studied	Score
3	80
5	90
2	75
6	80
7	90
1	50
2	65
7	85
1	40
7	100

On the y-axis, place scores from 0–100. On the x-axis, place hours studied from 0–8. Place one "point" on the graph for each row on the data table. Your scatter plot will look similar to this.

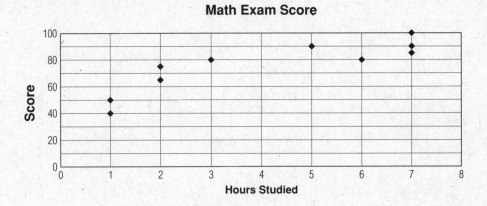

Math Exam Score

Hands-On Lab
Scatter Plots, continued

Think and Discuss

The data displayed on the graph resembles a line rising from left to right. What type of correlation does this show between the two sets of data? What does this mean in terms of the data compared?

_____

_____

_____

_____

_____

_____

Holt Mathematics

LESSON 9A **Hands-On Lab**

Scatter Plots, continued

Try This

Plot the following points on the graph below:

(0.5, 1.5), (1, 0.5), (1, 2), (1, 4), (2, 1), (2.5, 2), (2.5, 3),

(3, 4), (4, 1.5), (4, 3), (4, 3.5), (5, 2), (5, 3.5), (5, 5)

What type of correlation between data is represented on the scatter plot below?

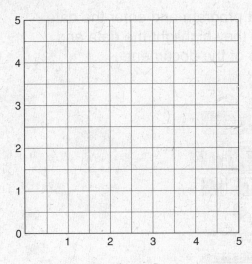

_____

_____

Holt Mathematics

Technology Lab 1
LESSON **9A** *Scatter Plots*

Activity

The 4th grade class has collected information from Internet research to make a scatter plot with. The class tracked the age of gym students and the number of pushups they were able to do. The data they collected is in the table below and they will use it with a spreadsheet program to make a scatter plot.

Age	10	19	15	20	13	17	16	12	14	15	18
Pushups	3	36	20	21	10	28	22	13	17	25	32

First they open a worksheet in the spreadsheet program and enter the data in the top left corner of a new worksheet. Then they highlight the data and select the Chart menu on the toolbar at the top of the document.

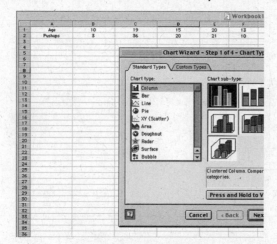

Select the Scatter Plot option and follow the instructions to select data and labels for the chart. The class makes the ages the X axis of the plot and the number of pushups the Y axis on the plot.

Holt Mathematics

LESSON
9A Technology Lab 1
Scatter Plots, continued

Think and Discuss

1. Do the data show a general correlation? If so, what is it?

   _____

   _____

2. If you extended the scatter plot data to cover the pushups done
   by people in their 20s, 30s, 40s, 50s, and 60s, would you expect
   the same correlation to hold and the same trend to continue?

   _____

Try This

You can choose to add a trendline that will show if there is a
correlation between the points on the scatter plot. This trendline is
the same as the line of best fit.

1. Click on the chart to select it.

2. From the main menu, choose **Chart,** and then choose **Add
   Trendline** from the Chart menu.

3. In the Add Trendline dialog box, choose **Linear.**

4. Click **OK.** A trendline appears, showing the line of best fit
   calculated by the spreadsheet software.

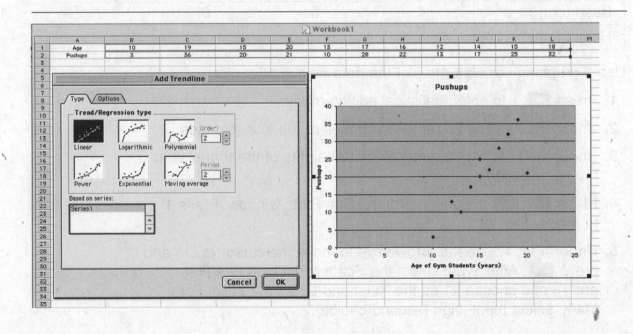

Holt Mathematics

LESSON 9A Technology Lab 2
Collect Data and Match to a Linear Function

You have learned that the sides of similar triangles are in proportion. You can verify that for yourself by measuring several similar triangles and seeing how accurately your measurements agree with the proportions the triangles should show. If your measurements are accurate, the heights of the triangles should be a linear function of the bases.

Activity

On a piece of 8.5 in. by 11 in. paper, use a centimeter ruler to draw four baselines with the following lengths: 4 cm, 5 cm, 6 cm, and 7 cm. Using a protractor, draw a ray at a 30° angle starting from the left end of the 4-cm line segment. From the right side of the 4-cm segment, draw a vertical segment intersecting the ray you just drew. Do the same with the other line segments to create four similar triangles.

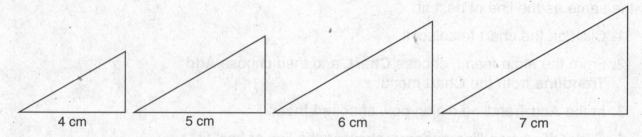

Measure the vertical line segments of the four triangles and complete the table below.

Base (cm)	4	5	6	7
Height (cm)				

Use a graphing calculator to plot the data as a scatter plot.

1. Press [STAT] 1 to enter statistical editing mode.

2. Under the heading L1, enter the bases of the four triangles.

3. Under the heading L2, enter the four heights of the triangles in the same order.

4. Press [2nd] [Y=] to summon up the Stat Plots window. Press 1 to modify Plot 1.

5. Under "Plot 1," use the arrow keys to move the cursor to On and press [ENTER]. After Type, select the Scatter Plot icon (the first entry), and choose L1 as the XList and L2 as the YList. For Mark, select the + sign (second choice).

Holt Mathematics

LESSON 9A Technology Lab 2
Collect Data and Match to a Linear Function, continued

6. Press [WINDOW]. Set Xmin as 0, Xmas as 7.5, Ymin as 0, and Ymax as 7.5.

7. Press [GRAPH]. Your measurements appear as a scatter plot.

8. Press [Y=] and press [ENTER] [÷] [2nd] [x²] 3 to enter the equation $y = x/\sqrt{3}$.

9. Press [GRAPH] again to see how well the linear function you just entered agrees with the data you obtained by measuring.

Think and Discuss

1. This activity calls for a centimeter ruler. Would an inch ruler be just as good? Explain.

   _____

   _____

   _____

2. How do you know that the four triangles you drew are similar triangles?

Try This

1. If the scatter plot and the function line are not showing, press [GRAPH] to display them. Press [TRACE] and use the forward and back arrow keys to check the y-values of the four points you plotted on the scatter plot. Then press the Down arrow to shift the trace onto the function line closest to each of your four plotted points. Read the y-value of the point as plotted on the function line and compare it with your measurement for that point. Were you close?

Holt Mathematics

Name _____ Date _____ Class _____

Review for Mastery
Scatter Plots

Two sets of data can be graphed as points in a **scatter plot**.
If there is a relationship between the data sets, a **line of best fit**
can be drawn.

Positive correlation:
both sets of data
increase together.

Negative correlation:
values of one set
increase while values of
the other set decrease.

No correlation: points
neither increase nor
decrease together.

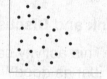

**Make a scatter plot. Include a line of best fit if there is a
correlation. Describe the correlation.**

1.

Time (hours)	1	2	2.5	6
Distance (miles)	50	150	175	270

The values for
time are: increasing

distance are: _____

So, there is a _____ correlation.

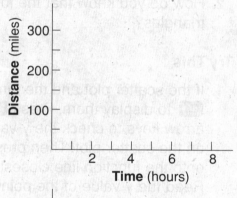

2.

Number of Workers	6	4	2	1
Number of Days	1	2	5	7

The values for
the number of workers are: _____

the number of days are: _____

So, there is a _____ correlation.

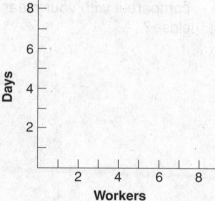

Holt Mathematics

Name _____ Date _____ Class _____

Homework and Practice

Scatter Plots

1. Use the given data to make a scatter plot.

Sandwich	Calories	Total Fat Grams
Chicken Breast	318	2
Chicken Teriyaki	374	1.5
Club	323	2
Cold Cut	441	7
Ham	288	1.5
Meatball	527	10
Roast Beef	293	2
Tuna	445	6
Turkey Breast	281	1.5
Veggie	226	1

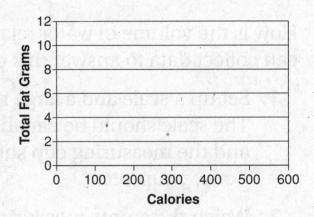

Do the data sets have a positive, a negative, or no correlation?

2. The type of car a person drives and the color of their hair.

3. The number of people working on a job and the hours to completion.

_____

4. The number of innings completed in a baseball game and the number of runs scored.

5. The number of shares of stock owned and the amount received in dividends.

_____

6. Use the data to predict the percent of U.S. Households with a computer in 1998.

Percent of U.S. Households with a Computer				
Year	1985	1990	1995	2000
Percent	8.2%	15%	24.1%	51%

In 1998, about _____% of U.S. households had a computer.

Holt Mathematics

Georgia Performance
Standards

M8D4.a, M8D4.b

9B Gathering Data and Lines of Best Fit

How is the volume of water related to the weight of water? You can collect data to answer this question.

1. Set up a scale and a large measuring cup in your classroom. The scale should be capable of showing weight in ounces, and the measuring cup should have markings for $\frac{1}{4}$ cup, $\frac{1}{2}$ cup, $\frac{3}{4}$ cup, etc.

2. Weigh the empty measuring cup and record the weight in the table below.

Amount of water	$\frac{1}{4}$ cup	$\frac{1}{2}$ cup	$\frac{3}{4}$ cup	1 cup	2 cups
Weight (oz)					

3. Weigh the amounts of water listed in the table. Subtract the weight of the empty container from each measurement and record your results.

Think and Discuss

4. **Tell** what kind of display you would use for this data.

5. **Discuss** the relationship between the amount of water and the weight of water. Do you think the relationship is linear? Why?

Holt Mathematics

Review for Mastery

LESSON 9B

Gathering Data and Lines of Best Fit

A *line of best fit* is a straight line that comes closest to all the data points on a scatter plot. When estimating a line of best fit, try to draw the line so that half of the data points are above the line and half are below the line.

Marcus recorded the miles he drove with different amounts of gasoline. Make a scatter plot of the data and draw a line of best fit. Use your line of best fit to find how many miles Marcus could drive with 10 gallons of gasoline.

Gasoline (gal)	3	5	6	7	12	15
Miles Driven	68	138	149	152	240	376

Plot the data on a scatter plot and draw a line of best fit. According to the graph, 10 gallons of gasoline should let Marcus drive about 225 miles.

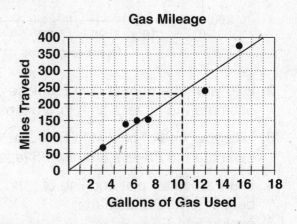

1. The table shows the temperature over time for a summer day. Make a scatter plot and draw a line of best fit. Use your line of best fit to estimate the temperature at 10:30 A.M.

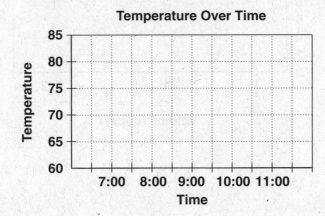

Time (A.M.)	Temp (°F)
7:00	68
8:00	73
9:30	74
11:00	80
11:30	82

Estimated temperature at 10:30 A.M.:

_____

Holt Mathematics

LESSON 9B

Homework and Practice
Gathering Data and Lines of Best Fit

1. The table shows the times for a driver practicing laps for a NASCAR race. Make a scatter plot for the data and draw a line of best fit.

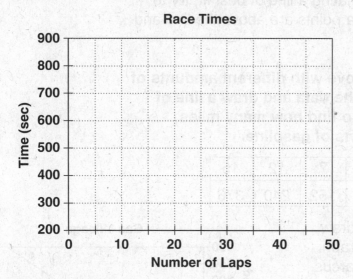

Race Times

Laps	Time (sec)
10	315
15	359
25	535
30	785
40	884

2. Use your line of best fit in Exercise 1 to estimate the driver's time for 20 laps. _____

3. Use your line of best fit in Exercise 1 to estimate the driver's time for 35 laps. _____

4. Draw a scatter plot and line of best fit for the data in the exploration.

5. Use your graph to estimate the weight of $1\frac{1}{2}$ cups of water.

_____

6. Weigh $1\frac{1}{2}$ cups of water. Is your estimate close?

_____

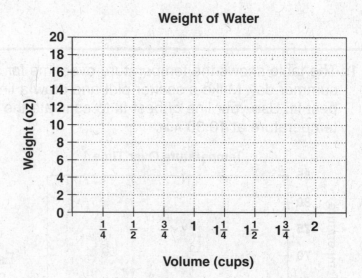

Weight of Water

Holt Mathematics

Answer these questions to summarize the important concepts from Chapter 9 in your own words.

1. Explain how to find the mean, median, mode, and range of the data set.

    45, 53, 78, 29, 84, 25, 74, 57, 29, 36

2. Explain how graphs can be misleading.

3. Explain when you should use different types of graphs.

For more review of Chapter 9:

- Complete the Chapter 9 Study Guide and Review on pages 510–512 of your textbook.

- Complete the Ready to Go On quizzes on pages 482 and 506 of your textbook.

Holt Mathematics

Project

Probability: Breaking the Code

Career: Cryptographer

10010011010111100000110100111001011100100
10001001000100100100110011101000111

Is this pattern of zeros and ones some kind of message or secret code? A cryptographer could find out. Cryptographers create and break codes by assigning number values to letters of the alphabet. Almost all text sent over the Internet is encrypted to ensure security for the sender. Codes made up of zeros and ones, or *binary codes*, are frequently used in computer applications. Use the table on the Code Breaking project worksheet to break the code above.

In this chapter project...you will come up with your own code and write a secret message. You will:

- Create what's called a *substitution cipher or code*. In this type of code, every letter of the alphabet is changed to a different letter.

- Write a message in your code and trade messages with a classmate.

- Use probability to help crack your classmate's code. For example, "e" is the most commonly used letter in English, so finding the most commonly used letter in your classmate's code is likely to be the coded version of "e." Research the frequency of letters of the alphabet to help you crack the rest of the code.

To get started, work through the Code Breaking worksheet on the next page.

This chapter project reinforces your understanding of these Georgia Performance Standards:

M8P1.c Apply and adapt a variety of appropriate strategies to solve problems.

M8P4.c Recognize and apply mathematics in contexts outside of mathematics.

---

go.hrw.com
Chapter Project Online
KEYWORD: MT7 Ch10

Holt Mathematics

Name _____ Date _____ Class _____

Code Breaking

You might think that only spies worry about codes but in this modern world that just isn't true any more. Today, anyone who sends electronic information wants it to be safe. Encrypting a code is the way to do it. Cryptographers are the people who create codes. If you like discovering and creating patterns then cryptography might be for you.

Use the chart to figure out the message below.

100100110101111000001101001100101110010011
0001001000100100100110011101000111

Letter	Code	Letter	Code
A	1000001	N	1001110
B	1000010	O	1001111
C	1000011	P	1010000
D	1000100	Q	1010001
E	1000101	R	1010010
F	1000110	S	1010011
G	1000111	T	1010100
H	1001000	U	1010101
I	1001001	V	1010110
J	1001010	W	1010111
K	1001011	X	1011000
L	1001100	Y	1011001
M	1001101	Z	1011010

What is the message? _____

Create a message of your own using the code above.
Exchange messages with your classmates.

Look at the code. What patterns do you see? _____
What other patterns might be used to create a code
using 1's and 0's? _____

Develop a code of your own. Write a message. See if a
classmate can decipher the message using your code.

Research: The code above uses the binary system of 1's and 0's.
What other uses for the binary system can you discover?

Holt Mathematics

Georgia Performance
Standards

M8D3.a

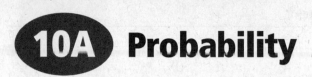
10A Probability

A plastic container contains 10 marbles: 4 red, 3 yellow, 2 green, and 1 blue. An experiment consists of shaking the container and then drawing a number of marbles.

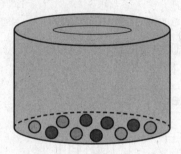

1. If you draw one marble, which color is it most likely to be?

2. If you draw one marble, which color is it least likely to be?

3. If you draw two marbles at the same time, which colors might you draw two of?

4. If you repeatedly draw one marble and return it to the container before the next draw, which color do you think you would draw most often?

Think and Discuss

5. **Discuss** real-world situations in which probability is used.

6. **Explain,** using the marble experiment, why the probability of drawing a blue marble is $\frac{1}{10}$. (*Hint:* Compare the number of blue marbles to the total number of marbles.)

Holt Mathematics

LESSON 10A Hands-On Lab
Probability

What you need: marbles (5 light-colored, 5 medium-colored, 10 dark-colored), bag or sack

Activity

1. Put 5 dark-colored (R), 5 light-colored (G), and 5 medium-colored (B) marbles in a bag. Pull out one marble. What color did you pull out? What is the probability that you pulled out a dark colored marble?

The probability that you pulled out a dark colored marble is given by:

$$\frac{\text{number of favorable outcomes}}{\text{number of total outcomes}}$$

$$P_{(R)} = \frac{5}{15} = \frac{1}{3} = 33.3\%$$

If you put 5 additional dark colored marbles in the bag, what is the probability that you will pull out a light colored marble?

$$P_{(G)} = \frac{5}{20} = \frac{1}{4} = 25\%$$

2. You have 10 dark-colored (R), 5 medium-colored (B), and 4 light-colored (G) marbles in the bag. What is the probability that you will pull out a light-colored marble? Pull out one marble. Repeat the process 20 times, always putting back into the bag the marble you pulled out. Record the outcomes in the table below and compute the probability.

1	2	3	4	5	6	7	8	9	10	11	12	13	14	15	16	17	18	19	20
R	R	G	B	B	R	R	R	B	G	R	R	R	B	B	G	G	R	R	R

$$P_{(G)} = \frac{4}{19} = 21.05\%$$

Holt Mathematics

Hands-On Lab

LESSON 10A

Probability, continued

Look back at the chart. How many times did a light-colored marble come out of the bag? Four times; that fits the probability.

Think and Discuss

1. In #2, if you were to repeat the process 100 times, how often would you expect to pull out a light-colored marble? Why would this be a more representative sample?

_____

_____

Try This

1. You have 7 dark-colored marbles, 3 medium-colored marbles, and 3 light-colored marbles in the bag. What is the probability that you pull out a dark-colored marble? Pull out one marble. Repeat the process 20 times. Record the outcomes in a table and then compute the probability. (Remember to put the marble you pulled out back into the bag.)

1	2	3	4	5	6	7	8	9	10	11	12	13	14	15	16	17	18	19	20

_____

_____

Holt Mathematics

LESSON 10A — Review for Mastery
Probability

The **probability** that something will happen is how often you can expect that **event** to occur. This depends upon how many outcomes are possible, the **sample space.**

In the spinner shown, the circle is divided into four equal parts. There are 4 possible outcomes.

So, in a single spin:

$$P(A) = P(B) = P(C) = P(D) = 25\% = \frac{1}{4}$$

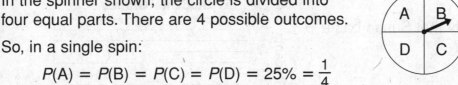

Complete to give the probability for each event.

1. A fair coin is tossed.   **2.** A number cube is rolled.

List all the possible outcomes.

_____   _____

_____   _____

How many outcomes in sample space?

_____   _____

Find the probability of the event shown. $P(\text{heads}) = $ _____ $P(5) = $ _____

- A probability of 0 means the event is **impossible,** or can never happen.
  On the spinner above, $P(F) = 0$.

- A probability of 1 means the event is **certain,** or has to happen.
  In one roll of a number cube, $P(\text{a whole number from 1 through 6}) = 1$.

Give the probability for each event.

3. selecting a rectangle from the set of squares

$P(\text{rectangle}) = $ _____

4. selecting a negative number from the set of whole numbers

$P(\text{negative number}) = $ _____

- The sum of the probabilities of all the possible outcomes in a sample space is 1.
  If the probability of *snow* is 30%, then the probability of *no snow* is 70%.
      $P(\text{snow}) + P(\text{no snow}) = 1$

5. If the probability of selecting a senior for a committee is 60%, then the probability of not selecting a senior is:

6. If the probability of choosing a red ball from a certain box is 0.35, then the probability of not choosing a red ball is:

_____   _____

269   **Holt Mathematics**

Review for Mastery

LESSON 10A *Probability (continued)*

To find the probability that an event will occur, add the probabilities of all the outcomes included in the event.

This bar graph shows the midterm grades of the 30 students in Ms. Lin's class.

What is the probability that Susan has a grade of C or higher?

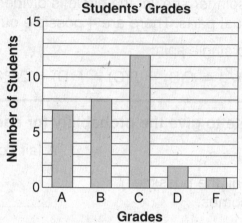

Students' Grades

The event "a grade of C or higher" consists of the outcomes C, B, A.

$$P(\text{C or higher}) = P(\text{C}) + P(\text{B}) + P(\text{A})$$

$$= \frac{12}{30} + \frac{8}{30} + \frac{7}{30} = \frac{12 + 8 + 7}{30} = \frac{27}{30} = \frac{9}{10} = 90\%$$

So, the probability that Susan's midterm grade is C or higher is $\frac{9}{10}$ or 90%.

Use the bar graph above to find each probability.

7. B or higher is honor roll. What is the probability that Ken made the honor roll?

$$P(\text{B or higher}) = P(\text{B}) + \underline{\hspace{1cm}}$$

$$= \frac{}{30} + \frac{}{30}$$

$$= \frac{}{30} = \underline{\hspace{1cm}}$$

So, the probability that Ken made the

honor roll is: _____ or _____%.

8. In this class, D is a failing grade. What is the probability that Tom failed?

$$P(\text{D or lower}) = P(\text{D}) + \underline{\hspace{1cm}}$$

$$= \frac{}{30} + \frac{}{30}$$

$$= \frac{}{30} = \underline{\hspace{1cm}}$$

So, the probability that Tom

failed is: _____ or _____%.

Holt Mathematics

Homework and Practice
LESSON 10A *Probability*

The following table indicates the
inventory totals for a shoe store. Find
the probability for choosing the
following types of shoes.

	Two-Tone	Black	White
High-Top	25	54	21
Low Cut	15	24	11

1. P(two-tone high-top)   **2.** P(black low cut)   **3.** P(white high top)

_____   _____   _____

4. P(black shoe)   **5.** P(two-tone)   **6.** P(two-tone low cut)

_____   _____   _____

7. P(blue shoe)   **8.** P(black or white)   **9.** P(low cut or high top)

_____   _____   _____

**Find the probability of drawing the following colored candies
from a jar containing 25 red, 15 blue, 20 green, 30 yellow, and
10 orange pieces of candy.**

10. P(yellow)   **11.** P(red)   **12.** P(orange)   **13.** P(blue)

_____   _____   _____   _____

14. P(purple)   **15.** P(blue or green)   **16.** P(candy)   **17.** P(red or yellow)

_____   _____   _____   _____

18. There are 25 red, 16 green, 30 purple, 14 white, 20 black, and
15 orange marbles in a bag. What is the probability of picking a
marble that is not purple?

_____

19. What is the probability of tossing a 4 on a regular numerical
cube?

_____

Holt Mathematics

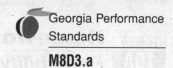

Georgia Performance
Standards

M8D3.a

10B Experimental Probability

Use a plastic lid to make a spinner such as the one below. Color $\frac{1}{2}$ of the lid red, $\frac{1}{4}$ yellow, and the other $\frac{1}{4}$ green. Use a paper clip to secure the spinner to the center.

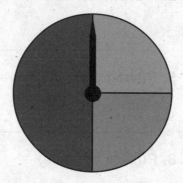

1. Spin the spinner 20 times, and record the results in the table.

Color	Number of Spins
Red	
Yellow	
Green	

a. Write a ratio to compare the number of spins for each color to 20, the total number of spins.

b. Add the three ratios in **a**. What is this sum equal to?

Think and Discuss

2. **Discuss** which color had the largest ratio in Problem **1a**.

3. **Explain** whether the sum in Problem **1b** is what you expected.

Holt Mathematics

Review for Mastery

LESSON 10B *Experimental Probability*

A machine is filling boxes of apples by choosing 50 apples at random from a selection of six types of apples. An inspector records the results for one filled box in the table below.

Type	Pink Lady	Red Delicious	Granny Smith	Golden Delicious	Fuji	MacIntosh
Number	8	12	6	4	15	5

The inspector then expands the table to find the experimental probability.

$$\text{probability} = \frac{\text{number of type of apple}}{\text{total number of apples}}$$

Type	Pink Lady	Red Delicious	Granny Smith	Golden Delicious	Fuji	MacIntosh
Experimental Probability (ratio)	$\frac{8}{50}$, or $\frac{4}{25}$	$\frac{12}{50}$, or $\frac{6}{25}$	$\frac{6}{50}$, or $\frac{3}{25}$	$\frac{4}{50}$, or $\frac{2}{25}$	$\frac{15}{50}$, or $\frac{3}{10}$	$\frac{5}{50}$, or $\frac{1}{10}$
Experimental Probability (percent)	16%	24%	12%	8%	30%	10%

Find each sum for the apple experiment.

1. The sum of the experimental probability ratios.

   $\text{probability} = \frac{8}{50} + \frac{12}{50} + \frac{6}{50} + \frac{4}{50} + \frac{15}{50} + \frac{5}{50} = \frac{}{50}$ or _____

2. The sum of the experimental probability percents.

   $\text{probability} = 16\% + 24\% + 12\% + 8\% + 30\% + 10\% = $ ____% or ____

Complete the table to find the experimental probability.

3. Five types of seed are inserted at random in a pre-seeded strip ready for planting.

Type	Marigold	Impatiens	Snapdragon	Daisy	Petunia
Number	40	100	80	60	120
Experimental Probability (ratio)	$\frac{}{400}$, or ___	$\frac{}{400}$, or ___	$\frac{}{400}$, or ___	$\frac{}{400}$, or ___	$\frac{}{400}$, or ___
Experimental Probability (percent)					

Holt Mathematics

LESSON 10B Homework and Practice
Experimental Probability

1. A number cube was thrown 125 times. The results are shown in the table below. Complete the table with the experimental probability for each outcome.

Outcome	1	2	3	4	5	6
Frequency	15	25	20	26	18	21
Probability	12%					

The school spirit wear shop sells special sweatshirts with the school logo imprinted on them in sizes small, medium, large, x-large and xx-large. In the first hour the store is open, the first 50 customers buy 2 small, 4 medium, 5 large, 15 x-large, and the rest buy xx-large. Find the probability of the purchase of each of the different size sweatshirts from the store.

2. P(x-large sweatshirt)

3. P(medium sweatshirt)

_____

_____

4. P(xx-large sweatshirt)

5. P(small or large sweatshirt)

_____

_____

If the store has 225 customers in the second hour they are open, predict how many sweatshirts of each size will be sold based on the purchases during the first hour.

6. number of small sweatshirts sold

7. number of medium sweatshirts sold

_____

_____

8. number of xx-large sweatshirts sold

9. number of large and x-large sweatshirts sold

_____

_____

10. Jay practiced his foul shots for the upcoming basketball game. He attempted 45 shots and made 36 of them. What is the probability that Jay would make the foul shot?

_____

11. If Jay took 20 foul shots in the basketball game, predict how many shots he would make based on his practicing.

_____

Holt Mathematics

EXPLORATION

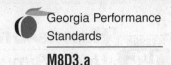

Georgia Performance
Standards

M8D3.a

10C Use a Simulation

You can use a calculator to simulate flipping a coin 30 times.

- Press the **MATH** key.

- Select **PRB.**

- Select **5:randInt(.**

- Key in 0, 1, 6.

- Press the **ENTER** key five times.

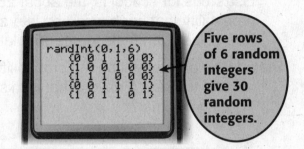

Five rows of 6 random integers give 30 random integers.

Assume that 1 means heads and 0 means tails to answer each question.

1. How many heads did you get in the 30 simulated flips?

2. How many tails did you get in the 30 simulated flips?

3. What is the experimental probability of flipping heads? (*Hint:* Write a fraction that compares the number of heads to 30 flips.)

4. What is the experimental probability of flipping tails? (*Hint:* Write a fraction that compares the number of tails to 30 flips.)

5. Use a calculator to simulate 100 flips, and compute the experimental probability of flipping heads.

Think and Discuss

6. **Explain** how to perform simulations on a calculator.

7. **Discuss** what you think would happen to the experimental probability as you increase the number of simulated flips.

275

Holt Mathematics

LESSON 10C Hands-On Lab
Use a Simulation

Activity

1. Use a computer or calculator to create a table of random numbers. Use the table to simulate the following probabilities.

   Lisa's bus for school is late about 25% of the time. What is the probability that her bus will be late at least 3 days in a week? Use at least ten trials for the simulation.

Step 1 The answer will be the probability that Lisa's bus will be late 3 of the next 5 days. What is this outcome, 3 out of 5, written as a decimal?

_____

Step 2 Group the numbers in the table in pairs.
Which numbers in the table will represent Lisa's bus being late?

_____

Step 3 Determine how many pairs of numbers will represent one trial. Since you want to find the probability that Lisa's bus will be late in the next 5 days, 5 pairs of numbers will make up a trial.

Step 4 For every 5 pairs of numbers, count the pairs of numbers that represent Lisa's bus being late.
For example, given the random numbers:
12 85 65 24 95

The probability that Lisa's bus will be late is $\frac{2}{5}$ or 0.4.

Step 5 Use at least 10 trials for the simulation. Of the 10 trials, how many represented a probability of Lisa's bus being late 60% of the time in the next 5 days?

Based on the fact that Lisa's bus is late only about 25% of the time, is your answer reasonable? Explain.

_____

_____

Holt Mathematics

LESSON 10C Hands-On Lab
Use a Simulation, continued

Think and Discuss

1. Redo the simulation of Lisa's bus being late using 25% as the
   probability that it will be late. What is the probability it will be late
   according to the simulation? Does this result support the
   usefulness of random-number simulations?

   _____

   _____

   _____

   _____

2. Describe what *random* means in your own words.

   _____

   _____

   _____

Try This

Create a table of random numbers to simulate the two situations.
Use at least 10 trials for each simulation.

1. 18 of the 20 students in a math class passed a quiz. What is the
   probability that one student randomly chosen from the class did
   not pass the quiz?

   _____

   _____

2. The probability that you will roll a 4 when you roll a number cube
   is $\frac{1}{6}$. What is the probability you will roll a 4 in 3 out of the next
   10 rolls ?

   _____

   _____

LESSON 10C

Review for Mastery

Use a Simulation

Situation: Strout's Market is having a contest. They give a puzzle piece to each customer at the checkout. A customer who collects all 10 different puzzle pieces gets $100 in store credit.

Using a table of random numbers, you can model the situation to estimate how many times a customer would have to shop to collect all 10 puzzle pieces.

3	1	9	4	1	1	8	8
5	7	4	5	7	7	9	0
7	0	3	0	1	3	5	0
0	4	3	8	9	5	3	8
2	6	1	7	6	7	6	9
0	8	2	6	5	5	9	2

• Start anywhere in the table. Count the numbers you pass as you "collect" the digits 0–9.

Suppose you start at the top of Column 3 and move to the right.
List each number until you have collected all the numbers 0–9.

9 4 1 1 8 8 5 7 4 5 7 7 9 0 7 0 3 0 1 3 5 0 0 4 3 8 9 5 3 8 2 6

You had to go through 32 numbers to get each number at least once (underscored).

• Do the experiment again.

Suppose you start at the bottom of Column 4 and move to the right.
When you reach the end of the row, go to the beginning of the table.

6 5 5 9 2 3 1 9 4 1 1 8 8 5 7 4 5 7 7 9 0

You had to go through 21 numbers to get each number at least once (underscored).

• Find the average of your results. $\frac{32 + 21}{2} = \frac{53}{2} = 26.5$

So, on average, you need to shop 27 times to get all 10 pieces to win $100 credit.

Model each situation. Use the list of random numbers shown above. Do two trials. Tell where you start for each trial.

1. A box of Whammos contains a toy dinosaur. If there are 10 different model dinosaurs in the collection, estimate how many boxes of Whammos you would have to buy to get all 10 dinosaurs.

_____

_____

2. For this spinner, estimate how many times you would have to spin the pointer to get the numbers 1–10.

_____

_____

Holt Mathematics

Homework and Practice

LESSON 10C *Problem Solving Strategy: Use a Simulation*

Use the table of random numbers for the problems below.

2596	3623	1053	2161	8550	9672	1044	9852	8935	8727
2393	1231	2795	2036	5138	7488	5814	2086	5397	8073
5086	9057	2050	7424	1706	1391	3585	3124	4164	9498
3274	5099	1789	7021	5636	2404	7180	3395	4734	0395
1387	7460	9196	0463	1388	5104	6408	7463	3289	9321
5891	8081	6222	9656	5606	8739	8698	3982	4974	9961
1544	2817	5296	1340	9750	3943	5697	1585	1097	8365
0442	3881	9080	7964	9357	8202	9987	5681	1288	7894
7170	4188	7099	7590	2158	0242	5299	4095	6986	3935
6039	5890	3996	0217	4045	6545	3744	8368	2034	8670

Ms. Patrick gave the same math test to all three of her math classes. In the first two classes, 70% of the students received a grade above C. Estimate the probability that at least 13 of 20 students will receive a grade above C in the third class.

1. Using the first row as the first trial, count the successful outcomes and name the unsuccessful outcomes.

   _____

2. Using the second row, count the successful outcomes and name the unsuccessful outcomes.

   _____

Determine the successful outcomes in the remaining rows of the random number table.

3. third row

4. fourth row

5. fifth row

6. sixth row

   _____   _____   _____   _____

7. seventh row

8. eighth row

9. ninth row

10. tenth row

   _____   _____   _____   _____

11. Based on the simulation, estimate the probability that at least 13 of 20 students will receive a grade above C.

Holt Mathematics

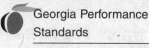
Georgia Performance
Standards

M8D3.a

10D Theoretical Probability

The *theoretical probability* of an event tells you the probability of the event without your having to conduct an experiment.

For example, the experiment of rolling two dice and adding the two numbers that each die shows does not have to be conducted to know the possible sums of numbers.

	2	3	4	5	6	7
	3	4	5	6	7	8
	4	5	6	7	8	9
	5	6	7	8	9	10
	6	7	8	9	10	11
	7	8	9	10	11	12

1. Use the number of times each sum occurs to complete the table.

Sum	2	3	4	5	6	7	8	9	10	11	12
Outcomes	1	2									
Theoretical Probability	$\frac{1}{36}$	$\frac{2}{36}$									

Think and Discuss

2. **Explain** which sum is most likely to occur.

Review for Mastery

LESSON 10D *Theoretical Probability*

The sample space for a fair coin has 2 possible outcomes: heads or tails. Both possibilities have the same chance of occurring; they are **equally likely**.

The probability of each outcome is $\frac{1}{2}$.

$$P(\text{heads}) = P(\text{tails}) = \frac{1}{2}$$

Complete to find each probability.

1.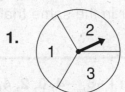

2.

How many outcomes in the sample space?   _____   _____

Are the outcomes equally likely?   _____   _____

What is the probability for each outcome?   _____   _____

For this spinner, there are 10 possible outcomes in the sample space. The outcomes are equally likely.

$$P(7) = \frac{1}{10} \qquad P(\text{even number}) = \frac{5}{10}, \text{ or } \frac{1}{2}$$

$$P(\text{a number greater than 4}) = \frac{6}{10}, \text{ or } \frac{3}{5}$$

When the possible outcomes are equally likely, you calculate the probability that an event E will occur by using a ratio.

$$P(E) = \frac{\text{number of favorable outcomes}}{\text{total number of possible outcomes}}$$

Find each probability.

3.

4.

5.

$P(C) = $ ____ $P(1) = $ ____, or ____ $P(2) = $ ____, or ____

$P(A) = $ ____ $P(\text{even}) = $ ____ $P(\text{odd}) = $ ____, or ____

Holt Mathematics

Review for Mastery
Theoretical Probability (continued)

For this spinner:

$P(\text{odd}) = \dfrac{3}{6}$, or $\dfrac{1}{2}$ $P(\text{even}) = \dfrac{1}{6}$

You cannot get an odd number
and an even number $P(\text{odd and even}) = 0$
in the same spin.

Events that cannot occur in the same trial are called **mutually
exclusive.**

**A number is drawn from {−6, −4, 0, 2, 4, 7, 9}.
List the possible favorable results for each event. Tell if the
events are mutually exclusive.**

6. *Event A*: get an odd number

_____

Event B: get a negative number

_____

Are *A* and *B* mutually exclusive? Explain.

_____

7. *Event C*: get a multiple of 3

_____

Event D: get an even number

_____

Are *C* and *D* mutually exclusive? Explain.

_____

For the spinner at the top of this page:

$P(\text{odd}) = \dfrac{3}{6}$, or $\dfrac{1}{2}$ $P(\text{even}) = \dfrac{1}{6}$ $P(\text{odd or even}) = \dfrac{3}{6} + \dfrac{1}{6} = \dfrac{4}{6}$, or $\dfrac{2}{3}$

**A number is drawn from {−6, −4, 0, 5, 6, 7, 9}.
Find the indicated probabilities.**

8. odd numbers are: 5, 7, 9

numbers < 0 are: _____

$P(\text{odd}) = \dfrac{\quad}{7}$

$P(\text{number} < 0) = \dfrac{\quad}{7}$

$P(\text{odd number or number} < 0) =$

$\dfrac{\quad}{7} + \dfrac{\quad}{7} = \dfrac{\quad}{7}$

9. numbers > 6 are: _____

even numbers: _____

$P(\text{number} > 6) =$ _____

$P(\text{even number}) =$ _____

$P(\text{number} > 6 \text{ or even number}) =$

_____ + _____ = _____

Holt Mathematics

LESSON 10D Homework and Practice
Theoretical Probability

An experiment consists of rolling two fair dice. Find each probability.

1. P(total shown = 4)

_____

2. P(total shown = 6)

_____

3. P(total shown = 10)

_____

4. P(total shown = 11)

_____

5. P(total shown = 1)

_____

6. P(total shown = 5)

_____

7. P(total shown ≥ 2)

_____

8. P(total shown ≤ 7)

_____

9. P(total shown > 8)

_____

Find the theoretical probability of having a thrown dart land in the indicated area.

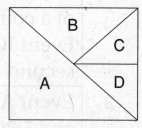

10. P(landing in area A)

_____

11. P(landing in area B)

_____

12. P(landing in area C)

_____

13. P(landing in area D)

_____

14. P(landing in areas A or C)

_____

15. What is the theoretical probability of winning a raffle if 375 tickets were sold and you bought 25?

_____

16. The second place winner of the raffle could choose between 12 envelopes each with money in them. Two of the envelopes contained a $20 bill, 4 contained $10 bills, and 6 contained $5 bills. What is the theoretical probability that the winner will choose an envelope with a $20 bill in it?

Holt Mathematics

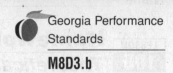

Georgia Performance
Standards

M8D3.b

10E Independent and Dependent Events

When the occurrence of one event affects the probability of a second event, the events are *dependent.* Otherwise, they are *independent.*

Classify each pair of events as dependent or independent.

	Events	Independent	Dependent
1.	**Event A:** Drawing a 3 from a deck without replacing it **Event B:** Drawing another 3 from the same deck.		
2.	**Event A:** Tossing heads on a flip of a coin **Event B:** Tossing heads on a second flip of the same coin		
3.	**Event A:** Running between 5:00 P.M. and 5:30 P.M. **Event B:** Drinking water between 5:30 P.M. and 6:00 P.M.		
4.	**Event A:** Drawing a blue marble and putting it back in a bag that contains 6 blue marbles and 4 red marbles **Event B:** Drawing another blue marble from the same bag		

Think and Discuss

5. Discuss real-world examples of dependent events and independent events.

Holt Mathematics

Hands-On Lab

LESSON 10E *Independent and Dependent Events*

Activity 1

1. Find the probability of tossing two 5's when you toss two six-sided number cubes.

Step 1 Decide whether the two events are dependent or independent.

Does the probability of tossing a 5 on one number cube depend on the probability of tossing a 5 on the other number cube? _____

Are the events dependent or independent? _____

Step 2 Determine the probability of tossing a 5 on one number cube. There are six possible numbers on a six-sided number cube. 5 is one of the numbers. What is the probability of tossing a 5 on the first number cube? _____

What is the probability of tossing a 5 on the second number cube? _____

Step 3 Multiply the probability of tossing a 5 on the first toss by the probability of tossing a 5 on the second toss.

_____

Activity 2

1. A bag has 3 blue socks, 2 red socks, and 5 white socks. Calculate the probability of pulling out a pair of blue socks. Make 10 slips of paper to represent the 10 socks. Place them in a bag.

Step 1 What is the probability of pulling out a blue sock on the first draw?

_____

Step 2 Pull out one blue sock from the bag. How many blue socks are left in the bag? _____

How many socks are left in the bag? _____

Step 3 What is the probability of pulling a blue sock out of 9 socks if 2 of the socks are blue?

_____

Step 4 Multiply the probability of pulling out the first blue sock by the probability of pulling out the second blue sock to find the probability of pulling out a pair of blue socks.

_____

Holt Mathematics

Name _____ Date _____ Class _____

LESSON 10E Hands-On Lab
Independent and Dependent Events, continued

Think and Discuss

1. Look back at the first activity where you calculated the probability of tossing double 5's on two number cubes. Find the experimental probability of this event happening in 36 trials. Toss two number cubes 36 times and record the number of times you toss double 5's. The experimental probability is the number of times you toss double 5's over the number of times you toss the number cubes. What is the experimental probability of tossing double 5's?

_____

_____

2. How is the experimental probability different or similar to the theoretical probability you calculated in the first activity?

_____

_____

_____

Try This

1. Calculate the probability of tossing heads each time when tossing a quarter 5 times. Show your work.

_____

2. Charlotte has 10 coins in her pocket. 3 coins are nickels, 3 are dimes, and 4 are quarters. What is the probability that when she pulls 3 coins out of her pocket, they will all be nickels? Show your calculations.

_____

_____

LESSON
10E
Review for Mastery
Independent and Dependent Events

Carlos is to draw 2 straws at random from a box of straws that
contains 4 red, 4 white, and 4 striped straws.

P(1st straw is striped) $= \dfrac{4}{12}$ ← number of striped straws
← total number of straws

If Carlos *returns* the 1st straw to the box before drawing the 2nd straw, the probability that the 2nd straw is striped remains the same.	If Carlos *does not return* the first straw to the box before drawing the second straw, the probability that the second straw is striped changes.
P(2nd straw is striped)	P(2nd straw is striped)
$= \dfrac{4}{12}$ ← same number of striped straws ← same total number of straws	$= \dfrac{3}{11}$ ← one striped straw has been taken ← one less straw in total number
When the 1st straw is returned before the 2nd draw, the 2nd draw occurs as though the 1st draw never happened, **independent events.**	When the 1st straw is not returned before the 2nd draw, the number of straws remaining is changed, **dependent events.**
P(striped, then striped) $= \dfrac{4}{12} \times \dfrac{4}{12}$ $= \dfrac{1}{3} \times \dfrac{1}{3} = \dfrac{1}{9}$	P(striped, then striped) $= \dfrac{4}{12} \times \dfrac{3}{11}$ $= \dfrac{1}{3} \times \dfrac{3}{11} = \dfrac{1}{11}$

Describe the events as independent or dependent.

1. Josh tosses a coin and spins a spinner.   _____

2. Ana draws a colored toothpick from a jar.
Without replacing it, she draws a second toothpick.   _____

3. Sue draws a card from a deck of cards and replaces it.
Then she draws a second card from the deck.   _____

**Each situation begins with a box of marbles that contains 2 red,
3 blue, 4 green, and 3 yellow marbles. Complete to find each
probability.**

4. A 1st marble is drawn and replaced.
Then a 2nd marble is drawn.

P(red, then blue) $= \dfrac{}{12} \times \dfrac{}{12} =$ _____

5. A 1st marble is drawn and not
replaced. A 2nd marble is drawn.

P(red, then blue) $= \dfrac{}{12} \times \dfrac{}{11} =$ _____

6. A 1st marble is drawn and replaced.
Then a 2nd marble is drawn.

P(red, then red) $= \dfrac{}{12} \times \dfrac{}{} =$ _____

7. A 1st marble is drawn and not
replaced. A 2nd marble is drawn.

P(red, then red) $= \dfrac{}{12} \times \dfrac{}{} =$ _____

Holt Mathematics

Homework and Practice

LESSON 10E *Independent and Dependent Events*

Determine if the events are dependent or independent.

1. spinning a spinner and rolling a numerical cube

   _____

2. drawing a card from a deck and not replacing it and then drawing another card

   _____

3. selecting a piece of cake and selecting a drink

   _____

A jar contains 4 white chips, 5 purple chips, and 1 black chip. Chips are selected randomly one at a time, and are not replaced. Find the probability of the following.

4. P(purple then black)   5. P(black then white)   6. P(white then purple)

   _____   _____   _____

7. P(purple then white)   8. P(2 whites)   9. P(2 purples)

   _____   _____   _____

10. P(2 black chips)   11. P(white, then purple,   12. P(3 whites)
                                then black)

   _____   _____   _____

13. Mrs. Benedict offers extra credit when she gives a math test. She writes the first 5 prime numbers on 5 separate cards and places them in a box. Students are permitted to draw one card to determine their extra credit when the test is finished. The cards are replaced after each student draws. What is the most extra credit a student can receive on a test? What is the probability of drawing that card?

   _____

   _____

Holt Mathematics

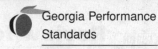

10F Making Decisions and Predictions

Georgia Performance
Standards

M8A1.a, M8A1.c,
M8A1.d, M8D3.b

Kate sells shirts and caps that have a school logo on them. Both the shirts and the caps are available in red or black. The table shows the number of shirts and caps that Kate sold during her first week of business.

	Red	Black
Shirts	125	75
Caps	60	40

1. What was the total number of shirts sold during the first week?

2. What fraction of the shirts that were sold were red shirts?

3. Kate assumes that future sales will be similar to the first week's sales. She plans to order 2000 more shirts. How many of these should be red shirts?

4. In general, when Kate sells a shirt, what is the probability that it is a red shirt?

5. What was the total number of caps sold during the first week?

6. What fraction of the caps that were sold were black caps?

7. Kate places an order for 5000 more caps. How many of these should be black caps?

Think and Discuss

8. **Explain** how you determined the number of red shirts that Kate should order in Problem 3.

9. **Explain** how you determined the number of black caps that Kate should order in Problem 6.

Holt Mathematics

LESSON 10F Review for Mastery
Making Decisions and Predictions

Probability can be used to make predictions about data.

The spinner has 5 equal sections. To predict how
many times you will land on the number 1 in 30 spins,
first find the probability of landing on 1 in one spin.
Then multiply 30 spins by that probability.

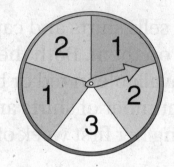

Step 1 Find the probability.

$$P(1) = \frac{\text{number of 1s}}{\text{number of equal sections}} = \frac{2}{5}$$

Step 2 Multiply the number of spins by the probability.

There are 30 spins and $P(1) = \frac{2}{5}$.

$$30 \times \frac{2}{5} = 6 \times 2 = 12$$

You will spin about 12 1s in 30 spins.

Use the spinner shown at right to answer the questions.

1. Predict how many times you will land on
   C in 32 spins.

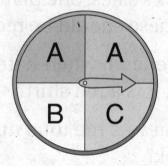

   a. $P(C) =$ _____

   b. $32 \times P(C) = 32 \times$ _____ $=$ _____

   c. about _____ times

2. Predict how many times you will
   land on B in 48 spins.

   a. $P(B) =$ _____

   b. $48 \times P(B) =$ _____ $=$ _____

   c. about _____ times

3. Predict how many times you will
   land on A in 50 spins.

   a. $P(A) =$ _____

   b. _____ $=$ _____

   c. about _____ times

Holt Mathematics

Name _____ Date _____ Class _____

Homework and Practice
Making Decisions and Predictions

An athletic wear store sells hooded sweatshirts in five colors. The table shows the colors of the last 60 sweatshirts sold. The manager plans to order 200 more.

Color	Number Sold
White	6
Red	12
Blue	13
Green	9
Black	20

1. How many white sweatshirts should the manager order? _____

2. How many red sweatshirts should the manager order? _____

3. How many green sweatshirts should the manager order? _____

Use the diagram of the spinner for Exercises 4 and 5.

4. Predict the number of times the spinner will land on 5 in 24 spins.

   a. total possible outcomes = _____

   b. number of possible 5 outcomes = _____

   c. $P(5)$ = _____

   d. The spinner will land on 5 about _____ times.

5. Predict the number of times the spinner will land on an odd number in 40 spins.

   a. number of possible odd outcomes = _____

   b. $P(\text{odd})$ = _____

   c. The spinner will land on an odd number about _____ times.

6. A bag contains 4 blue marbles, 3 red marbles, and 7 yellow marbles. Decide whether the game is fair. Player A draws a marble. If it is yellow, player A wins. Otherwise, player B wins.

   _____

Holt Mathematics

10G Odds

When you find the *odds in favor* of an event, you compare the number of favorable outcomes to the number of unfavorable outcomes. With *probability,* you compare the number of favorable outcomes to the total number of outcomes.

The plastic container at right contains 10 marbles: 4 red, 3 yellow, 2 green, and 1 blue. The odds in favor of drawing a green marble are 2 to 8, because 2 marbles are green and 8 marbles are not green.

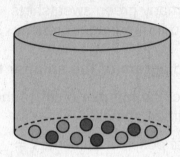

Use the definitions of *odds in favor* and *probability* to complete the table.

	Probability	Odds in Favor
Drawing a green marble	$\frac{2}{10} = \frac{1}{5}$	2:8
1. Drawing a red marble		
2. Drawing a yellow marble		
3. Drawing a blue marble		

Think and Discuss

4. Explain the difference between odds and probability.

Holt Mathematics

Name _____ Date _____ Class _____

Review for Mastery
Odds

Baseball fans do not usually ask "What is the probability that the New York Yankees will win the World Series this year?"

Fans who want to know the chances of a team winning usually ask "What are the *odds* that the Yankees will win?"

Odds that an event E will or will not occur can be defined as a ratio of probabilities.

$$\text{odds in favor} = \frac{P(E)}{P(\text{not } E)} \qquad\qquad \text{odds against} = \frac{P(\text{not } E)}{P(E)}$$

What are the odds in favor of getting a 4 in one roll of a numbered cube?

$$P(4) = \frac{1}{6} \quad P(\text{not } 4) = \frac{5}{6} \quad \text{odds}(4) = \frac{P(4)}{P(\text{not } 4)} = \frac{\frac{1}{6}}{\frac{5}{6}} = \frac{1}{5}$$

So, the odds in favor of getting a 4 are 1 to 5.

Complete to find the indicated odds. In each case, a cube numbered 1–6 is rolled once.

1. Find the odds in favor of getting a number greater than 4.

$$P(> 4) = \underline{\quad} \quad P(\text{not} > 4) = \underline{\quad} \quad \text{odds } (> 4) = \frac{P(> 4)}{P(\text{not} > 4)} = \underline{\quad} = \underline{\quad}, \text{ or } \underline{\quad}$$

So, the odds in favor of getting a number greater than 4 are _____ to _____.

2. Find the odds against getting a 3.

$$P(3) = \underline{\quad} \quad P(\text{not } 3) = \underline{\quad} \quad \text{odds}(\text{not } 3) = \frac{P(\text{not } 3)}{P(3)} = \underline{\quad} = \underline{\quad}$$

So, the odds against getting a 3 are _____ to _____.

3. Find the odds in favor of getting an even number.

$$P(\text{even}) = \underline{\quad} P(\text{not even}) = \underline{\quad} \quad \text{odds}(\text{even}) = \frac{P(\text{even})}{P(\text{not even})} = \underline{\quad} = \underline{\quad}, \text{ or } \underline{\quad}$$

So, the odds in favor of getting an even number are _____ to _____.

LESSON 10G Review for Mastery
Odds, continued

Convert each probability ratio to an odds ratio.

4. The probability of winning a prize is $P(\text{win}) = \frac{2}{25}$.

$P(\text{not win}) = 1 - \frac{2}{25}$, or $\frac{}{25}$ $\text{odds(win)} = \frac{P(\text{win})}{P(\text{not win})} = \dfrac{\frac{2}{25}}{\frac{}{25}}$ or $\dfrac{2}{}$, or 2 to _____

5. The probability of not winning a prize $P(\text{not win}) = \frac{100}{109}$.

$P(\text{win}) = 1 - \frac{100}{109}$, or $\frac{}{109}$ $\text{odds(not win)} = \frac{P(\text{not win})}{P(\text{win})} = \dfrac{\frac{100}{109}}{\frac{}{109}}$ or _____, or 100 to _____

Reconsider a problem in finding odds by using probabilities.

What are the odds in favor of getting a 4 in one roll of a numbered cube?

$P(4) = \frac{1}{6}$ $P(\text{not } 4) = \frac{5}{6}$ $\text{odds}(4) = \frac{P(4)}{P(\text{not } 4)} = \dfrac{\frac{1}{6}}{\frac{5}{6}} = \frac{1}{5}$

Study the ratio for odds with respect to its relation to the probability ratios.

$\dfrac{1}{5}$ ← numerator of probability in favor
← numerator of probability against $1 + 5 = 6$ ← denominator of probability ratio

If the odds in favor of an event are $\frac{a}{b}$, or $a{:}b$, then the probability that the event will occur is $\frac{a}{a + b}$.

If the odds in favor of being chosen for a committee are 2:3,

then the probability of being chosen is $\frac{2}{2 + 3}$, or $\frac{2}{5}$.

Convert each odds ratio to a probability ratio.

6. The odds in favor of winning a prize are 3:20.

The probability of winning a prize is: $\dfrac{3}{3 + }$, or _____.

7. The odds against winning a prize are 100:7.

The probability of not winning a prize is: $\dfrac{100}{}$, or _____.

Holt Mathematics

LESSON 10G Homework and Practice
Odds

1. If the probability of Courtney winning the raffle is $\frac{7}{12}$, what are the odds in favor of Courtney winning the raffle?

_____

2. The odds in favor of the New York Yankees winning the World Series are 5 to 3. What is the probability that the Yankees will win the World Series?

_____

A bag contains 18 red jelly beans, 12 green jelly beans, 10 purple jelly beans, 6 yellow jelly beans, and 4 orange jelly beans.

3. Find P(green jelly bean)   **4.** Find P(red jelly bean)   **5.** Find P(yellow jelly bean)

_____   _____   _____

6. Find the odds in favor of choosing a red jelly bean.

_____

7. Find the odds against choosing a red jelly bean.

_____

8. Find the odds in favor of choosing an orange jelly bean.

_____

9. Find the odds against choosing a purple jelly bean.

_____

10. Find the odds in favor of choosing a green jelly bean.

_____

11. Find the odds against choosing a yellow jelly bean.

_____

12. Find the odds in favor of not choosing an orange jelly bean.

_____

Holt Mathematics

Georgia Performance
Standards

**M8D2.a, M8D2.b,
M8D3.a**

10H Counting Principles

A movie theater sells popcorn in small, medium, or large containers. Each size is also available for regular or lightly buttered popcorn.

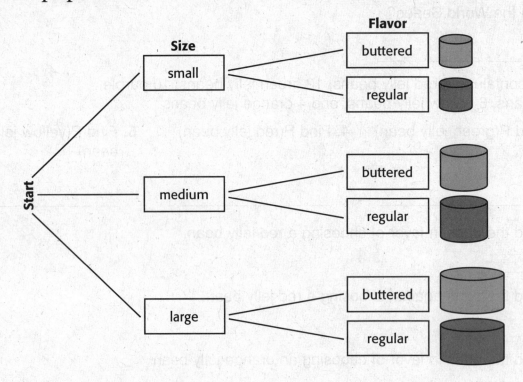

1. How many possible options are there for buying popcorn at the movie theater?

2. How many options are there if the theater adds two new flavors—cheddar cheese and caramel?

Think and Discuss

3. **Explain** how you counted the number of options in Problem 2.

4. **Discuss** whether the number of options in Problem 1 would be different if you were to start with flavor followed by size.

296

Holt Mathematics

LESSON 10H Technology Lab
The Fundamental Counting Principle

Activity

Warehouses use a combination of letters and numbers to identify their stock.

Description of Item	ID Number
Champion Spark Plug Tecumseh RJ12YC	2B3a5735

2 = second floor
B = aisle
Bin = 3
a = Bin Drawer
5735 = Stock Number

The warehouse has floors 1–3, aisles A–P, and bins 1–5, and drawers a–c.

What is the maximum of items this warehouse can stock?

Use the Counting Principle:

$$3 \cdot 16 \cdot 5 \cdot 3 \cdot 10 \cdot 10 \cdot 10 \cdot 10$$

Use your calculator to compute the different identification numbers.

There are 7,200,000 different ID numbers.

Think and Discuss

1. Why did you compute 10^4 for the stock number when applying the counting principle?

   _____

   _____

   _____

   _____

Holt Mathematics

LESSON
10H

Technology Lab
The Fundamental Counting Principle, continued

2. What would give more possible outcomes, adding another floor or adding another bin drawer?

_____

_____

_____

_____

Try This

The Library of Congress call numbers are a combination of letters and numbers. The first letter indicates the subject area. The second letter indicates a category of the subject area. For example, Q stands for General Science and QA stands for mathematics.

Suppose a call number for a math book is QA1589.

1. Use your calculator to compute the numbers of different call numbers for math books.

_____

_____

2. If each letter stands for a different category of general science, compute the number of different call numbers for General Science books.

_____

_____

Holt Mathematics

Name _____ Date _____ Class _____

Review for Mastery
Counting Principles

The Fundamental Counting Principle can help you solve some problems about situations that involve more than one activity.

| the number of ways in which one activity can be performed | × | the number of ways in which a second activity can be performed | = | the total number of ways in which both activities can be performed |

Apply the Fundamental Counting Principle to find the total number of possibilities in each situation.

1. Kelly has 6 shirts and 4 coordinating pants.
   The number of possible shirt-pants outfits is: _____, or _____

2. The menu for dinner lists 2 soups, 4 meats,
   and 3 desserts. How many different meals
   that have one soup, one meat, and one
   dessert are possible? _____, or _____

A **tree diagram** helps you see all the possibilities in a sample space.

If three coins are tossed at the same time, list all the possible outcomes.

List, in a column, the 2 possibilities for the 1st coin.

For each possibility for the 1st coin, list the 2 possibilities for the 2nd coin.

For each possibility for the 2nd coin, list the 2 possibilities for the 3rd coin.

Read the diagram across to write the list of all possible outcomes.

In this situation, there are
2 × 2 × 2 = 8 possible outcomes.

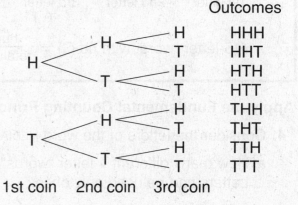

			Outcomes
		H	HHH
	H	T	HHT
H		H	HTH
	T	T	HTT
		H	THH
	H	T	THT
T		H	TTH
	T	T	TTT
1st coin	2nd coin	3rd coin	

Draw a tree diagram and list the outcomes.

3. A vendor is selling cups of ice cream.
   There are 2 different sizes of cups:
   small (S), or large (L). There are 2
   different flavors of ice cream: vanilla
   (V) or chocolate (C). There are 2
   different toppings: fudge (F) or
   pineapple (P).

Holt Mathematics

LESSON 10H

Review for Mastery

Counting Principles (continued)

How many different 5-letter "words" are possible using the letters of TRIANGLE? Letters can be used only once in each "word."

There are 8 choices for the 1st letter, 7 choices for the 2nd letter,

6 choices for the 3rd letter, 5 choices for the 4th letter, and 4 choices for the 5th.

Apply the Fundamental Counting Principle.

$$\underset{\text{1st letter}}{8} \times \underset{\text{2nd letter}}{7} \times \underset{\text{3rd letter}}{6} \times \underset{\text{4th letter}}{5} \times \underset{\text{5th letter}}{4} = 6720 \text{ possibilities}$$

If a "word" is selected at random from the 6720 possibilities, what is the probability that it will be the "word" ANGLE?

There is only one outcome ANGLE. $P(\text{ANGLE}) = \dfrac{1}{6720}$

If a "word" is selected at random from the 6720 possibilities, what is the probability that it will not contain the letter G?

Find the number of favorable outcomes.

Eliminate the letter G from the choices. So, there are 7 choices to begin.

$$\underset{\text{1st letter}}{7} \times \underset{\text{2nd letter}}{6} \times \underset{\text{3rd letter}}{5} \times \underset{\text{4th letter}}{4} \times \underset{\text{5th letter}}{3} = 2520 \text{ possibilities}$$

$$P(\text{5-letter "word" with no G}) = \frac{\text{number of favorable outcomes}}{\text{total number of possible outcomes}} = \frac{2520}{6720}, \text{ or } \frac{3}{8}$$

Apply the Fundamental Counting Principle.

4. Consider the letters of the word MEDIAN.

   a. How many different 4-letter "words" are possible?
      Letters can be used only once.

      $$\underset{\text{1st letter}}{\underline{\hspace{2cm}}} \times \underset{\text{2nd letter}}{\underline{\hspace{2cm}}} \times \underset{\text{3rd letter}}{\underline{\hspace{2cm}}} \times \underset{\text{4th letter}}{\underline{\hspace{2cm}}} = \underline{\hspace{1.5cm}} \text{ possibilities}$$

   b. If a 4-letter "word" is selected at random
      from all the possibilities, then: $P(\text{DEAN}) = \underline{\hspace{1.5cm}}$

   c. If a 4-letter "word" is selected at random from all the possibilities,
      what is the probability that it will not contain the letter D?

      $$\text{favorable outcomes: } \underset{\text{1st letter}}{\underline{\hspace{2cm}}} \times \underset{\text{2nd letter}}{\underline{\hspace{2cm}}} \times \underset{\text{3rd letter}}{\underline{\hspace{2cm}}} \times \underset{\text{4th letter}}{\underline{\hspace{2cm}}} = \underline{\hspace{1.5cm}}$$

      $$P(\text{4-letter "word" with no D}) = \frac{\text{number of favorable outcomes}}{\text{total number of possible outcomes}} = \underline{\hspace{1.5cm}}, \text{ or } \underline{\hspace{1cm}}$$

Holt Mathematics

Homework and Practice

The Fundamental Counting Principle

**School identification codes at Truman School contain 1 letter
followed by 3 numbers. All codes are equally likely.**

1. Find the number of possible identification codes.

   _____

2. Find the probability that an ID code of the school does not
   contain the number 0.

   _____

3. The Dairy King Shop serves 3 flavors of ice cream: vanilla,
   chocolate, and vanilla/chocolate swirl. The ice cream can be
   served in a dish, sugar cone, or waffle cone and may be a small,
   medium, large, or jumbo size. Make a tree diagram indicating
   the possible outcomes for each ice cream served.

4. How many different ice cream selections does the Dairy King
   Shop have?

   _____

**Find the probability for each of the following. Assume all
selections are equally likely.**

5. P(dish of ice cream)

   _____

7. P(medium size)

   _____

6. P(vanilla and small ice cream)

   _____

8. P(not a dish)

   _____

Holt Mathematics

Georgia Performance Standards

M8D2.b

10I Permutations and Combinations

Alfonso and Barb race against each other in a 5K race. There are two ways they can finish.

First Place	Second Place
Alfonso	Barb
Barb	Alfonso

1. Carl joins Alfonso and Barb. Complete the table to show all of the different ways they can finish.

	First Place	Second Place	Third Place
	Alfonso	Barb	Carl
a.			
b.			
c.			
d.			
e.			

2. Complete the table to show all of the different ways 2 of the 3 runners can finish in a tie for first place.

	First Place (tie)	Second Place
	Alfonso and Barb	Carl
a.		
b.		

Think and Discuss

3. **Explain** how you could find the number of ways 5 runners could finish.

Holt Mathematics

LESSON 101 Hands-On Lab
Odds

Activity

1. You roll a single die. What is the probability that you roll a four?

$$\text{Probability} = \frac{\text{number of favorable outcomes}}{\text{number of total outcomes}}$$

$$\text{Probability} = \frac{1}{6} \approx 16.7\%$$

The idea of odds is a little different from the idea of probability. What are the odds in favor of rolling a four?

$$\text{Odds in favor} = \frac{\text{number of favorable outcomes}}{\text{number of unfavorable outcomes}}$$

On a single die, there is one 4, so the number of favorable outcomes is 1. There are 5 other numbers on the die, so the number of unfavorable outcomes is 5.

$$\text{Odds in favor} = \frac{1}{5} = 1{:}5$$

2. You roll a fair die. What are the odds that you will roll an even number? First, figure the probability that you will roll an even number.

$$\text{Probability} = \frac{3}{6} = \frac{1}{2}$$

$$\text{Odds} = 1{:}(2 - 1) = 1{:}1$$

Holt Mathematics

LESSON
101

Hands-On Lab
Odds, continued

Think and Discuss

1. Explain the difference between odds and probability.

_____

_____

_____

_____

Try This

1. Roll a die 10 times and record your outcomes in a table.

1	2	3	4	5	6	7	8	9	10

2. How many times did you roll a number less than 3? What is the probability of rolling a number less than 3?

_____

3. What are the odds of doing so?

_____

_____

Holt Mathematics

Hands-On Lab

LESSON 101

Odds, continued

4. Roll three dice 50 times and record your outcomes in a table. What is the probability that you roll three numbers less than 4?

_____

5. What is the probability that you will roll three numbers greater than 4? Is it the same as above? Why or why not?

_____

_____

_____

_____

Holt Mathematics

Name _____ Date _____ Class _____

LESSON
101

Technology Lab 1
Permutations and Combinations

Activity

1. Washington state is famous for its apples. At an apple festival
   prizes are awarded for the best apple pies. Fifteen pies have
   made it to the last round. Prizes are awarded for first, second,
   and third best-tasting pie. How many permutations of three
   winning pies are possible?

$$_{15}P_3 = 15 \cdot 14 \cdot 13 = 2730$$

There are 2730 permutations.

If a prize were awarded for fourth place as well, how many different
permutations would there be?

$$_{15}P_4 = 15 \cdot 14 \cdot 13 \cdot 12 = 32{,}760$$

2. The judges cannot decide which one pie tastes best. So they
   are giving first prizes to the three best-tasting pies. How many
   choices do the judges have for awarding 1st prize to the three
   best-tasting pies?

$$_{15}C_3 = \frac{_{15}P_3}{3!} = \frac{15 \cdot 14 \cdot 13}{3 \cdot 2} = 455$$

The judges have 455 choices.

Copyright © by Holt, Rinehart and Winston.
All rights reserved.

306

Holt Mathematics

Technology Lab 1

LESSON 10I

Permutations and Combinations, continued

Think and Discuss

1. Why is the number of combinations of a set smaller than the number of permutations of the same set?

_____

_____

_____

_____

_____

Try This

1. Find the value of each expression. Use your calculator.

$_{20}P_4$	
$_{12}P_5$	
$_8P_4$	
$_8C_4$	
$_{12}C_8$	
$_9C_4$	
$_{23}C_3$	

Holt Mathematics

Technology Lab 2
LESSON 10I
Permutations and Combinations

Graphing calculators have features to help with computing factorials, permutations, and combinations.

Activity

1 In a stock-car race, 11 cars finish the race. The number of different orders in which they can finish is 11! A calculator can help you do the computation. Both ways are shown–the direct way, using the definition of *factorial*, and the calculator factorial command.

To compute 11! on a graphing calculator, enter 11 [MATH], press [>] to go to the **PRB** menu, and select **4:!** [ENTER].

The number of ways the 11 cars can finish first, second, third, and fourth is given by $11 \cdot 10 \cdot 9 \cdot 8$, or in *permutation* notation, $_{11}P_4$, 11 things taken 4 at a time. Both the direct and calculator *nPr* command methods are shown. The *nPr* command is also found in the **PRB** menu.

To compute $_{11}P_4$, enter 11, press [MATH], press [>] to go to the **PRB** menu, select **2:nPr**, type 4, and press [ENTER].

2 Twenty girls try out for 5 open places on a hockey team. Since order is not considered, the number of different *combinations* of these girls that can be chosen is given by $_{20}C_5$, the number of combinations of 20 things taken 5 at a time. Both the direct and calculator *nCr* command computations are shown.

To compute $_{20}C_5$, press 20 [MATH], press [>] to go to the PRB menu, select **3:nCr**, and press 5 [ENTER].

Technology Lab 2

LESSON 10I

Permutations and Combinations, continued

Think and Discuss

1. Explain why *nPr* is usually greater than *nCr* for the same values of *n* and *r*.

_____

_____

2. Can *nPr* ever equal *nCr*?

_____

_____

Try This

Compute each value by direct calculator multiplication and division and by using the calculator permutation and combination commands.

1. $_{14}P_6$

2. $_{25}P_{17}$

3. $_8P_3$

_____

4. $_8C_3$

5. $_{16}C_4$

6. $_{40}C_6$

_____

309

Holt Mathematics

Review for Mastery

Permutations and Combinations (continued)

When using fewer than the available number of items in an arrangement, instead of the Fundamental Counting Principle, you can use a formula to find the number of possible permutations.

To arrange _n_ things _r_ at a time, the number of possible permutations _P_ is: $_nP_r = \dfrac{n!}{(n-r)!}$

Find how many permutations are possible using 4 letters 2 at a time, with no repetitions.

$_4P_2 = \dfrac{4!}{(4-2)!} = \dfrac{4!}{2!} = \dfrac{4 \cdot 3 \cdot 2 \cdot 1}{2 \cdot 1} = 12$ possible 2-letter arrangements

Complete to apply the permutations formula.

7. In how many ways can 6 people be seated on a bench that seats 4?

$_6P_4 = \dfrac{6!}{(6-\quad)!} = \dfrac{\quad!}{\quad!} = $ _____ = _____ possible seating arrangements

8. How many 3-digit numbers can be made using the digits 7, 4, 2, 1, 8 without repetitions?

$_5P____ = \dfrac{5!}{(5-\quad)!} = \dfrac{\quad!}{\quad!} = $ _____ = _____ possible 3-digit numbers

Combination: an arrangement in which order is not important

How many 2-letter combinations can be made from the 4 letters _w_, _x_, _y_, _z_ without repetition?

The combinations _w x_ and _x w_ are the same. After all the same combinations are removed, there are 6 different combinations possible.

wx	x̶w̶	y̶w̶	z̶w̶
wy	xy	yx	z̶x̶
wz	xz	yz	z̶y̶

There are fewer combinations than permutations.

$_nC_r = \dfrac{_nP_r}{r!} = \dfrac{n!}{(n-r)!\,r!}$

The number of combinations _C_ of _n_ things taken _r_ at a time is:

$_4C_2 = \dfrac{_4P_2}{2!} = \dfrac{4!}{(4-2)!\,2!} = \dfrac{4!}{2!\,2!} = \dfrac{4^2 \cdot 3 \cdot 2 \cdot 1}{2 \cdot 1 \cdot 2 \cdot 1} = 2 \cdot 3 = 6$

Complete to apply the combinations formula.

9. How many different 4-person committees can be formed from a group of 6 people?

$_6C_4 = \dfrac{_6P_4}{4!} = \dfrac{6!}{(6-\quad)!\,\quad!} = \dfrac{6!}{\quad!\,\quad!} = $ _____ = _____ possible 4-person committees

Holt Mathematics

LESSON	**Review for Mastery**
10	*Permutations and Combinations (continued)*

When using fewer than the available number of items in an arrangement, instead of the Fundamental Counting Principle, you can use a formula to find the number of possible permutations.

To arrange *n* things *r* at a time,
the number of possible permutations *P* is: $\quad {}_nP_r = \dfrac{n!}{(n-r)!}$

Find how many permutations are possible using 4 letters 2 at a time, with no repetitions.

$${}_4P_2 = \dfrac{4!}{(4-2)!} = \dfrac{4!}{2!} = \dfrac{4 \cdot 3 \cdot 2 \cdot 1}{2 \cdot 1} = 12 \text{ possible 2-letter arrangements}$$

Complete to apply the permutations formula.

7. In how many ways can 6 people be seated on a bench that seats 4?

$${}_6P_4 = \dfrac{6!}{(6-\;\;)!} = \dfrac{\;\;!}{\;\;!} = \underline{\hspace{3cm}} = \underline{\hspace{1.5cm}} \text{ possible seating arrangements}$$

8. How many 3-digit numbers can be made using the digits 7, 4, 2, 1, 8 without repetitions?

$${}_5P\underline{\hspace{0.8cm}} = \dfrac{5!}{(5-\;\;)!} = \dfrac{\;\;!}{\;\;!} = \underline{\hspace{3cm}} = \underline{\hspace{1.5cm}} \text{ possible 3-digit numbers}$$

Combination: an arrangement in which order is not important

How many 2-letter combinations can be made from the 4 letters *w*, *x*, *y*, *z* without repetition?

The combinations *w x* and *x w* are the same. After all the same combinations are removed, there are 6 different combinations possible.

wx	x̸w̸	y̸w̸	z̸w̸
wy	xy	y̸x̸	z̸x̸
wz	xz	yz	z̸y̸

There are fewer combinations than permutations.

$${}_nC_r = \dfrac{{}_nP_r}{r!} = \dfrac{n!}{(n-r)!\,r!}$$

The number of combinations *C* of *n* things
taken *r* at a time is:

$${}_4C_2 = \dfrac{{}_4P_2}{2!} = \dfrac{4!}{(4-2)!\,2!} = \dfrac{4!}{2!\,2!} = \dfrac{4^2 \cdot 3 \cdot 2 \cdot 1}{2 \cdot 1 \cdot 2 \cdot 1} = 2 \cdot 3 = 6$$

Complete to apply the combinations formula.

9. How many different 4-person committees can be formed from a group of 6 people?

$${}_6C_4 = \dfrac{{}_6P_4}{4!} = \dfrac{6!}{(6-\;\;)!\;\;!} = \dfrac{6!}{\;\;!\;\;!} = \underline{\hspace{3cm}} = \underline{\hspace{1.5cm}} \text{ possible 4-person committees}$$

Holt Mathematics

Homework and Practice
Permutations and Combinations

Evaluate each expression.

1. 12!

_____

2. 9!

_____

3. 13! − 10!

_____

4. 11! − 8!

_____

5. $\dfrac{22!}{19!}$

_____

6. $\dfrac{20!}{15!}$

_____

7. $\dfrac{18!}{(24 - 12)!}$

_____

8. $\dfrac{21!}{(21 - 5)!}$

_____

9. $\dfrac{17!}{(23 - 14)!}$

_____

10. How many different 3 people committees can be formed from a group of 25 people?

_____

11. From a class of 28 students, how many different ways can 4 students be selected to serve on the student council as president, vice president, secretary and treasurer?

_____

12. The boys' volleyball team has 24 players. If the coach chooses 9 boys to play at a time, how many different teams can be formed?

_____

13. The golf tournament has 120 players signed up to play. How many different 4-person sets can be formed?

_____

14. Mr. Cruz bought new tires for his car. The dealer advised Mr. Cruz to have the tires rotated every 5,000 miles. If Mr. Cruz takes the advice of the dealer and has the tires rotated a different way every 5,000 miles, how many possible miles would he drive before using all the possible rotations?

_____

Holt Mathematics

CHAPTER 10 Big Ideas

Answer these questions to summarize the important concepts from Chapter 10 in your own words.

1. A marble is randomly drawn out of a bag and then replaced. There were 40 red marbles drawn, 65 green marbles drawn, 85 blue marbles drawn, and 10 yellow marbles drawn from the bag. Explain how to find the probability of randomly drawing a blue marble from the bag.

2. An experiment consists of rolling a fair number cube. Explain how to find the probability of rolling an odd number.

3. An experiment consists of tossing three coins. Explain how to find the probability of each coin landing on heads.

4. Explain the difference between a permutation and a combination.

For more review of Chapter 10:

- Complete the Chapter 10 Study Guide and Review on pages 572–574 of your textbook.

- Complete the Ready to Go On quizzes on pages 538 and 568 of your textbook.

Holt Mathematics

Project
Multi-Step Equations and Inequalities: Riding the Rapids

Career: Hydrologist

Hydrologists measure water flow between rivers, streams, lakes, and oceans. They map their results to record locations and movement of water above and below the earth's surface. Hydrologists are involved in projects such as water-resource studies, field irrigation, flood management, soil-erosion prevention, and the study of water discharge from creeks, streams, and rivers.

In this chapter project...you will make a drawing of a man-made river that you could go white-water rafting on. You will:

• Learn how the size of a river (cross section), water velocity, and water discharge are related mathematically.

• Research the properties of rivers that have white-water rapids. Use this information to design a river that would have rapids.

• Using your research, determine the velocity of water and cross section of your river. Use this data to find the discharge of the river.

• Make a scale drawing of your river and label the dimensions of the cross section. Include the discharge and water velocity in your diagram.

To get started, work through the Water Flows Downhill worksheet on the next page.

This chapter project reinforces your understanding of these Georgia Performance Standards:

M8A1.d Solve equations involving several variables for one variable in terms of the others.

M8P5.a Create and use representations to organize, record, and communicate mathematical ideas.

go.hrw.com
Chapter Project Online
KEYWORD: MT7 Ch11

Holt Mathematics

Name _____ Date _____ Class _____

CHAPTER 11

Project Recording Sheet
Multi-Step Equations and Inequalities

Water Flows Downhill

You are monitoring a river in which the water's velocity has been changing. What is the effect of this velocity change on the amount of water flowing past the measuring station? The river is 30 m across with a mean depth of 2.5 m. Use the relationships below to complete the table.

Discharge (m^3/s) = water velocity (m/s) × stream cross section (m^2)
Stream cross section = width (m) × mean depth (m)
1 m^3 = 264.4 gallons
1 hour = 3,600 seconds

My River
Stream Cross Section (75 m^2)

Velocity (m/s)	Discharge (m^3/s)	Hourly Discharge (m^3)	Hourly Discharge (gallons)
0.49	36.75	132,300	34,980,120
0.76			
1.22			
1.86			
2.10			

Answer the following questions:

1. Dixon Creek in Texas has a discharge of 0.11 m^3/s. What happens to the discharge:

   a. if the velocity of the stream doubles? _____

   b. if the cross section becomes smaller? _____

   c. if both the velocity and cross section triple? _____

2. The Mississippi River at Pointe Coupee Parish has a typical discharge of 16,735 m^3/s.

   a. How many billions of gallons of water pass in a typical day? _____

   b. If the flow has a velocity of 2.0 m/s what might the cross section be? _____

3. Create a river of your own. Draw a picture to demonstrate its flow. What would its characteristics be during:

   a. normal times? _____

   b. drought? _____

   c. flood season? _____

Holt Mathematics

EXPLORATION

11A Simplifying Algebraic Expressions

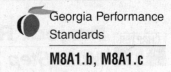

Georgia Performance
Standards

M8A1.b, M8A1.c

Like terms are combined separately from unlike terms.
Look at how the like terms are combined in the diagram.

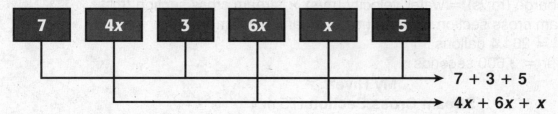

Express the perimeter of each figure with all the like terms combined.

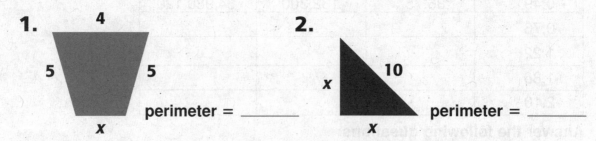

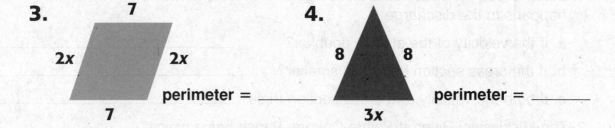

Think and Discuss

5. Explain what it means to combine like terms.

6. Describe a real-world situation in which you combine like terms.

Holt Mathematics

Name _____ Date _____ Class _____

Hands-On Lab
Model Combining Like Terms

KEY			REMEMBER:
▢ = 1	▯ = x	▢ = x^2	Like terms in an equation have the same variable and exponent. They do not need to have the same coefficient.

You can use algebra tiles to help combine like terms.

Activity

To simplify an expression such as $3x^2 + x + 2 + 2x^2 + 3x + x^2 + 1$, combine the like terms.

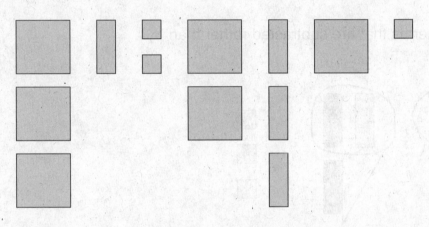

$$3x^2 + x + 2 + 2x^2 + 3x + x^2 + 1$$

Group the similar tiles together. Simplify.

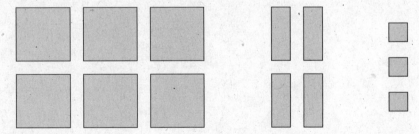

317
Holt Mathematics

LESSON 11A Hands-On Lab

Model Combining Like Terms, continued

1. Use algebra tiles to model and simplify each expression.

a. $2 + x^2 + 3x + 2x^2 + 2$ _____

b. $2x + 3x^2 + 3x + 2x^2 + 2 + x^2 + x + 1$ _____

c. $x + x^2 + 2x + x^2 + 1 + x^2 + x + 1 + x^2 + x^2 + 1$

_____

d. $x^2 + 2x + x + 2x^2 + x^2 + 3 + 3x + 1 + x^2 + 3x^2$

_____

Black tiles can represent terms that are subtracted rather than added.

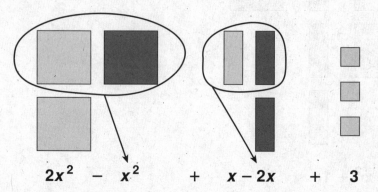

$$2x^2 \; - \; x^2 \quad + \quad x - 2x \quad + \quad 3$$

Take away any pairs of tiles that are the same size but different colors. Then simplify.

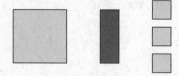

Holt Mathematics

Hands-On Lab

LESSON 11A *Model Combining Like Terms, continued*

2. Use algebra tiles to model and solve each equation.

a. $2 - x^2 + 2x + 2x^2 - 2$ _____

b. $3x^2 - 3x - 2x^2 + 2 - x^2 + x - 1$ _____

c. $-x - x^2 - 2x + 2x^2 - 1 + x^2 - x^2 + 3$ _____

d. $x^2 - 2x - 2x^2 + x^2 - 3 + 3x + 1 - x^2 + 3x^2$

_____

Think and Discuss

1. How would you model expressions that include x^3 terms?

_____

_____

2. How you would model the expression $x^2 + 2y + y^2 + 1 + x$ that has two variables, x and y?

_____

_____

Holt Mathematics

Hands-On Lab
Model Combining Like Terms, continued

3. Explain why you can take away a pair of tiles that have the same shape but different colors.

_____

Try This

Use algebra tiles to model and simplify each expression.

1. $3x^2 - x + 2x - x^2 - 2$

_____

2. $x^2 - 2x - x^2 + 1 + 2x^2 + x - 1$

_____

3. $x + y^2 - 2x + 2x^2 - 1 + 2y^2 - x^2 + 3 + y$

_____

LESSON 11A — Review for Mastery

Simplifying Algebraic Expressions

The parts of an expression separated by plus or minus signs are called **terms**.

The expression shown has four terms. You can combine two of these terms to **simplify** the expression.

$$5a + 7b - 3a + 6a^2$$
$$5a - 3a + 7b + 6a^2$$
$$2a + 7b + 6a^2$$

$$5a + 7b - 3a + 6a^2$$

Like terms have the same variable raised to the same power.

Equivalent expressions have the same value for all values of the variables.

Some algebraic equations can be solved by first combining like terms.
Solve $4w - w = 24$.

$4w - w = 24$	Identify like terms; w is $1w$.
$3w = 24$	Combine coefficients of like terms.
$\dfrac{3w}{3} = \dfrac{24}{3}$	Divide both sides by 3.
$w = 8$	

Complete to combine like terms.

1. $9z + 4z$

$(9 + \underline{})z$

$\underline{} z$

2. $9r + 5q - 2r$

$(9 - \underline{})r + 5q$

$\underline{} r + 5q$

3. $5t + 12f - t - 3f$

$(5 - \underline{})t + (12 - \underline{})f$

$\underline{} t + \underline{} f$

Simplify.

4. $7m + 3n - m + 2n$

5. $15r + 4 - 3r - 2$

6. $6x + 3z - y$

Complete to solve.

7. $5h + 2h = 21$

$\underline{} h = 21$

$\dfrac{\underline{} h}{\underline{}} = \dfrac{21}{\underline{}}$

$h = \underline{}$

8. $16w - 5w = 44$

$\underline{} w = 44$

$\dfrac{\underline{} w}{\underline{}} = \dfrac{44}{\underline{}}$

$w = \underline{}$

9. $48 = 13x - x$

$48 = \underline{} x$

$\dfrac{48}{\underline{}} = \dfrac{\underline{} x}{\underline{}}$

$\underline{} = x$

Holt Mathematics

Homework and Practice
Combining Like Terms

Combine like terms.

1. $11b + 6b$

2. $9m - 3m$

3. $5x + 8x + 7$

_____

_____

_____

4. $8w + 9x + 7w$

5. $13r + 10r - 8t$

6. $9g + 4m - 8g$

_____

_____

_____

7. $12b + 14p - 7$

8. $7a + 11a - a$

9. $15 + 3x - 9 + 8x$

_____

_____

_____

10. $6x + y + x + 9y$

11. $8m + 14 + 7m - 11$

12. $13x - 4 - 12x + 9$

_____

_____

_____

Simplify.

13. $5(x + 4) - 7$

14. $9(6 + y) + 3y$

15. $6(7 + 2a) - 8a$

_____

_____

_____

Solve.

16. $5r + 2r = 21$

17. $15t - 9t = 54$

18. $6x + 8x = 42$

_____

_____

_____

19. Janelle has *d* dimes and *n* nickels. Her sister has 5 times as many dimes and 6 times as many nickels as Janelle has. Write the sum of the number of coins they have, and then combine like terms.

_____

20. If Janelle has 9 dimes and 18 nickels, how many total coins do Janelle and her sister have?

_____

Holt Mathematics

LESSON 11B Technology Lab 1
Solving Multi-Step Equations, continued

Step 3 Now that you can see what the triangle might look like, it is easier to set up the equation:

Perimeter = side a + side b + side c, let side a = the variable x

Side b is 10 centimeters less than side a, so side $b = x - 10$.

Side c is 4 centimeters more than half of side a, so side $c = (x \div 2) + 4$.

To solve the equation, the sum of all three sides of the triangle should equal the perimeter of 74 cm.

$x + (x - 10) + [(x \div 2) + 4] = 74$

$$x + x + \frac{x}{2} - 10 + 4 = 74$$

$$\frac{5x}{2} - 6 = 74$$

$$\frac{5x}{2} = 80$$

$$5x = 160$$

$$x = 32$$

side $b = 32 - 10$, or 22   side $c = (32 \div 2) + 4$, or 20

Check your answer by substituting the side values into the original equation.

Perimeter = side a + side b + side c, or $74 = 32 + 22 + 20$

Holt Mathematics

LESSON 11B Technology Lab 1
Solving Multi-Step Equations, *continued*

Think and Discuss

1. What if you had been given the area of the triangle above and the same descriptions of the side lengths? Could you have found the length of each side in the same way as you found the perimeter? Explain.

_____

_____

_____

_____

_____

Try This

1. You know the perimeter of a right triangle is 48 cm. You do not know the lengths of the sides, but you do know that the second side is 4 centimeters shorter than the first side, and you know that the third side is 4 centimeters shorter than 2 times the second side.

   Figure out the lengths of the sides and then draw the triangle.

   Show your work.

   _____

LESSON **Technology Lab 2**
11B *Solving for a Variable*

A variable is a value that can change. It changes depending on its relationship with other parts in an equation. In order to solve for a variable, you have to have the rest of the equation and the variable's relationship to that equation.

Activity

A city estimates budgets and how much it will spend on certain public needs.

Education (e)   Police (p)   Construction (c)   Waste (w)

Each need gets a percentage of the Budget (b), depending on how much money is available. Equations for each section of the budget are as follows.

e_1% of $b = e$ p_1% of $b = p$ c_1% of $b = c$ w_1% of $b = w$

Budgets for cities, even small ones, can be very large. It can be useful to use a calculator when solving for these variables. Suppose $b = \$488,590,000$.

$e_1 = 45\%$ $p_1 = 22\%$ $c_1 = 26\%$ $w_1 = 7\%$

Use your calculator to solve for each of the remaining variables.

For e_1% of $b = e$, use the following keystrokes on your calculator.

| 4885900 | X | 45 | % | 219865500 |

For p_1% of $b = p$, use the following keystrokes on your calculator.

| 4885900 | X | 22 | % | 107489800 |

Follow the same example for the remaining two variables. You should come up with these answers:

$488,590,000 \times 0.26 = 127,033,400$

$488,590,000 \times 0.07 = 34,201,300$

Holt Mathematics

Technology Lab 2

LESSON 11B *Solving for a Variable, continued*

Think and Discuss

1. What if the city in the activity above determined it needed more money to pay for a new Civic Arts Center downtown? It found a way to raise the money, but it kept the same amounts for each of education, police, construction, and waste. Which variables in the equations above would change and why?

_____

_____

_____

_____

Try This

1. The earth is more than 71% covered by water. Only 29% of the earth's surface is covered by land. If the water area of the earth is 140,000,000 square miles, what is the total area of the earth? Use your calculator to help you find the answer.

_____

_____

2. How much of the earth is covered by land?

_____

Holt Mathematics

Review for Mastery

LESSON 11B · *Solving Multi-Step Equations*

To combine like terms, add (or subtract) coefficients.

$$2m + 3m = (2 + 3)m = 5m \qquad x - 3x = (1 - 3)x = -2x$$

To solve an equation that contains like terms, first combine the like terms.

$2m + 3m = 35 - 25$ | **Check:** Substitute into the original.

$5m = 10$ Combine like terms.

$\dfrac{5m}{5} = \dfrac{10}{5}$ Divide by 5.

$m = 2$

$$2m + 3m = 35 - 25$$
$$2(2) + 3(2) \overset{?}{=} 35 - 25$$
$$4 + 6 \overset{?}{=} 10$$
$$10 = 10 \ ✔$$

$x + 6 - 3x + 5 = 13$ | **Check:** $x + 6 - 3x + 5 = 13$

$-2x + 11 = 13$ Combine like terms.

$\underline{\quad -11 \quad -11 \quad}$ Subtract 11.

$-2x = 2$

$\dfrac{-2x}{-2} = \dfrac{2}{-2}$ Divide by -2.

$x = -1$

$$-1 + 6 - 3(-1) + 5 \overset{?}{=} 13$$
$$-1 + 6 + 3 + 5 \overset{?}{=} 13$$
$$-1 + 14 \overset{?}{=} 13$$
$$13 = 13 \ ✔$$

Complete to solve and check each equation.

1. $4z - 7z = -20 - 1$ **Check:** $\quad 4z - 7z = -20 - 1$

_____z = _____   Combine like terms. $4(\underline{\quad}) - 7(\underline{\quad}) \overset{?}{=} -20 - 1$

$\dfrac{\underline{\quad}z}{\underline{\quad}} = \underline{\quad}$ Divide. $\underline{\quad} - \underline{\quad} \overset{?}{=} \underline{\quad}$

$z = \underline{\quad}$ $\underline{\qquad\qquad}$

2. $t + 1 - 4t + 8 = 21$ **Check:** $\quad t + 1 - 4t + 8 = 21$

_____t _____ = _____   Combine like terms. $\underline{\quad} + 1 - 4(\underline{\quad}) + 8 \overset{?}{=} \underline{\quad}$

$\underline{\qquad\qquad}$ _____   Subtract. $\underline{\quad} + 1 + \underline{\quad} + 8 \overset{?}{=} 21$

$\underline{\quad}t = \underline{\quad}$ $\underline{\quad} + \underline{\quad} \overset{?}{=} 21$

$\dfrac{\underline{\quad}t}{\underline{\quad}} = \underline{\quad}$ Divide. $\underline{\qquad\qquad}$

$t = \underline{\quad}$

Holt Mathematics

Review for Mastery

LESSON 11B *Solving Multi-Step Equations (continued)*

To clear fractions in an equations, multiply every term by the

least common denominator (LCD)

$$\frac{x}{4} + 3 = \frac{1}{2}$$ The LCD of 4 and 2 is 4.   **Check:** $\frac{1}{4}(-10) + 3 \overset{?}{=} \frac{1}{2}$

$$4 \cdot \frac{x}{4} + 4 \cdot 3 = 4 \cdot \frac{1}{2}$$ Multiply *every* term by LCD. $\frac{-10}{4} + \frac{12}{4} \overset{?}{=} \frac{1}{2}$

$$x + 12 = 2$$ $\frac{2}{4} \overset{?}{=} \frac{1}{2}$

$$\underline{\quad -12 \quad -12 \quad}$$ Subtract 12. $\frac{1}{2} = \frac{1}{2} \checkmark$

$$x = -10$$

Complete to solve and check.

3. $\frac{t}{2} + \frac{t}{6} = 2$ Determine the LCD. **Check:** $\frac{1}{2}(\underline{\quad}) + \frac{1}{6}(\underline{\quad}) \overset{?}{=} 2$

$$\underline{\quad} \cdot \frac{t}{2} + \underline{\quad} \cdot \frac{t}{6} = \underline{\quad} \cdot 2$$ Multiply *every* term by LCD. $\overline{\quad 2 \quad} + \overline{\quad 2 \quad} \overset{?}{=} 2$

$$\underline{\quad} t + t = \underline{\quad}$$ The fractions are cleared. $\overline{\quad 2 \quad} \overset{?}{=} 2$

$$\underline{\quad} t = \underline{\quad}$$ Combine like terms.

$$\frac{\underline{\quad} t}{\quad} = \frac{\overline{\quad}}{\underline{\quad}}$$ Divide.

$$t = \underline{\quad}$$

4. $\frac{m}{3} + \frac{m}{4} - 1 = \frac{5}{2}$ Determine the LCD.

$$\underline{\quad} \cdot \frac{m}{3} + \underline{\quad} \cdot \frac{m}{4} - \underline{\quad} \cdot 1 = \underline{\quad} \cdot \frac{5}{2}$$ Multiply *every* term by the LCD.

$$\underline{\quad} m + \underline{\quad} m - \underline{\quad} = \underline{\quad}$$ The fractions are cleared.

$$\underline{\quad} m - \underline{\quad} = \underline{\quad}$$ Combine like terms.

Add.

$$\frac{\underline{\quad} m}{\quad} = \frac{\underline{\quad}}{\quad}$$

$$\frac{\underline{\quad} m}{\quad} = \frac{\overline{\quad}}{\underline{\quad}}$$ Divide.

$$m = \underline{\quad}$$ **Check:** $\frac{\quad}{3} + \frac{\quad}{4} - 1 \overset{?}{=} \frac{5}{2}$

$$\frac{\quad}{12} + \frac{\quad}{12} - \frac{\quad}{12} \overset{?}{=} \frac{\quad}{12}$$

       Holt Mathematics

LESSON 11B Homework and Practice
Solving Multistep Equations

Solve.

1. $8y - 4 - 7y = 11$

2. $2x + 2 + 5x = 23$

3. $8 = 7a - 8 - 3a$

_____

_____

_____

4. $r + 5r + 5 = -25$

5. $9w - 12w - 2 = 7$

6. $38 = 24 - 7x + 5x$

_____

_____

_____

7. $\frac{2}{7}y - \frac{5}{6} + \frac{5}{7}y = 1\frac{1}{6}$

8. $\frac{5}{8}x + 1 - \frac{7}{8}x = \frac{3}{4}$

9. $6x + 16 - 15x = -11$

_____

_____

_____

10. $\frac{4}{9}w + 6 - \frac{1}{3}w = 4$

11. $0.05d - 0.2d - 17 = 13$

12. $0.6m - 4.4 - 4.8m = 2.4$

_____

_____

_____

13. $8.2s + 4 - 13.7s = -7$

14. $11y - 7.5 - 6y = 2$

15. $13x - 4.6x - 3.9 = 8.7$

_____

_____

_____

16. The measure of an angle is 34° less than its supplement. Find the measure of each angle.

_____

17. The measure of an angle is 9° more than twice its complement. Find the measure of each angle.

_____

18. If the perimeter of the triangle is 139. Find the measure of each side.

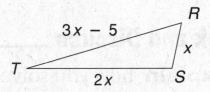

_____

Holt Mathematics

11C Solving Equations with Variables on Both Sides

Georgia Performance Standards

M8A1.a, M8A1.c, M8A1.d

Samara wants to rent a kayak. Two rental places offer the following deals.

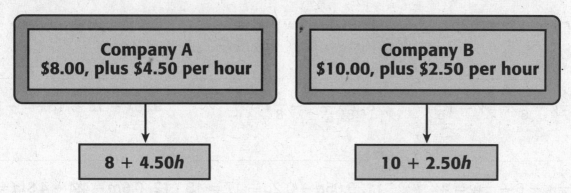

Company A
$8.00, plus $4.50 per hour

Company B
$10.00, plus $2.50 per hour

8 + 4.50*h*

10 + 2.50*h*

Use the expressions above to solve each problem.

1. Find the cost of a 1-hour rental from company A ($h = 1$).

2. Find the cost of a 1-hour rental from company B ($h = 1$).

3. Find the cost of a 2-hour rental from company A ($h = 2$).

4. Find the cost of a 2-hour rental from company B ($h = 2$).

5. Find the number of hours that a kayak would need to be rented from both companies to make the costs equal by solving $8 + 4.50h = 10 + 2.50h$ for h. (*Hint:* Combine like terms first.)

Think and Discuss

6. **Explain** how you solved the equation in Problem 5.
7. **Discuss** what it means to set $8 + 4.50h$ equal to $10 + 2.50h$.

Holt Mathematics

LESSON 11C Technology Lab
Solve Two-Step Equations by Graphing

A graphing calculator is another tool used to solve equations.

Activity

To solve the equation $2x - 3 = 4x + 1$, use the Y= menu.
Enter the left side of the equation in **Y1** and the right side in **Y2**.

1 Press Y= 2 X,T,θ,n — 3 ENTER 4 X,T,θ,n + 1.

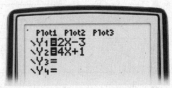

2 To select the standard viewing window and graph the two
equations, press ZOOM **6:Zstandard.**

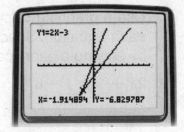

On the figure, the two graphs *appear* to intersect at the point
$(-2, -7)$. The coordinates -2 and -7 are *approximations*.
The solution of the original equation is the x-coordinate of the
point of intersection of the two lines. The solution is
approximately $x = -2$.
If the equation is solved algebraically by adding $-4x$ and 3 to
both sides, the result is $2x - 3 + (-4x) + 3 = 4x + 1 + (-4x)$
$+ 3$. This becomes $- 2x = 4$, or $x = -2$, thus confirming the
estimated graphical solution.

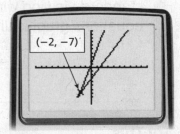

3 Press TRACE and the left arrow key 9 times to get the
screen shown. As you press the arrow keys,
observe how the coordinates change. This is as
close to $x = -2$ as you can get using this window.
The x-value $-1.914...$is only an estimate of the
exact solution, -2.

Holt Mathematics

Technology Lab

LAB 11C *Solve Two-Step Equations by Graphing, continued*

Think and Discuss

1. Explain why using the [TRACE] key may show only estimates.

_____

_____

_____

2. Graph both sides of the equation $x + 4 = -2x + 7$ in the standard viewing window. What must be done to solve the equations graphically?

_____

_____

Try This

Use a graphing calculator to find an approximate solution to each equation. Specify the window used. Confirm your estimate by solving algebraically.

1. $2x + 1 = x - 4$

_____

2. $\frac{1}{2}x - 3 = 2x + 4$

_____

3. $3x - 5 = 2x + 6$

_____

4. $3x + 5 = 4 - 2x$

_____

Holt Mathematics

Review for Mastery

LESSON 11C *Solving Equations with Variables on Both Sides*

If there are variable terms on both sides of an equation,
first collect them on one side. Do this by adding or subtracting.

If possible, collect the variable terms on the side where the on
coefficient will be positive.

$\dfrac{5x = 2x + 12}{-2x \quad -2x}$	To collect on left side, subtract $2x$.	**Check:** Substitute into the original equation.
$3x = 12$		$5x = 2x + 12$
$\dfrac{3x}{3} = \dfrac{12}{3}$	Divide by 3.	$5(4) \overset{?}{=} 2(4) + 12$
$x = 4$		$20 \overset{?}{=} 8 + 12$
		$20 = 20$ ✔

$\dfrac{-6z + 28 = 9z - 2}{+6z \qquad\quad +6z}$	To collect on right side, add $6z$.	
$28 = 15z - 2$		**Check:** $-6z + 28 = 9z - 2$
$\dfrac{}{+2} \qquad \dfrac{}{+2}$	Add 2.	$-6(2) + 28 \overset{?}{=} 9(2) - 2$
$30 = 15z$		$-12 + 28 \overset{?}{=} 18 - 2$
$\dfrac{30}{15} = \dfrac{15z}{15}$	Divide by 15.	$16 = 16$ ✔
$2 = z$		

Complete to solve and check each equation.

1. $9m = 4m - 25$ To collect on
   $\underline{} \quad \underline{}$ left, subtract.

   $5m = -25$

   $\dfrac{m}{} = \dfrac{-25}{}$ Divide.

   $m = \underline{}$

Check: $9m = 4m - 25$

$9(\underline{}) \overset{?}{=} 4(\underline{}) - 25$

$\underline{} \overset{?}{=} \underline{} - 25$

$\underline{}$

2. $3h - 7 = 5h + 1$ To collect on
   $\underline{} \quad \underline{}$ right, subtract.

   $-7 = \underline{} h + 1$

   $\underline{} \quad \underline{}$ Subtract.

   $\underline{} = \underline{} h$

   $\dfrac{\underline{}}{} = \dfrac{h}{}$ Divide.

   $\underline{} = h$

Check: $3h - 7 = 5h + 1$

$3(\underline{}) - 7 \overset{?}{=} 5(\underline{}) + 1$

$\underline{} - 7 \overset{?}{=} \underline{} + 1$

$\underline{}$

Holt Mathematics

Name _____ Date _____ Class _____

Review for Mastery
Equations with Variables on Both Sides (continued)

To solve multi-step equations with variables on both sides: 1) *clear* fractions, 2) *combine* like terms, 3) *collect* variable terms on one side, and 4) *isolate* the variable by using properties of equality.

$\frac{t}{3} - \frac{5t}{6} + \frac{1}{2} = t - 1$ To clear fractions, determine LCD = 6.

$6 \cdot \frac{t}{3} - 6 \cdot \frac{5t}{6} + 6 \cdot \frac{1}{2} = 6 \cdot t - 6 \cdot 1$ Multiply *every* term by the LCD.

$2t - 5t + 3 = 6t - 6$ The fractions are cleared.

$-3t + 3 = 6t - 6$ Combine like terms.

$\underline{+3t \qquad +3t}$ To collect variable terms, add $3t$ to both sides.

$3 = 9t - 6$

$\underline{\quad +6 \qquad +6}$ Add 6 to both sides.

$9 = 9t$

$\frac{9}{9} = \frac{9t}{9}$ Divide both sides by 9.

$1 = t$

Complete to solve.

3. $\frac{w}{4} + \frac{w}{2} + \frac{1}{4} = w$ Find the LCD of 2 and 4.

   $\underline{\quad} \cdot \frac{w}{4} + \underline{\quad} \cdot \frac{w}{2} + \underline{\quad} \cdot \frac{1}{4} = \underline{\quad} \cdot w$ Multiply *every* term by the LCD.

   $\underline{\quad} w + \underline{\quad} w + \underline{\quad} = \underline{\quad} w$

   $\underline{\quad} w + \underline{\quad} = \underline{\quad} w$ Combine like terms.

   $- \underline{\quad} \qquad - \underline{\quad}$ Subtract.

   $\underline{\quad} = w$

4. $3m + 17 - m = 10 - m - 2$ **Check:** $3m + 17 - m = 10 - m - 2$

   $\underline{\quad} m + \underline{\quad} = \underline{\quad} - m$ $3 (\underline{\quad}) + 17 - (\underline{\quad}) \overset{?}{=}$

   $\underline{+ \quad} \qquad \underline{+ \quad}$ $10 - (\underline{\quad}) - 2$

   $\underline{\quad} m + 17 = \underline{\quad}$ $-9 + 17 \underline{\quad} \overset{?}{=} 10 \underline{\quad} - 2$

   $\underline{- \quad} \quad \underline{- \quad}$ $\underline{\quad} + \underline{\quad} \overset{?}{=} \underline{\quad} - 2$

   $m = \underline{\quad}$ $\overline{\qquad\qquad}$

   $m = \underline{\quad}$

Holt Mathematics

Name _____ Date _____ Class _____

Homework and Practice
LESSON 11C *Solving Equations with Variables on Both Sides*

Solve.

1. $5x - 1 = 21 + 3x$

2. $9y + 3 = 6y - 15$

3. $7w - 3 = w - 12.6$

_____

4. $12 + 8a = 3a - 3$

5. $\frac{2}{9}n - 5 = 2 + \frac{5}{9}n$

6. $1.8d + 31 = 3.4d + 19$

_____

7. $2b + 30 = 4b + 3$

8. $4x + 2.3 = 2x - 3.7$

9. $3(m - 5) = m - 7$

_____

10. $5(3h - 2) = 2(h + 8)$

11. $5 + \frac{1}{2}y = \frac{3}{8}y + 6$

12. $2\left(x - \frac{1}{2}\right) = 4\left(x + \frac{1}{4}\right)$

_____

13. $4(3r - 2) = 4 - 12r$

14. $\frac{1}{4}x - 7 = \frac{1}{3}x + 8$

15. $\frac{3a - 4}{2} = 5 - 2a$

_____

16. Mandy and Mackenzie spent the same amount of money at the arcade. They both played the same number of games. Mandy played $0.50 games and spent $10 on refreshments. Mackenzie played $0.75 games and spent $6 on refreshments. How many games did each person play?

_____

17. The square and the equilateral triangle at the right have the same perimeter. Find the lengths of the sides of the square.

 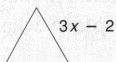

_____

Holt Mathematics

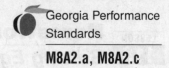

Georgia Performance Standards

M8A2.a, M8A2.c

11D Inequalities

An inequality states that two values are not equal or may not be equal. When one of the values is expressed as a variable, there are four different inequality relationships possible.

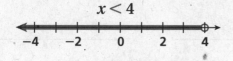

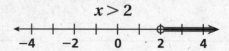

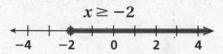

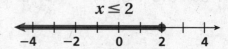

Graph each inequality on the number line.

1. $x > 2$

2. $x < -1$

3. $x \geq -3$

4. $x \leq 0$

Think and Discuss

5. Explain how you determined which direction the arrow should point on your graphs in Problems **1–4**.

6. Explain what an inequality is.

Holt Mathematics

LESSON 11D Technology Lab
Inequalities

You will need a graphing calculator.

Activity

An inequality is a statement that two amounts are not equal. Below are symbols expressing inequalities:

< means less than

> means more than

≤ means less than or equal to

≥ means more than or equal to

Use the table feature of a graphics calculator to explore the inequality of: $x - 9 > 6$.

Step 1 Press **Y=** then enter $x - 9$ next to Y1=

Step 2 Press **2nd** **WINDOW**

Step 3 On the "Table Setup," select: **TblStart=0;**

△Tbl=1; Indpnt: auto ; Depend: auto

Step 4 Choose and press **2nd** **GRAPH**.

Step 5 Use **▶** to move to the *y*- column and **▼** to scroll down.

Step 6 Name the corresponding value of *x: x* = 15.

So, to obtain *y* values greater than 6, *x* must be greater than 15.

Holt Mathematics

Technology Lab
Inequalities, continued

Think and Discuss

1. In the equation $x - 9 > 6$, the solution is $x > 15$. What does this mean?

   _____

2. How is the equation $x - 9 \geq 6$ different from the equation above?

   _____

   _____

Try This

1. Solve the inequality $a + 6 > 9$. Then graph the solution on a number line.

   _____

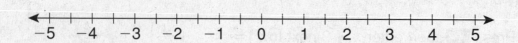

Holt Mathematics

LESSON 11D Review for Mastery
Inequalities

An equation is a statement that says two quantities are equal. An **inequality** is a statement that says two quantities are **not** equal.

The chart shows symbols and phrases that indicate inequalities.

<	>	≤	≥
Less than	Greater than	Less than or equal to	Greater than or equal to
Fewer than	More than	At most	At least
Below	Above	No more than	No less than

Complete the inequality for each situation.

1. No more than 200 people can be seated in the restaurant.

   number of people seated in restaurant ☐ 200

2. The waiting time for a table is at least 20 minutes.

   waiting time ☐ 20 minutes

3. The price of all special dinner entrees is below $10.

   special dinner entrees ☐ $10

4. The Yoshida family spent more than $40 for dinner.

   Yoshida family spent ☐ $40

An inequality can be shown on a graph.

The graph shows:	Inequality	Graph
All numbers greater than 3	$x > 3$	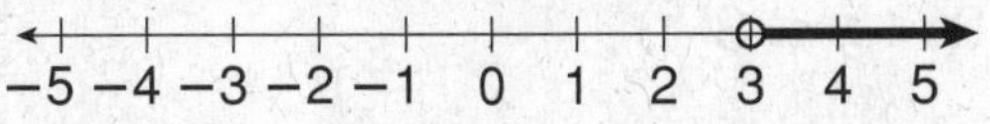 ←––+––+––+––+––+––+––+––+––○——→ −5 −4 −3 −2 −1　0　1　2　3　4　5 The *open circle* at 3 shows that the value 3 is **not** included in the graph.
All numbers greater than or equal to 3	$x \geq 3$	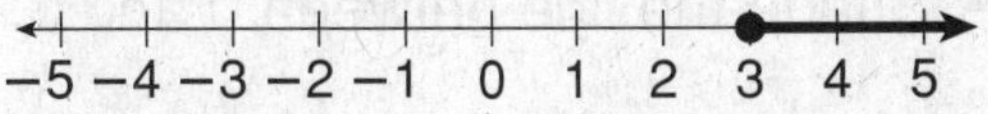 ←––+––+––+––+––+––+––+––+––●——→ −5 −4 −3 −2 −1　0　1　2　3　4　5 The *closed circle* at 3 shows that the value 3 **is** included in the graph.
All numbers less than 3	$x < 3$	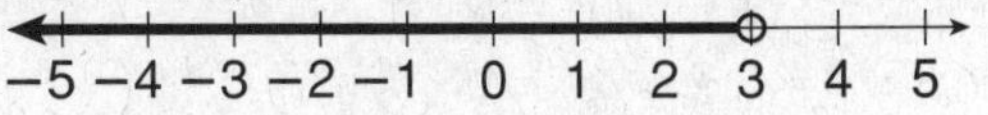 ←——○––+––+––+––+––+––+––+––+→ −5 −4 −3 −2 −1　0　1　2　3　4　5
All numbers less than or equal to 3	$x \leq 3$	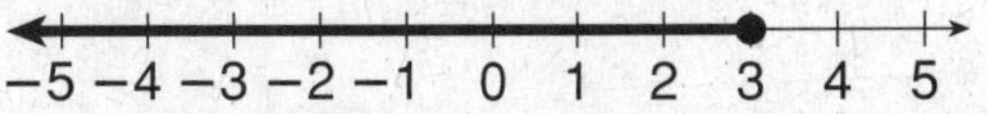 ←——●––+––+––+––+––+––+––+––+→ −5 −4 −3 −2 −1　0　1　2　3　4　5

Holt Mathematics

LESSON
11D

Review for Mastery
Inequalities (continued)

Graph each inequality.

5. $x > -4$

- Draw an open circle at −4.
- Read $x > -4$ as "x is greater than −4."
- Draw an arrow to the right of −4.

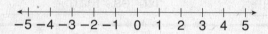

6. $x \leq 1$

- Draw a closed circle at 1.
- Read $x \leq 1$ as "x is less than or equal to 1."
- Draw an arrow to the left of 1.

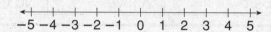

7. $a > -1$

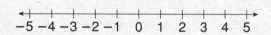

8. $y \leq 3$

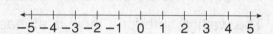

A **compound inequality** is a combination of two inequalities.

The graph shows:	Inequality	Graph
All numbers from −2 to 2	$-2 \leq x \leq 2$	
All numbers greater than 2 *or* less than −2	$x > 2$ or $x < -2$	

Graph each compound inequality.

9. $0 < x \leq 3$

- Draw an open circle at 0 and a closed circle at 3.
- Shade the line between 0 and 3.

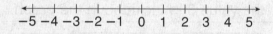

10. $x \geq 4$ or $x \leq -1$

- Draw a closed circle at −1 and a closed circle at 4.
- Shade the line to the left of −1 and to the right of 4.

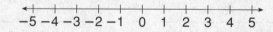

Holt Mathematics

Name _____ Date _____ Class _____

LESSON 11D Homework and Practice
Inequalities

Write an inequality for each situation.

1. Today's attendance will be at least 250 people. _____

2. Tomorrow's attendance will be less than 200 people. _____

3. Last weekend, there were more than 75 birds in
   the sanctuary. _____

4. Next weekend, there will be at most 90 birds in the
   sanctuary. _____

Graph each inequality.

5. $x > -3$

6. $a \le 5$

7. $g < -1$

8. $m \ge 2\frac{3}{4}$

Graph each compound inequality.

9. $-2 \le y < 0$

10. $d \le -3$ or $d > 3$

11. $r < -4$ or $r > 1$

12. $0 \le s < 5$

13. $c < -1$ or $c \ge 4$

Holt Mathematics

11E Solving Inequalities by Adding or Subtracting

Georgia Performance
Standards

M8A2.a, M8A2.b,
M8A2.c

Algebra tiles, which are commonly used for equations, can also be used to model adding or subtracting the same number from each side of an inequality. The model below shows the inequality $x + 4 > -1$.

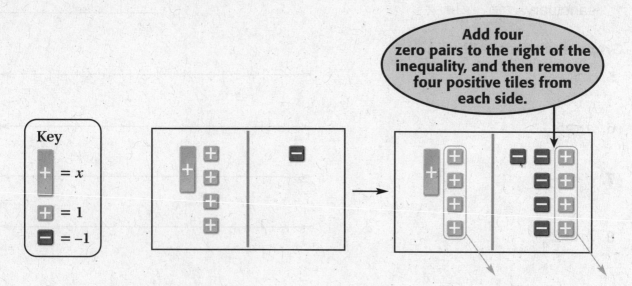

Add four zero pairs to the right of the inequality, and then remove four positive tiles from each side.

Key

$+$ = x

$+$ = 1

$-$ = -1

So the solution to $x + 4 > -1$ is $x > -5$. In other words, any number that is greater than -5 is a solution to the inequality.

Use a model to solve each inequality.

1. $x + 5 > -2$ **2.** $x - 5 < -4$

3. $8 + x < -1$ **4.** $4 - x < -4$

Think and Discuss

5. Discuss why inequalities have many solutions.

6. Explain how to solve the inequality $x + 4 < 10$ mentally.

Holt Mathematics

LESSON
11E

Review for Mastery
Solving Inequalities by Adding or Subtracting

Inequalities with variables may have more than one solution. All the solutions of an inequality are called the **solution set**.

You can solve an inequality involving addition or subtraction just as you would solve an equation.

Complete the steps to solve, graph, and check the inequality.

1. $n - 13 < 7$

$n - 13 +$ _____ $< 7 +$ _____

$n <$ _____

Graph the inequality.

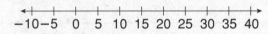
$-10\ -5\quad 0\quad 5\quad 10\ 15\ 20\ 25\ 30\ 35\ 40$

Check:

Pick any number in the solution set
of $n < 20$.
$19 < 20$

Substitute 19 into the inequality.

$n - 13 < 7$

_____ $\overset{?}{-}\ 13 < 7$

_____ $\overset{?}{<}\ 7$ ✔

2. $x + 18 \geq 2$

$x + 18 -$ _____ $\geq 2 -$ _____

$x \geq$ _____

Graph the inequality.

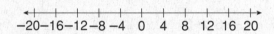
$-20\ -16\ -12\ -8\ -4\quad 0\quad 4\quad 8\quad 12\ 16\ 20$

Check:

Pick any number in the solution set
of $x \geq -16$.
$0 \geq -16$

Substitute 0 into the inequality.

$x + 18 \geq -2$

_____ $\overset{?}{+}\ 18 \geq -2$

_____ $\overset{?}{\geq}\ -2$ ✔

Solve. Then graph each solution set.

3. $d + 3 > -5$ _____

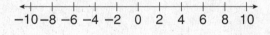
$-10\ -8\ -6\ -4\ -2\quad 0\quad 2\quad 4\quad 6\quad 8\quad 10$

4. $s - 10 < -6$ _____

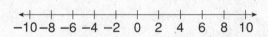
$-10\ -8\ -6\ -4\ -2\quad 0\quad 2\quad 4\quad 6\quad 8\quad 10$

Solve. Check each answer.

5. $y + 9 > 20$

6. $h + 17 \leq -6$

7. $a - 4 \geq -18$

_____   _____   _____

Holt Mathematics

Homework and Practice
Solving Inequalities by Adding or Subtracting

Solve. Then graph each solution set on a number line.

1. $a + 2 < -3$ _____   ←—+—+—+—+—+—+—+—+—+—+—+—→

2. $c - 6 \geq 4$ _____   ←—+—+—+—+—+—+—+—+—+—+—+—→

3. $z - 4 \leq -3$ _____   ←—+—+—+—+—+—+—+—+—+—+—+—→

4. $j + 12 > 5$ _____   ←—+—+—+—+—+—+—+—+—+—+—+—→

5. $r - 1 \leq 13$ _____   ←—+—+—+—+—+—+—+—+—+—+—+—→

6. $m + 6 \geq 0$ _____   ←—+—+—+—+—+—+—+—+—+—+—+—→

Solve. Check each answer.

7. $v - 21 \leq -13$ 8. $32 + y < 43$ 9. $p + 44 > 19$

_____   _____   _____

10. $t + 3.5 \geq 8.9$ 11. $d - 1.9 < -8.7$ 12. $f - 3\frac{1}{3} > 2\frac{5}{6}$

_____   _____   _____

346   **Holt Mathematics**

EXPLORATION

11F Solving Inequalities by Multiplying or Dividing

Georgia Performance Standards

M8A2.a, M8A2.b, M8A2.c, M8A2.d

You can discover an important property of inequalities by looking for patterns.

1. Multiply both sides of each inequality by 2. Write the resulting numbers under the original inequality as shown in **1a.** Then insert the correct inequality symbol, < or >, to make the new inequality true.

    a.

3	>	2
6		4

    b.

−4	<	−1

    c.

2	>	−3

2. Multiply both sides of each inequality by −2. Write the resulting numbers under the original inequality as shown in **2a.** Then insert the correct inequality symbol, < or >, to make the new inequality true.

    a.

3	>	2
−6		−4

    b.

−4	<	−1

    c.

2	>	−3

Think and Discuss

3. **Describe** any patterns you notice.

4. **Explain** what happens when you multiply both sides of an inequality by a negative number.

Holt Mathematics

LESSON 11F Hands-On Lab
Solving Inequalities

KEY

□ = 1

■ = −1

□ + ■ = 0

▯ = x

REMEMBER:
It will not change the
value of an expression if
you add or remove zero.

Algebra tiles can also help you solve inequalities.

Activity

Solving inequalities is similar to solving equations. You must get the
variable alone on one side of the inequality sign. You can add or
remove tiles as long as you add the same amount or remove the
same amount on both sides. Solve the inequality $x + 4 < 7$.

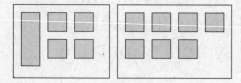 →

$x + 4$ $<$ 7   Remove 4 tiles from each side. x $<$ 3

1. Use algebra tiles to model and solve each inequality.
 a. $x + 1 < 6$ **b.** $x + 2 < 7 + 1$ **c.** $x + 3 > 9$ **d.** $x + 5 > 3$

_____   _____   _____   _____

If the inequality includes negative values, you can add tiles to each
side. Solve the inequality $x + (-4) < 5$.

$x + (-4)$ $<$ 5   Add 4 tiles to each side. $x + (-4) + 4$ $<$ $5 + 4$

Holt Mathematics

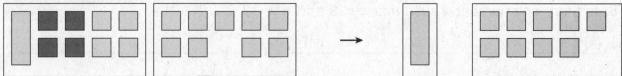

LESSON 11F Hands-On Lab
Solving Inequalities, continued

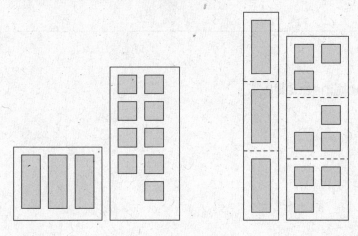

$x + (-4) + 4$ $<$ $5 + 4$ Combine terms x $<$ **9**

2. Use algebra tiles to model and solve each inequality.

a. $x + (-1) < 7$ **b.** $x + (-9) < 3$ **c.** $x + (-3) > -1$ **d.** $x + (-6) > -4$

_____   _____   _____   _____

Both sides of inequalities can be multiplied or divided by the same number. Solve the inequality $3x < 9$.

3x $<$ **9**   Regroup   **x** $<$ **3**

3. Use algebra tiles to model and solve the following equations.
a. $2x < 2$ **b.** $4x < 12$ **c.** $3x > -9$ **d.** $5x > 10$

_____   _____   _____   _____

Think and Discuss

1. How are inequalities different from equations?

_____

_____

2. If $a < b$ and $b < c$, then what is the relation between a and c?

_____

_____

Holt Mathematics

Hands-On Lab
Solving Inequalities, continued

3. Is there any number x such that $x < 3$ and $x > 3$?

_____

_____

4. What is the first step in solving an inequality such as $3x - 9 > 6$?

_____

_____

5. Describe the steps required to get x alone on one side of the inequality $4x + 5 < 25$.

_____

_____

Try This

Use algebra tiles to model and solve each inequality.

1. $x - 4 > 6$ _____

2. $x - 1 < 3$ _____

3. $x + 3 > 6$ _____

Holt Mathematics

Name _____ Date _____ Class _____

LESSON 11F Hands-On Lab
Solving Inequalities, continued

4. $x + (-4) > 1$ _____

5. $x + (-8) > 1$ _____

6. $x - 6 < 2$ _____

7. $2x > 12$ _____

8. $4x < 8$ _____

Holt Mathematics

Name _____ Date _____ Class _____

LESSON
11F

Review for Mastery
Solving Inequalities by Multiplying or Dividing

To solve an inequality, multiply and divide the same way you would
solve an equation. But, if you multiply or divide by a negative
number, you must reverse the inequality sign.

Divide by a Positive Number

$2x < 14$

$\dfrac{2x}{2} < \dfrac{14}{2}$

$x < 7$

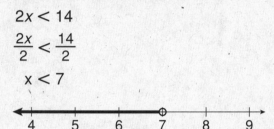

To check your solution, choose two
numbers from the graph and substitute
them into the original equation. Choose
a number that should be a solution and
a number that should not be a solution.

Divide by a Negative Number

$-2x < 14$

$\dfrac{-2x}{-2} > \dfrac{14}{-2}$ Reverse the inequality sign.

$x > -7$

Check

According to the graph, −6 should
be a solution, but −8 should not be.

$$-2x < 14 \qquad -2x < 14$$

$$\dfrac{-2 \cdot -8}{-2} \overset{?}{>} \dfrac{14}{-2} \quad \dfrac{-2 \cdot -6}{-2} \overset{?}{>} \dfrac{14}{-2}$$

$$-8 > -7 \; \times \qquad -6 > -7 \; ✔$$

Complete to solve. Then graph the equation and check.

1. $-3y \geq 24$

$\dfrac{-3y}{-3}$ ____ $\dfrac{24}{}$

y ____ ____

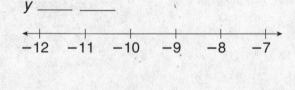

_____

_____

_____

_____

2. $\dfrac{s}{-9} < 4$

____ · $\dfrac{s}{-9}$ ____ ____ · 4

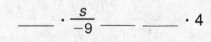

s ____ _____

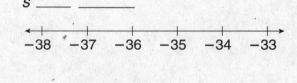

_____

_____

_____

_____

Holt Mathematics

Homework and Practice
LESSON 11F *Solving Inequalities by Multiplying or Dividing*

Solve.

1. $6x > -36$

2. $-9c \le 90$

3. $\dfrac{m}{-8} < -4$

_____

_____

_____

4. $\dfrac{z}{4} \le -7$

5. $-15f \ge 75$

6. $\dfrac{n}{-6.1} > -3$

_____

_____

_____

Solve. Check each answer.

7. $15r \ge -45$

8. $-9p < 15$

9. $18j \le 48$

_____

_____

_____

10. $\dfrac{h}{-1} < 6$

11. $\dfrac{b}{9} \ge \dfrac{5}{3}$

12. $-\dfrac{3}{4}s > 6$

_____

_____

_____

13. It costs Elizabeth $220 to make the clothes that she sells in her store. How many shirts must she sell at $15 each to make a profit?

_____

Holt Mathematics

EXPLORATION

11G Solving Two-Step Inequalities

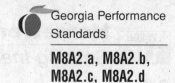

Georgia Performance Standards

M8A2.a, M8A2.b, M8A2.c, M8A2.d

Rosa is offered two telephone service options when she buys her new cell phone.

Cell phone option A
$25, plus 12.5¢ per minute

Cell phone option B
$90, plus unlimited minutes

1. Complete the table to compare the costs under each option for the given number of minutes.

Minutes	Cost Under Option A	Cost Under Option B
220	$25 + 0.125 \cdot 220 = \$52.50$	$90
320		
420		
520		
620		

2. Solve the inequality $25 + 0.125x < 90$. What does the solution tell you about option A and option B?

3. Solve the inequality $25 + 0.125x > 90$. What does the solution tell you about option A and option B?

Think and Discuss

4. **Explain** how you solved the inequalities in Problems 2 and 3.

Holt Mathematics

Hands-On Lab
Solving Two–Step Inequalities

Activity

An inequality is a statement that two amounts are not equal. Solve
the inequalities below and graph the solutions on a number line.
To solve the inequalities, use the same rules used for solving
equations.

$9a + 2 \geq a + 10$

Step 1	$9a + 2 \geq a + 10$	Given.
Step 2	$9a - a + 2 \geq a - a + 10$	Subtract a from both sides.
Step 3	$8a + 2 \geq 10$	Simplify.
Step 4	$8a - 2 + 2 \geq 10 - 2$	Subtract 2 from both sides.
Step 5	$8a \geq 8$	Simplify.
Step 6	$a \geq 1$	Divide both sides by 8.

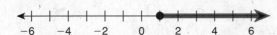

$c - 12 \leq 3$

Step 1	$c - 12 \leq 3$
Step 2	$c - 12 + 12 \leq 3 + 12$
Step 3	$c \leq 15$

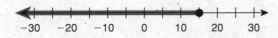

Holt Mathematics

Hands-On Lab

LESSON 11G *Solving Two–Step Inequalities, continued*

Think and Discuss

In the first inequality, what if $9a + 2$ had been $-9a + 2$? How would that have changed the method for solving the inequality?

_____

_____

_____

_____

_____

Try This

Solve the inequality $8a - 7 \leq 12a + 1$.

_____

_____

_____

LESSON 11G

Review for Mastery

Solving Two-Step Inequalities

To solve an inequality, undo operations the same way you would with an equation. But, when multiplying or dividing by a negative number, reverse the inequality symbol.

$3x + 2 > 11$	To undo addition,
$\underline{\quad -2 \quad -2\quad}$	subtract 2.
$3x \qquad > 9$	To undo multiplication,
$\dfrac{3x}{3} \quad > \dfrac{9}{3}$	divide by 3.
$x \qquad > 3$	

The solution set contains all real numbers greater than 3.

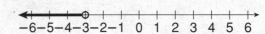

$-3x + 2 > 11$	To undo addition,
$\underline{\quad -2 \quad -2\quad}$	subtract 2.
$-3x \qquad > 9$	To undo multiplication,
$\dfrac{-3x}{-3} \quad < \dfrac{9}{-3}$	divide by -3 and
$x \qquad < -3$	change > to <.

The solution set contains all real numbers less than -3.

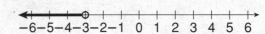

Complete to solve and graph.

1. $2t + 1 \le 9$ To undo addition,

    $\underline{\qquad}\ \underline{\quad}$ subtract.

    $2t \quad \le \underline{\quad}$ To undo multiplication,

    $\dfrac{2t}{\underline{\quad}} \ \underline{\dfrac{\quad}{\quad}}$ divide.

    $t \qquad \underline{\quad}$

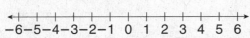

2. $-2t + 1 \le 9$ To undo addition,

    $\underline{\qquad}\ \underline{\quad}$ subtract.

    $-2t \quad \le 8$ To undo multiplication,

    $\dfrac{-2t}{\underline{\quad}} \ \underline{\dfrac{\quad}{\quad}}$ divide by -2 and

    $t \qquad \underline{\quad}$ change $\le$ to $\ge$.

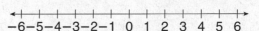

3. $-3z - 2 > 1$

    $\underline{\qquad}\qquad \underline{\qquad}$

    $-3z \ > \underline{\qquad}$

    $\underline{-3z}\qquad \underline{\quad}$

    $z \quad \underline{\qquad}$

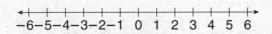

4. $3z - 2 > 1$

    $\underline{\qquad}\qquad \underline{\qquad}$

    $3z \ > \underline{\qquad}$

    $\underline{3z}\qquad \underline{\quad}$

    $z \quad \underline{\qquad}$

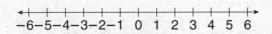

Holt Mathematics

LESSON 11G

Review for Mastery

Solving Two-Step Inequalities (continued)

To solve multistep inequalities, you may need to clear fractions.
Multiply both sides by the LCD.

$\dfrac{v}{4} + \dfrac{1}{4} > -\dfrac{1}{2}$ The LCD is 4.

$4 \cdot \dfrac{v}{4} + 4 \cdot \dfrac{1}{4} > 4 \cdot -\dfrac{1}{2}$ Multiply by the LCD.

$v + 1 > -2$

$\underline{-1 \qquad -1}$ Subtract from both sides.

$v \quad > -3$

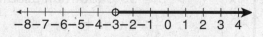

Complete to solve and graph.

5.

$-\dfrac{b}{4} - \dfrac{7}{12} \le \dfrac{2}{3}$ Find the LCD.

$\underline{\quad} \cdot -\dfrac{b}{4} - \underline{\quad} \cdot \dfrac{7}{12} \le \underline{\quad} \cdot \dfrac{2}{3}$ Multiply by the LCD.

$\underline{\quad} b - \underline{\quad} \le \underline{\quad}$

$\underline{\quad} \quad \underline{\quad}$ Add.

$\underline{\quad} b \le \underline{\quad}$

$\underline{\quad b} \underline{\quad} \underline{\quad}$ Divide and change symbol.

$b \underline{\quad}$ Check direction.

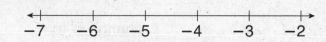

-7   -6   -5   -4   -3   -2

6.

$\dfrac{2}{7} + \dfrac{y}{14} \ge -\dfrac{1}{2}$

$\underline{\quad} \cdot \dfrac{2}{7} + \underline{\quad} \cdot \dfrac{y}{14} \ge \underline{\quad} \cdot -\dfrac{1}{2}$

$\underline{\quad} + \underline{\quad} \ge \underline{\quad}$

$\underline{\quad} \quad \underline{\quad}$

$\underline{\quad} \ge \underline{\quad}$

-12   -11   -10   -9   -8   -7

7.

$-\dfrac{1}{3} > \dfrac{x}{9} + \dfrac{2}{3}$

$\underline{\quad} \cdot -\dfrac{1}{3} > \underline{\quad} \cdot \dfrac{x}{9} + \underline{\quad} \cdot \dfrac{2}{3}$

$\underline{\quad} > x + \underline{\quad}$

$\underline{\quad} \quad \underline{\quad}$

$\underline{\quad} > x$

$x \underline{\quad} \underline{\quad}$

-12   -11   -10   -9   -8   -7

Holt Mathematics

Name _____ Date _____ Class _____

Homework and Practice
LESSON 11G *Solving Multistep Inequalities*

Solve and graph.

1. $5x + 3 \geq 28$

_____

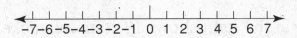

2. $10 - \frac{1}{2}w > 12$

_____

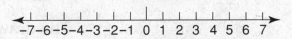

3. $7y - 15 - 4y \leq -18$

_____

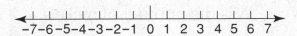

4. $7a < 12a + 10$

_____

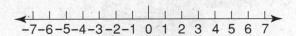

5. $19 - 4m > 4m + 11$

_____

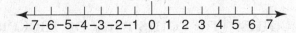

6. $-\frac{5}{6}d + 8 > 13$

_____

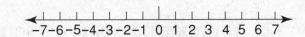

7. $2(3x + 1) \leq 4(2x - 3)$

_____

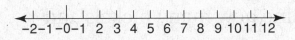

8. $14.1 - \frac{2}{5}h \geq 13.9 - \frac{3}{10}h$

_____

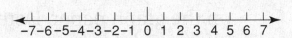

9. Six more than three-fourths a number is greater than or equal to one more than twice the number. Find the number.

_____

10. Ms. Garcia wants to carpet her bedroom which requires 24 square yards. Her budget will allow her to spend no more than $600 for the project. If the installation of the carpet will cost $162, what is the most she can pay per square yard for the carpeting?

_____

Holt Mathematics

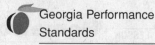

Georgia Performance
Standards

**M8A5.a, M8A5.b,
M8A5.d**

11H Solving Systems of Equations Graphically

You can solve a system of equations by sketching a graph. Check
if your solution makes sense given the context of the situation.

The drawing at the right shows 16 coins, all nickels
and dimes. They have a value of $1.60.

If you want to know how many coins are nickels
and how many are dimes, you can graph the system

$N + D = 16$ N is the number of nickels,

$5N + 10D = 160$ and D is the number of dimes.

1. You and a partner can solve problems like the one above.
   You will need 5 dimes, 5 nickels, a pencil, and graph paper.

2. Your partner removes some coins. The coins may be nickels
   or dimes. Your partner then tells you how many coins were
   removed, and the value of the remaining coins.

3. Write a system of equations. Graph the system accurately
   on the graph paper. Determine how many nickels and
   dimes remain.

Think and Discuss

4. **Describe** what the expression $5N + 10D$ represents.
5. **Simplify** the equation $5N + 10D = 160$ from the example.
   Why is it useful to do this before graphing?
6. **Explain** why the solution $(N, D) = (4, 2.5)$ is not a solution in
   the context of this problem.

Holt Mathematics

LESSON
11H

Review for Mastery

Solving Systems of Equations Graphically

To graph a system of equations, it is not always necessary to solve each equation for y. You can also use the intercepts to graph an equation.

Solve the system by graphing. $2x - y = -4$
$$y + 3x = -1$$

$2x - y = -4$

When $x = 0$, $y = 4$: $(0, 4)$
When $y = 0$, $x = -2$: $(-2, 0)$

$y + 3x = -1$

Solve for y: $y = -3x - 1$. The slope is -3 and the y-intercept is -1.

Graph:

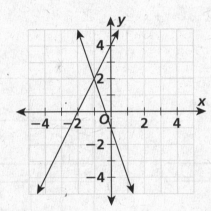

Use the intercepts to sketch $2x - y = -4$.

Use the y-intercept and slope to sketch $y + 3x = -1$.

The graphs appear to intersect at $(-1, 2)$.

Check:

$2x - y = -4$ $y + 3x = -1$
$2(-1) - 2 = -2 - 2 = -4$ ✔ $2 + 3(-1) = 2 - 3 = -1$ ✔

The solution is $(-1, 2)$.

Solve each system by graphing. Check your solution algebraically.

1. $x + y = 3$
   $2y = 2 - x$

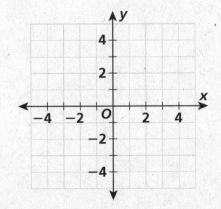

2. $y - x = -1$
   $x + y = 7$

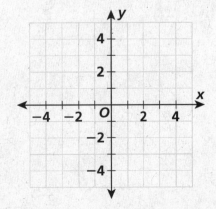

Holt Mathematics

LESSON	**Review for Mastery**
11H	*Solving Systems of Equations Graphically (continued)*

Some systems can be difficult to solve graphically on paper. This is especially true when the *x*- and *y*-values of the solution are not integers. For such systems, you can use technology to solve by graphing.

Solve the system by graphing: $x - 2y = -2$
$$4y = 3x - 1$$

Solve each equation for *y*.

$$x - 2y = -2 \qquad\qquad 4y = 3x - 1$$

$$-2y = -x - 2 \qquad\qquad y = \frac{3}{4}x - \frac{1}{4}$$

$$y = \frac{1}{2}x + 1$$

Enter the equations into the equation editor as Y₁ and Y₂. Then graph the equations in the standard window.

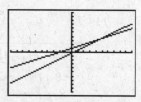

Use the intersect feature or a similar feature to find the intersection point.

The solution is (5, 3.5).

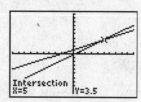

Solve each system by graphing. Use a graphing calculator.

3. $4x - 3y = 2$
$-2y = 3 - 4x$

4. $3x + 2y = 4$
$1 - 3x = 3y$

Holt Mathematics

Homework and Practice
LESSON 11H *Solving Systems of Equations Graphically*

Write an appropriate system of linear equations for the problem. Then solve the system of equations graphically. Be sure to simplify your equations before graphing.

1. Danielle has a purse with only nickels and dimes in it. It contains 29 coins that have a value of $2.00. How many nickels and dimes are in the purse?

System:

_____

_____

Solution:

_____

_____

2. Together, Hadi and Betsy sell 90 tickets to the school play. Betsy sells 12 more tickets than Hadi. How many tickets do they sell each?

System:

_____

_____

Solution:

_____

_____

Holt Mathematics

EXPLORATION

11I Systems of Equations

Georgia Performance
Standards

M8A5.a, M8A5.b,
M8A5.c

You can compare Celsius temperatures with Fahrenheit temperatures by graphing each formula as an equation using the variables x and y.

To convert °C to °F

$$F = \frac{9}{5} \cdot C + 32$$

$$y = \frac{9}{5} \cdot x + 32$$

To convert °F to °C

$$C = \frac{5}{9} \cdot (F - 32)$$

$$y = \frac{5}{9} \cdot (x - 32)$$

The calculator screens below show how to graph the two equations.

  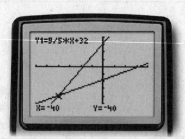

1. Which temperature is the same in both degrees Celsius and degrees Fahrenheit?

2. Substitute the temperature you found in Problem 1 for x in each equation above.

Think and Discuss

3. **Discuss** what happened when you substituted the temperature found in Problem 1 in each equation.

4. **Explain** what the point of intersection of the two graphs represents.

Holt Mathematics

LESSON 11L Review for Mastery

Systems of Equations

Two or more equations considered together form a **system of equations**.
To solve a system of equations, you can use a method of substitution.

Solve the system: $y = 3x$
$\qquad\qquad\qquad y - 5x = 20$

Use the first equation to substitute for y in the second equation.	$y - 5x = 20$ $3x - 5x = 20$	second equation Replace y with $3x$.
Solve the resulting equation for x.	$-2x = 20$	Combine like terms.
	$\dfrac{-2x}{-2} = \dfrac{20}{-2}$	Divide by -2.
	$x = -10$	
Substitute the x-value into the first equation to get the corresponding y-value.	$y = 3x$ $y = 3(-10) = -30$	

Check: Substitute both values in each of the original equations.

$y = 3x$ $\qquad\qquad\qquad$ $y - 5x = 20$

$-30 \overset{?}{=} 3(-10)$ $\qquad\qquad$ $-30 - 5(-10) \overset{?}{=} 20$ $\qquad$ $x = -10$ and $y = -30$

$-30 = -30$ ✔ $\qquad\qquad$ $-30 + 50 \overset{?}{=} 20$ $\qquad\qquad$ So, the solution of the

$\qquad\qquad\qquad\qquad\qquad\qquad\qquad$ $20 = 20$ ✔ $\qquad\qquad$ system is $(-10, -30)$.

Solve and check this system.

1. $y = 2x$
$\quad\; 6x + y = 16$

Use the first equation to substitute for y in the second equation.

$6x +$ ____ $= 16$

Solve the resulting equation for x.

_____

_____

_____

Substitute the x-value to get the corresponding y-value.

$\qquad y = 2x$

$\qquad y = 2($ ____ $) =$ ____

Check both values in each of the original equations.

$y = 2x \qquad\qquad 6x + y = 16$

____ $\overset{?}{=} 2($ ____ $) \quad 6($ ____ $) +$ ____ $\overset{?}{=} 16$

_____ $\qquad$ _____ $\overset{?}{=} 16$

So, the ordered pair _____ is the solution of the system.

Review for Mastery

LESSON 11I Systems of Equations (continued)

Sometimes, you first have to solve one equation for a variable.

Solve the system: $y + 3x = 7$
$x + 2y = 4$

Solve the first equation for y.	$y + 3x = 7$	
	$\underline{\; -3x \qquad -3x}$	Subtract $3x$.
	$y \qquad\;\; = 7 - 3x$	

Substitute for y in the second equation.	$x + 2y = 4$	second equation
Solve for x.	$x + 2(7 - 3x) = 4$	Replace y with $7 - 3x$.
	$x + 14 - 6x = 4$	Distributive property
	$-5x + 14 = 4$	Combine like terms.
	$\underline{\; -14 \quad\; -14}$	Subtract 14.
	$\dfrac{-5x}{-5} = \dfrac{-10}{-5}$	Divide by -5.
	$x = 2$	

Substitute the x-value into the first equation to get the corresponding y-value.

$$y + 3x = 7$$
$$y + 3(2) = 7$$
$$y + 6 = 7$$
$$y + 6 - 6 = 7 - 6$$
$$y = 1$$

Check: Substitute both values in each of the original equations.

$y + 3x = 7$	$x + 2y = 4$	$x = 2$ and $y = 1$
$1 + 3(2) \overset{?}{=} 7$	$2 + 2(1) \overset{?}{=} 4$	The solution of the
$7 = 7 ✔$	$4 = 4 ✔$	system is (2, 1).

Solve and check this system.

2. $y - 2x = 0$
$x - 2y = 6$

Solve the first equation for y.
$y - 2x = 0$

$y = $ _____

Use the result to substitute for y in the second equation.
$x - 2y = 6$
$x - 2(\_\_\_) = 6$

Solve the resulting equation for x.

$x = $ _____

Substitute the x-value to get the corresponding y-value.

_____

_____

$y = $ _____

Check:

$y - 2x = 0 \qquad x - 2y = 6$

So, the ordered pair _____ is the solution of the system.

Holt Mathematics

Homework and Practice

LESSON 11I *Systems of Equations*

Determine if the ordered pair is a solution of each system of equations.

1. $(-1, 3)$
$y = -x + 2$
$y = x + 4$

_____

2. $(1, 2)$
$y = 2x$
$y - x = 1$

_____

3. $(3, 5)$
$x - y = 8$
$x + y = -2$

_____

4. $(-1, -4)$
$x = 4y$
$3x + 4y = -4$

_____

5. $(2, 4)$
$3x + 2y = 14$
$2x = y$

_____

6. $(-2, -8)$
$2x + y = 4$
$3x + y = 2$

_____

7. $(-1, 2)$
$3x + y = 1$
$6x + 2y = -2$

_____

8. $(0, 0)$
$y = 3x - 4$
$y - 3x = -4$

_____

9. $(1, -3)$
$2x = y + 5$
$2x + y = -1$

_____

Solve each system of equations.

10. $x + y = 12$
$x - y = 0$

_____

11. $2x + y = 10$
$x - y = -4$

_____

12. $x + y = -8$
$2x - y = -4$

_____

13. $3x + 2y = 0$
$x + 2y = 8$

_____

14. The sum of two numbers is 206. The second number is 48 more than the first. Find the numbers. Write a system of equations and solve.

_____

15. Ryan and Juan collect baseball cards. Together they have 880 cards. Juan has 125 less than twice as many as Ryan. How many cards does each have? Write a system of equations and solve.

_____

Holt Mathematics

Big Ideas

Answer these questions to summarize the important concepts from Chapter 11 in your own words.

1. Explain how to simplify the expression $4(7x - 3) + 2x$.

2. Explain how to solve the equation $6x + 10 + 12x - 14 = 50$.

3. Explain how to solve the equation $4b + 8 - 6b = -18 + 2b + 10$.

4. Explain how to solve the inequality $12 \leq \dfrac{c}{-5}$.

5. Explain what an open circle and a closed circle means when graphing inequalities on a number line.

For more review of Chapter 11:

- Complete the Chapter 11 Study Guide and Review on pages 616–618 of your textbook.

- Complete the Ready to Go On quizzes on pages 598 and 612 of your textbook.

Holt Mathematics

Project
Graphing Lines: Life Lines

Career: Wildlife Ecologist

Whatever happened to the California parakeet and the passenger pigeon, two species of birds that once inhabited the United States? They are now extinct as *Tyrannosaurus rex.* The primary focus of wildlife ecologists is to keep other animals from becoming extinct. They have been successful with the whooping crane, the largest wild bird in North America.

In this chapter project...you will collect data on the population of a local animal. You will:

• Learn how to graph the changing population of an animal and how to draw a line to fit the data.

• Research local animals in your area. You may choose an endangered species or a more common animal.

• Keep track of population numbers of the animals over several months. You can do this through observation or by getting information from an official source, like the World Wildlife Fund or the U.S. Department of Fish and Wildlife.

• Graph the data you collected and draw a line to fit the data. Make conclusions about whether the population is increasing, decreasing, or staying the same. Prepare a poster including your graph, your conclusions, facts about the animal, and any photos of the animal you can find.

To get started, work through the Whooping It Up worksheet on the next page.

This chapter project reinforces your understanding of these Georgia Performance Standards:

M8D4.b Estimate and determine a line of best fit from a scatter plot.

M8P5.a Create and use representations to organize, record, and communicate mathematical ideas.

---

go.hrw.com
Chapter Project Online
KEYWORD: MT7 Ch12

Holt Mathematics

CHAPTER 12 **Project Recording Sheet**
Graphing Lines

Whooping it Up

Whooping Cranes reach almost five feet tall when standing and weigh about 14–16 pounds. The adult birds are snow white with black-tipped eight-foot wingspans. Each family group produces one or two offspring. The migration route from Wood Buffalo National Park in northern Alberta province to the Aransas National Wildlife Refuge in Texas is approximately 2400 miles long and only about 140 miles wide. The population of Whooping Cranes was likely never very large. The original population even before the European settlement of North America is estimated to be only 500 to 1400.

Year												
1940	1945	1950	1955	1960	1965	1970	1975	1980	1985	1990	1995	2000
Cranes 15	17	33	28	36	44	57	49	79	82	142	129	202

1. Plot a graph of the wild population from 1940 to 2000.

2. Draw a straight line that best conforms to the data. What is the slope of the line? Write an equation for the line.

_____

_____

3. What are your feelings about endangered species such as the Whooping Crane? Species of animals and plants have been disappearing from the Earth for millions of years. Should we try and protect all of them? Why or why not?

_____

_____

_____

_____

_____

Holt Mathematics

12A Graphing Linear Equations

Georgia Performance Standards

M8A3.h, M8A3.i, M8A4.c, M8A4.f

The calculator screens show the graphs of $y = x + 1$ and $y = x + 3$.

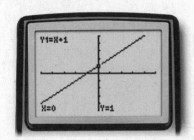
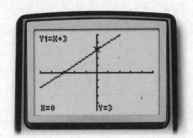

1. Why is the graph of $y = x + 3$ higher along the y-axis than the graph of $y = x + 1$?

The calculator screens show the graphs of $y = x + 2$ and $y = 2x + 2$.

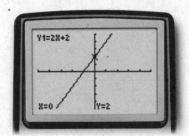

2. Why is the graph of $y = x + 2$ flatter than the graph of $y = 2x + 2$?

Think and Discuss

3. Discuss how the two graphs for Problem **1** are similar and different.

4. Discuss how the two graphs for Problem **2** are similar and different.

Holt Mathematics

Name _____ Date _____ Class _____

Hands-On Lab
Graphing Linear Equations

If all of the variables in an equation are raised only to the first power, the equation is known as a linear equation. The equation $y = 3x + 7$ is a linear equation because both x and y are raised to the first power.

Activity

1. Complete the following table.

x	1	2	3	4	5	6	8	10
$y = 3x + 7$	10							

2. Predict what the graph of the data you have generated would look like.

_____

3. Graph the data from part 1.

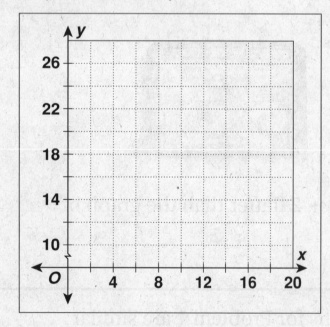

Holt Mathematics

Hands-On Lab
Graphing Linear Equations, continued

4. Complete the following table and draw a graph as in part 1.

x	1	2	3	4	5
$y = x^2$					

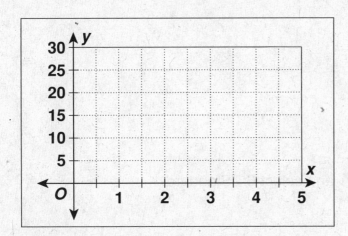

Explain why linear equations are called linear.

_____

Think and Discuss

1. Which of the following are linear equations?

  a. $y = 3x$ **b.** $x + 6 = y - 3$ **c.** $y = x^2$ **d.** $y = 3x^3 + 2x^2 + x$

_____   _____   _____   _____

2. Is the equation $y = \sqrt{x + 2}$ a linear equation? Explain your answer.

_____

_____

Try This

1. Which of the following are linear equations?

  a. $y = 2x - 7$ **b.** $x = y - 8$ **c.** $3y = x^2 + 3$ **d.** $y = \frac{3}{x}$

_____   _____   _____   _____

Holt Mathematics

LESSON 12A Technology Lab
Graphing Linear Equations

Activity

Graph the following equation on a graphics calculator:

$$y = x - 3$$

Step 1: Enter the equation by pressing [Y=] [X,T,θ,n] [−] [3] [ENTER].

Step 2: Set viewing window. Press [ZOOM] and select 6:ZStandard.

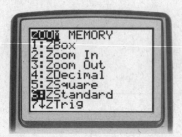

Step 3: Graph the equation. Press [GRAPH] if needed.

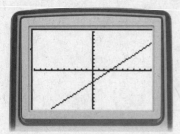

Notice that the graph of $y = x - 3$ is a straight line.

Holt Mathematics

Technology Lab

LESSON 12A *Graphing Linear Equations, continued*

Think and Discuss

1. In the function table below, discuss how *x* is related to *y* and write an equation to show this relationship.

x	y
−6	−2
−3	1
1	5
7	11
9	13

_____

_____

Try This

1. Translate "*y* is 4 more than twice *x*" into an equation and use your graphing calculator to graph the equation.

_____

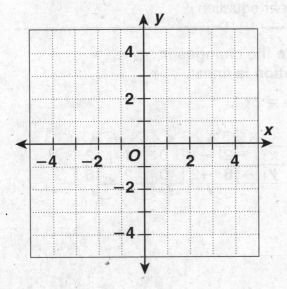

Holt Mathematics

LESSON 12A

Review for Mastery

Graphing Linear Equations

The graph of a **linear equation** is a straight line.

The line shown is the graph of $y = \frac{3}{2}x + 1$.

All the points on the line are solutions of the equation.

Each time the x-value increases by 2, the y-value increases by 3. So, a constant change in the x-value corresponds to a constant change in the y-values.

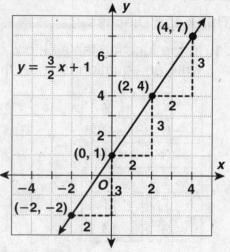

$y = 3x - 4$

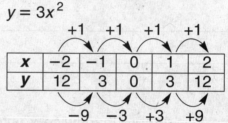

x	−2	−1	0	1	2
y	−10	−7	−4	−1	2

+3 +3 +3 +3

Since a constant change in the x-value corresponds to a constant change in the y-value, $y = 3x - 4$ is a linear equation.

$y = 3x^2$

+1 +1 +1 +1

x	−2	−1	0	1	2
y	12	3	0	3	12

−9 −3 +3 +9

Since a constant change in the x-value does not correspond to a constant change in the y-value, $y = 3x^2$ is not a linear equation.

Each equation has a table of solutions. Indicate the changes in x-values and in y-values. Tell whether the equation is linear.

1. $y = 2x - 5$

x	−2	−1	0	1	2
y	−9	−7	−5	−3	−1

_____

2. $y = 2x^3$

x	−2	−1	0	1	2
y	−16	−2	0	2	16

_____

Holt Mathematics

Review for Mastery

LESSON 12A *Graphing Linear Equations (continued)*

To graph a linear equation, make a table to find several solutions.
Choose *x*-values that are easy to graph. Substitute each *x*-value into
the equation to find the corresponding *y*-value. Plot your solutions
and draw a line connecting them.

x	$\frac{1}{2}x - 3$	y	(x, y)
−4	$\frac{1}{2}(-4) - 3$	−5	(−4, −5)
−2	$\frac{1}{2}(-2) - 3$	−4	(−2, −4)
0	$\frac{1}{2}(0) - 3$	−3	(0, −3)
6	$\frac{1}{2}(6) - 3$	0	(6, 0)

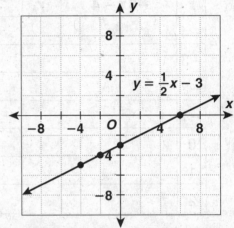

Complete the table for each equation and then graph the equation.

3. $y = 3x - 1$

x	3x − 1	y	(x, y)
−2	3(−2) − 1		(−2,)
0	3( ) − 1		(0,)
1	3( ) − 1		(1,)
3	3( ) − 1		(3,)

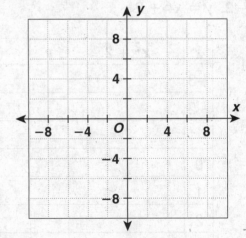

4. $y = -\frac{3}{2}x + 1$

x	$-\frac{3}{2}x + 1$	y	(x, y)
−2	$-\frac{3}{2}(\quad) + 1$		(−2, 4)
0	$-\frac{3}{2}(\quad) + 1$		
2	$-\frac{3}{2}(\quad) + 1$		
4	$-\frac{3}{2}(\quad) + 1$		

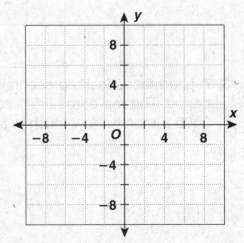

Holt Mathematics

Homework and Practice

Graphing Linear Equations

Graph each equation and tell whether it is linear.

1. $y = -3x - 4$

x	−3x − 4	y	(x, y)
−4			
−3			
−2			
−1			
0			
1			
2			

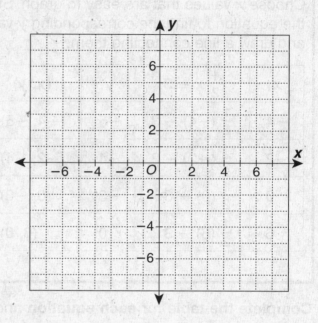

2. $y = x^2 + 2$

x	$x^2 + 2$	y	(x, y)
−3			
−2			
−1			
0			
1			
2			
3			

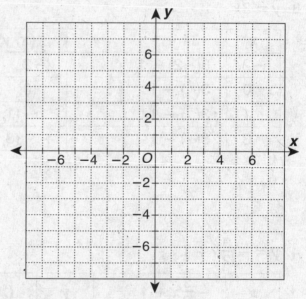

3. A pharmaceutical representative sells $48,000 in a one month period. The rep earns 5.5% commission plus base salary of $400 a month. How much is the rep paid that month?

_____

Holt Mathematics

EXPLORATION

12B Slope of a Line

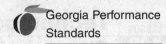

Georgia Performance
Standards

**M8A3.i, M8A4.a,
M8A4.f**

Joseph plots a graph of his 300-mile trip to the coast.

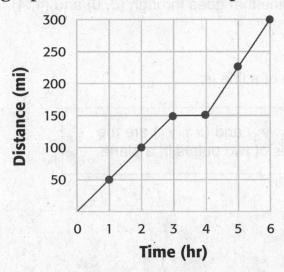

1. Calculate his average speed for the first 3 hours.
   (*Hint:* Divide the distance traveled during the first
   three hours by 3.)

2. What happens between hours 3 and 4?

3. Calculate his average speed for the last 2 hours.
   (*Hint:* Divide the distance traveled during the last
   two hours by 2.)

Think and Discuss

4. **Discuss** how you could find Joseph's average speed between
   hours 3 and 4.

5. **Discuss** how average speed is related to the shape of the graph.

Holt Mathematics

Technology Lab
LESSON 12B
Slope of a Line

Activity

Slope tells how much a line slants. When a line rises from left to right, the slope is positive; when a line falls from left to right, the slope is negative. Graph the line that goes through (0, 0) and (4, 4) on a graphing calculator.

Step 1: Find the slope.

The formula for the slope (*m*) of a line is:

$$m = \frac{y_2 - y_1}{x_2 - x_1}$$ Where (x_1, y_1) and (x_2, y_2) are the coordinates of two points in a plane.

Substitute: $m = \frac{4 - 0}{4 - 0}$

$$= \frac{4}{4} = 1$$

Step 2: Graph the equation.

Since the line goes through (0, 0), its equation is in the form $y = mx$. You know the slope is 1 from Step 1, so the equation is $y = 1x$ or $y = x$.

Enter the equation in Y1 and press `GRAPH`.

Technology Lab
LESSON 12B *Slope of a Line, continued*

Think and Discuss

1. What happens to your graph if you make the value of *m* higher? Lower? Negative?

_____

_____

_____

_____

Try This

1. Write and graph the equation of the line that goes through (0, 0) and (2, 6).

_____

2. Write and graph the equation of the line that goes through (0, 0) and (−3, 9).

_____

3. Find the slope of a line that passes through the points (4, 2) and (−6, −3).

_____

_____

Holt Mathematics

LESSON 12B Review for Mastery
Slope of a Line

The **slope** of a line is a measure of its tilt, or slant.

The slope of a straight line is a constant ratio, the "rise over run," or the **vertical change** over the **horizontal change**.

You can find the slope of a line by comparing any two of its points. The vertical change is the difference between the two *y*-values. And the horizontal change is the difference between the two *x*-values.

$$\text{slope} = \frac{y_2 \, y_1}{x_2 \, x_1}$$

point *A*: (3, 2)   point *B*: (4, 4)

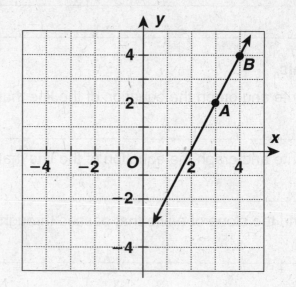

Make point *A* (x_1, y_1).
Make point *B* (x_2, y_2).

$$\text{slope} = \frac{4 - 2}{4 - 3}$$
$$= \frac{2}{1}, \text{ or } 2$$

So, the slope of the line is 2.

You can make point *A* (x_2, y_2) and point *B* (x_1, y_1).

$$\text{slope} = \frac{2 - 4}{3 - 4}$$
$$= \frac{-2}{-1}, \text{ or } 2$$

So, the slope remains 2.

Find the slope of the line that passes through each pair of points.

1. (1, 5) and (2, 6)

2. (0, 3) and (2, 7)

3. (2, 5) and (3, 4)

_____

_____

_____

4. (6, 9) and (2, 7)

5. (6, 5) and (8, −1)

6. (7, −4) and (4, −2)

_____

_____

_____

Holt Mathematics

Review for Mastery

12B *Slope of a Line (continued)*

A straight line has a constant slope, so it shows a **constant rate of change**. The same change in *y* always results in the same change in *x*.

From point *C* to point *B*:

$$\frac{\text{change in y}}{\text{change in x}} = \frac{2}{3}$$

From point *B* to point *A*:

$$\frac{\text{change in y}}{\text{change in x}} = \frac{2}{3}$$

A curved line doesn't have a constant slope, so it shows a **variable rate of change**.

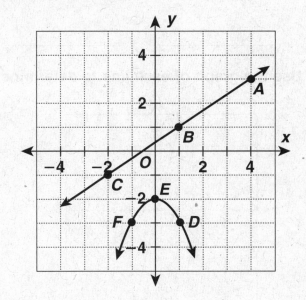

Between point *F* and point *E*, the curved line has a positive slope.
Between point *E* and point *D*, the curved line has a negative slope.

So, the curved line has a variable rate of change.

Determine whether each graph shows a constant or a variable rate of change. Write *constant* or *variable*.

7.

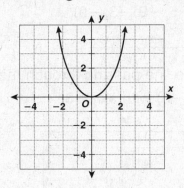

_____

8.

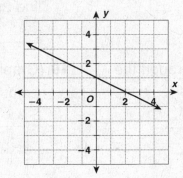

_____

9.

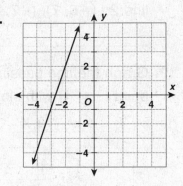

_____

Holt Mathematics

Name _____ Date _____ Class _____

Homework and Practice
Slope of a Line

Find the slope of the line passing through each pair of points.

1. (5, 7), (6, 9)   **2.** (2, 8), (8, 2)   **3.** (−2, 6), (−2, −4)   **4.** (−8, −7), (−9, −1)

_____   _____   _____   _____

Use the graph of each line to determine its slope.

5.

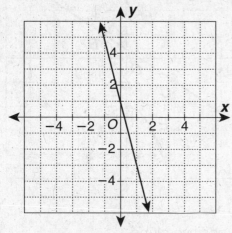

6.

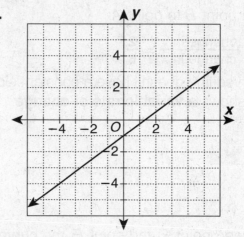

_____   _____

Tell whether the lines passing through the given points are parallel or perpendicular.

7. line 1: (−1, −2), (−4, −8)
    line 2: (−6, 7), (−7, 5)

8. line 1: (6, 8), (6, 10)
    line 2: (−5, −9), (3, −9)

_____   _____

9. Graph the line passing through the point (−1, 4) with slope $-\frac{1}{2}$.

10. Graph the line passing through the point (1, −3) with slope 3.

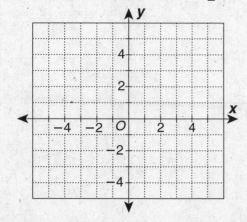

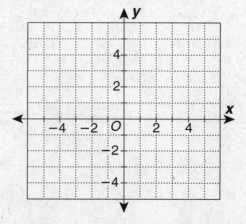

Holt Mathematics

EXPLORATION

12C Using Slopes and Intercepts

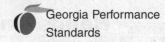

Georgia Performance Standards

M8A3.i, M8A4.a, M8A4.b, M8A4.c, M8A4.d, M8A4.f

On the graph below, 40 is called the *y-intercept* and 8 is called the *x-intercept*.

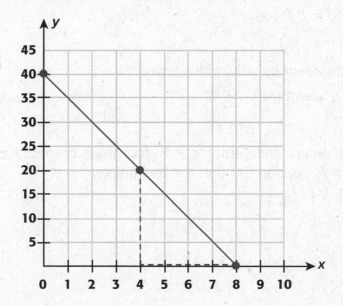

1. How do the rise and run compare to the intercepts?

2. Find the slope of the line by dividing the *y*-intercept by the *x*-intercept and then changing the sign of the quotient. Express the slope as a fraction in simplest form.

3. Consider the triangle drawn along the dashed lines below the line. Divide the vertical distance (20) by the horizontal distance (4), change the sign, and then compare this fraction with the fraction you found in Problem **2**.

Think and Discuss

4. **Explain** how to calculate the slope of a line using the *x*- and *y*-intercepts.

5. **Explain** how to calculate the slope of a line using any two points on the line.

385

Holt Mathematics

Name _____ Date _____ Class _____

Hands-On Lab 1
Using Slopes and Intercepts

Activity 1

Find the *x*-intercept and *y*-intercept of the linear equation $2x + y = 8$.
Use the intercepts to graph the equation.

Step 1 Find the *x*-intercept by solving for *x* when $y = 0$.

Solve $2x + 0 = 8$ for *x*.

$x =$ _____

Step 2 Find the *y*-intercept by solving for *y* when $x = 0$.

Solve $2(0) + y = 8$ for *y*.

$y =$ _____

Step 3 Plot the *x*-intercept and *y*-intercept on the graph below. Draw
the line of the equation through the two points.

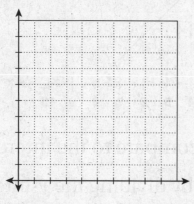

Holt Mathematics

LESSON 12C Hands-On Lab 1
Using Slopes and Intercepts, continued

Think and Discuss

1. How would you find the *x*-intercept and *y*-intercept of an equation that is not written in standard form, such as $2y = 10 - 5x$? Find the *x*-intercept and *y*-intercept of this equation.

_____

_____

_____

2. Write the equation $4 - 3x = y$ in standard form.

_____

Try This

1. Graph each of the following linear equations on the graph below by finding the x-intercept and y-intercept of each. How is the slope of the two lines different?

   Equation 1: $x - 3y = 9$

   Equation 2: $x + 3y = 9$

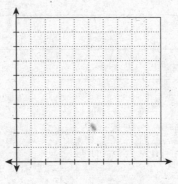

_____

_____

_____

_____

Holt Mathematics

Hands-On Lab 2
Using Slopes and Intercepts

Activity 1

Write the equation in slope-intercept form and graph the line.

$4x + y = 12$

Step 1 Subtract $4x$ from both sides.

$-4x + 4x + y = 12 - 4x$

$y = 12 - 4x$

Step 2 Rewrite the equation to match slope-intercept form.

$y = -4x + 12$

What is the y-intercept of the equation?

_____

What is the slope of the equation?

_____

Step 3 Graph the line on a separate sheet of graph paper. To graph the equation, plot the y-intercept. Then use the slope of the line to plot another point on the line. The slope is negative so the line will slant downward from left to right.

_____

_____

_____

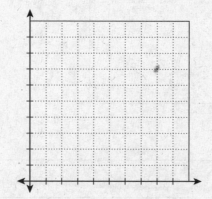

Name _____ Date _____ Class _____

LESSON
12C

Hands-On Lab 2
Using Slopes and Intercepts, continued

Think and Discuss

1. How can you find the equation of a line if you know two points
   on the line?

   _____

   _____

   _____

2. For every 1 hour that Emily babysits, she earns $7.00. Write an
   equation in slope-intercept form to describe this situation.

   _____

Try This

1. Jaden's parents gave him $50 to start a savings account. Each
   week he has to put $5.00 of his allowance into his savings
   account. Write an equation in slope-intercept form for the line that
   describes how much money Jaden has in his savings account.

   What is the slope of the line?

   _____

   What is the *y*-intercept of the line?

   _____

   Draw the line on the graph below.

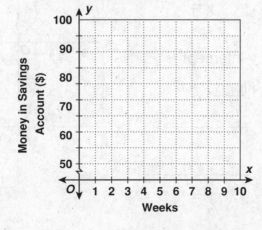

Holt Mathematics

Name _____ Date _____ Class _____

Review for Mastery
Using Slopes and Intercepts

x-intercept: the x-coordinate of the point
at which a line crosses the x-axis

y-intercept: the y-coordinate of the point
at which a line crosses the y-axis

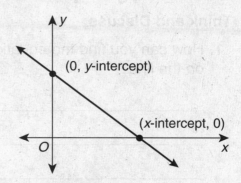

You can find the intercepts of a line from its equation.
Then you can use the intercepts to graph the line.

Find the intercepts of the line $3x + 4y = 24$.

For the x-intercept, let $y = 0$.	For the y-intercept, let $x = 0$.
$3x + 4y = 24$	$3x + 4y = 24$
$3x + 4(0) = 24$	$3(0) + 4y = 24$
$3x + 0 = 24$	$0 + 4y = 24$
$3x = 24$	$4y = 24$
$\dfrac{3x}{3} = \dfrac{24}{3}$	$\dfrac{4y}{4} = \dfrac{24}{4}$
$x = 8$	$y = 6$
The x-intercept is 8.	The y-intercept is 6.

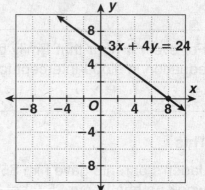

Find the intercepts of each line.
Draw both graphs on the same grid.

1. $2x + 3y = 12$

for x-intercept

$2x + 3(\_\_\_) = 12$

for y-intercept

$2(\_\_\_) + 3y = 12$

_____

_____

$x = \_\_\_$

_____

_____

$y = \_\_\_$

2. $6y - 3x = 6$

for x-intercept

$6(\_\_\_) - 3x = 6$

for y-intercept

$6y - 3(\_\_\_) = 6$

_____

_____

$x = \_\_\_$

_____

_____

$y = \_\_\_$

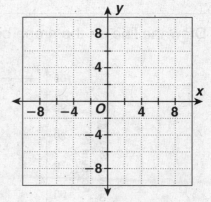

Holt Mathematics

Review for Mastery

LESSON 12C *Using Slopes and Intercepts (continued)*

slope-intercept form

$$y = mx + b$$

slope   y-intercept

In this form, the coefficient of x is the slope and the constant term is the y-intercept.

To rewrite an equation in slope-intercept form, *isolate y*.

$$
\begin{array}{ll}
2x + 3y = -12 & \\
\underline{-2x \qquad -2x} & \text{Subtract } 2x. \\
3y = -2x - 12 & \\
\dfrac{3y}{3} = \dfrac{-2}{3}x - \dfrac{12}{3} & \text{Divide by 3.} \\
y = \dfrac{-2}{3}x - 4 &
\end{array}
$$

So, $m = -\dfrac{2}{3}$ and $b = -4$.

Write each equation in slope-intercept form and then find the slope and y-intercept.

3. $3y = 4x + 15$

$\dfrac{3y}{} = \dfrac{4}{}x + \dfrac{15}{}$ Divide by 3.

_____

_____

4. $3x - 2y = 6$

Subtract $3x$.

_____ _____

_____

_____

Given two points of a line, you can write its equation.

$(2, 5)$ and $(-1, -4)$

$$\text{slope} = \frac{y_2 y_1}{x_2 x_1} = \frac{-4 - 5}{-1 - 2} = \frac{-9}{-3} = 3$$

To find b, substitute the slope and the values from one of the points into the slope-intercept equation.

$$
\begin{array}{rl}
y = mx + b \quad \rightarrow & 5 = 3(2) + b \\
& 5 = 6 + b \\
& -1 = b
\end{array}
$$

So, the equation for the line that passes through $(2, 5)$ and $(-1, -4)$ is $y = 3x - 1$.

Write the equation of the line that passes through each pair of points in slope-intercept form.

5. $(2, 11)$ and $(0, 3)$ **6.** $(-1, 3)$ and $(4, -2)$ **7.** $(10, 1)$ and $(6, -1)$

_____ _____ _____

Holt Mathematics

Name _____ Date _____ Class _____

Homework and Practice
Using Slopes and Intercepts

Find the *x*-intercept and *y*-intercept of each line. Use the intercepts to graph the equation.

1. $x = y + 5$

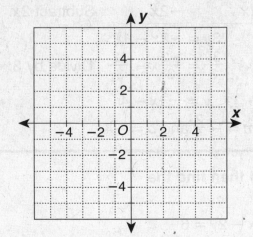

2. $3x - 2y = 6$

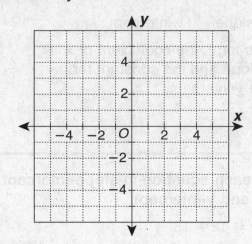

_____

_____

_____

_____

Write each equation in slope-intercept form and then find the slope and *y*-intercept.

3. $2x = y - 4$ **4.** $4x - 3y = -9$ **5.** $x - 4y = 8$

_____

_____

Write the equation of the line that passes through each pair of points in slope-intercept form.

6. $(-1, 7), (4, -3)$ **7.** $(2, 5), (-8, 15)$ **8.** $(8, 4), (-10, -5)$

_____

9. Thad's father gives him \$10 for a passing report card plus \$5 for every grade of A. Write an equation of a line in slope-intercept form to express *y*, the amount received with *x* grades of A. State the slope, *x*-intercept, and *y*-intercept of the equation.

_____

Holt Mathematics

Georgia Performance
Standards

M8A3.i, M8A4.b,
M8A4.d, M8A4.e,
M8A4.f

12D Point-Slope Form

The graph shows the point (2, 4).

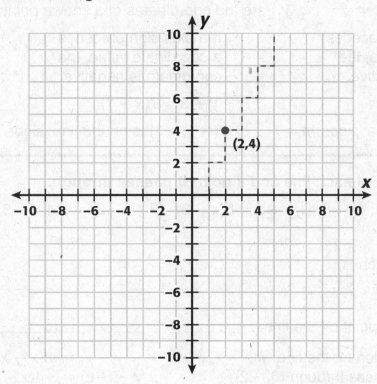

1. Draw a line that rests on the "stairs" drawn with a dashed line and that passes through the point (2, 4).

2. Calculate the slope of the line by dividing the vertical distance of each step by the horizontal distance of each step of the stairs.

3. Use the *point-slope form* $y - y_1 = m(x - x_1)$ to find the equation for the line. (*Hint:* $y_1 = 4$, $x_1 = 2$, and $m =$ the slope you found in Problem **2**.)

Think and Discuss

4. **Explain** why the equation $y - y_1 = m(x - x_1)$ is called the point-slope form of a line.

Holt Mathematics

LESSON 12D Review for Mastery
Point-Slope Form

$$y - y_1 = m(x - x_1)$$

slope

(x_1, y_1) are the coordinates of a known point on the line.

If a minus sign precedes a coordinate value, the coordinate is positive.	If a plus sign precedes a coordinate value, the coordinate is negative.
$y - 3 = 7(x - 1)$	$y + 3 = 7(x + 1)$
$(1, 3)$ is on the line; slope $m = 7$	$(-1, -3)$ is on the line; slope $m = 7$

Identify the slope of each line and a point it passes through.

1. $y + 2 = 5(x - 3)$ **2.** $y - 4 = -3(x + 5)$

$m =$ _____ $m =$ _____

Which sign for each
coordinate? _____ _____

Coordinates of a point on the line: _____ _____

To write an equation for the line with slope -4 that passes through $(6, -2)$, substitute $m = -4$, $x_1 = 6$, $y_1 = -2$ into the point-slope form.	$y - y_1 = m(x - x_1)$ $y - (-2) = -4(x - 6)$ $y + 2 = -4(x - 6)$

Write the point-slope form of the equation with the given slope that passes through the given point.

3. $m = 3$; $(x_1, y_1) = (7, 2)$ **4.** $m = -5$; $(x_1, y_1) = (2, 6)$

$y - y_1 = m(x - x_1)$ $y - y_1 = m(x - x_1)$

$y -$ ____ $=$ ____ $(x -$ ____ $)$ $y -$ ____ $=$ ____ $(x -$ ____ $)$

5. $m = \frac{1}{2}$; $(x_1, y_1) = (-8, 1)$ **6.** $m = -\frac{3}{4}$; $(x_1, y_1) = (0, -1)$

$y - y_1 = m(x - x_1)$ $y - y_1 = m(x - x_1)$

$y -$ ____ $=$ ____ $(x$ ____ $)$ y ____ $=$ ____ $(x -$ ____ $)$

Holt Mathematics

Homework and Practice
LESSON 12D *Point-Slope Form*

Identify a point the line passes through and the slope of the line, given the point-slope form of the equation.

1. $y - 6 = 3(x - 2)$ **2.** $y + 4 = -2(x + 1)$ **3.** $y - 5 = -1(x - 8)$

_____   _____   _____

_____   _____   _____

4. $y + 3 = 4(x + 2)$ **5.** $y - 7 = -6(x - 1)$ **6.** $y - 4 = 9(x + 6)$

_____   _____   _____

_____   _____   _____

7. $y + 5 = -7(x - 9)$ **8.** $y - 7 = \frac{1}{3}(x + 9)$ **9.** $y - 3 = 3.2(x + 8)$

_____   _____   _____

_____   _____   _____

Write the point-slope form of the equation with the given slope that passes through the indicated point.

10. the line with slope -3 passing through $(4, 3)$

     11. the line with slope -1 passing through $(6, -2)$

_____   _____

12. the line with slope 5 passing through $(-7, 1)$

     13. the line with slope 7 passing through $(-8, -4)$

_____   _____

14. the line with slope 2 passing through $(-9, -6)$

     15. the line with slope -8 passing through $(7, -3)$

_____   _____

16. Write an equation of a line in point-slope form that is parallel to $y = -4x + 7$ and passes through the $(8, -5)$

_____

Holt Mathematics

12E Direct Variation

Georgia Performance Standards

M8A3.h, M8A3.i,
M8A4.f, M8A4.g

In a *direct variation,* when one quantity increases or decreases, the other quantity does the same. The table below shows the number of stamps *x* and the price *y* for each number.

Notice that when the number of stamps is doubled, the price is also doubled.

Stamps *x*	1	2	3	4	5	6
Price *y*	$0.37	$0.74	$1.11	$1.48	$1.85	$2.22

1. Use each pair of values (*x, y*) in the table to complete the graph.

2. To find the *constant of proportionality,* divide each price in the table by each number of stamps.

3. What feature of the graph tells you that the graph is of a direct variation?

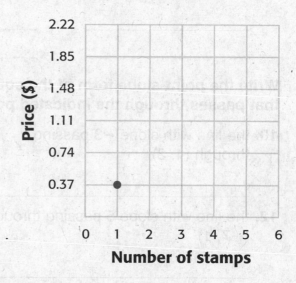

Think and Discuss

4. **Explain** the relationship between a constant of proportionality and the slope of the line.

5. **Give** a real-world example of a direct variation.

Holt Mathematics

Name _____ Date _____ Class _____

Review for Mastery
Direct Variation

Two data sets have **direct variation** if they are related by a constant ratio, the **constant of proportionality.** A graph of the data sets is linear and passes through (0, 0).

$y = kx$ **equation of direct variation,**
where k is the constant ratio

To determine whether two data sets have direct variation, you can compare ratios. You can also graph the data sets on a coordinate grid.

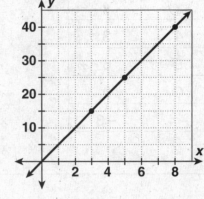

x	3	5	8
y	15	25	40

$\frac{y}{x} = \frac{15}{3} = \frac{25}{5} = \frac{40}{8} = \frac{5}{1}$ ← constant ratio

$k = 5 \rightarrow y = 5x$

The graph of the data sets is linear and passes through (0, 0).

So, the data sets show direct variation.

Determine whether the data sets show direct variation. If there is a constant ratio, identify it and write the equation of direct variation. Plot the points and tell whether the graph is linear.

1.
x	1	2	4	8
y	8	4	2	1

constant ratio? _____

If yes, equation. _____

Is the graph linear? _____

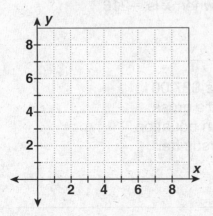

2.
x	0	2	3	5
y	0	20	30	50

constant ratio? _____

If yes, equation. _____

Is the graph linear? _____

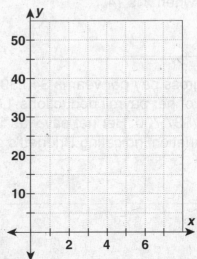

Holt Mathematics

LESSON
12E

Homework and Practice
Direct Variation

Make a graph to determine whether the data set shows direct variation.

1.

x	y
4	3
8	6
0	0
−4	−3

_____

_____

2. Write the equation of direct variation
for exercise 1.

_____

Find each equation of direct variation, given that *y* varies directly with *x*.

3. *y* is 27 when *x* is 3

_____

4. *y* is 8 when *x* is −40

_____

5. *y* is −54 when *x* is −12

_____

6. *y* is 21 when *x* is 49

_____

7. *y* is −31.5 when *x* is 14

_____

8. *y* is 180 when *x* is −216

_____

9. Bridgett's gross pay per year is $40,300. Her net pay is $27,001
as a result of her payroll deductions. Last year Bridgett's gross
salary was $37,700. Her net pay was $25,259. Write an equation
of direct variation indicating Bridgett's gross pay, *x*, versus her
net pay, *y*.

_____

Holt Mathematics

12F Graphing Inequalities in Two Variables

Georgia Performance Standards

M8A3.i, M8A4.b, M8A4.c, M8A4.d, M8A4.e, M8A4.f

The linear equation $y = 2x + 1$ is graphed at right.

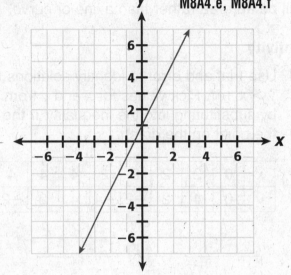

1. Substitute the point (1, 6) into each inequality.

	Point Above Line	Substituted into Inequality
$y > 2x + 1$	(1, 6)	
$y < 2x + 1$	(1, 6)	

2. Which inequality does the point (1, 6) satisfy?

3. Substitute the point (2, −4) into each inequality.

	Point Below Line	Substituted into Inequality
$y > 2x + 1$	(2, −4)	
$y < 2x + 1$	(2, −4)	

4. Which inequality does the point (2, −4) satisfy?

Think and Discuss

5. **Discuss** which points (those above or those below the line) you would expect to satisfy the inequalities $y > 2x + 1$ and $y < 2x + 1$.

Holt Mathematics

Hands-On Lab
Graphing Inequalities in Two Variables

An inequality with two variables can be graphed. However, the graph
will be an area rather than a line or curve.

Activity

1. Use trial and error to identify solutions to the inequality
   $y > x + 1$. Pick values for x and y from the table and test each
   by substituting into the inequality. If the value is a solution, plot
   the point on the graph.

x	0	2	2	2	2	4	4	4	4	−2	−2	−2	−2	−4	−4	−4	−4
y	0	4	2	−2	−4	4	2	−2	−4	4	2	−2	−4	4	2	−2	−4

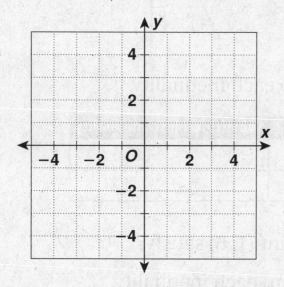

2. The equation $y = x + 1$ is known as the related equation for
   $y > x + 1$. Graph this equation on the same set of coordinates.
   Use a dashed line for the graph.

3. Lightly shade the area above and to the left of the graph of
   $y = x + 1$.

Holt Mathematics

Hands-On Lab

LESSON 12F *Graphing Inequalities in Two Variables, continued*

Think and Discuss

1. What is the relationship between the points you plotted in part 1 and the graph of the equation you constructed in part 2?

   _____

   _____

2. What does the shaded area represent?

   _____

   _____

3. Is the graph of $y = x + 1$ part of the solution set of the inequality $y > x + 1$?

   _____

   _____

4. Describe a procedure that can be used to graph any linear inequality.

   _____

   _____

401
Holt Mathematics

Hands-On Lab

LESSON 12F

Graphing Inequalities in Two Variables, continued

Try This

Graph the following inequalities.

1. $y > x - 1$

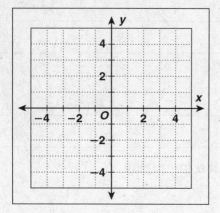

2. $y > 3x$

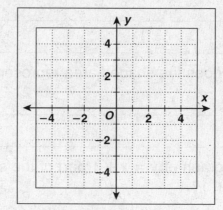

3. $y < x$

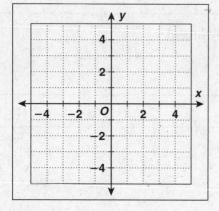

4. $y < x - 1$

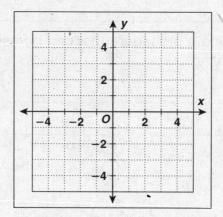

Holt Mathematics

LESSON 12F Technology Lab
Graph Inequalities In Two Variables

A graphing calculator can be used to graph the solution of an inequality in two variables.

Activity

1 To graph the inequality $y > 2x - 4$ using a graphing calculator, use the **Y=** menu, and enter the equation $y = 2x - 4$.

Press **Y=** 2 **X,T,θ,n** **−** 4 **GRAPH**

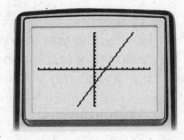

The line representing the graph of the equation represents the *boundary* of the solution region of the inequality. The graph of the inequality is either the region above the line or the region below the line. Use a test point to decide which region represents the graph of the inequality.

The point (0, 0) is a good test point if it is not on the line. Substituting 0 for both *x* and *y*, $0 > 2 \cdot 0 - 4$, or $0 > -4$, which is *true*. The solution graph is the region above the line.

To graph this region, press **Y=** **◄** **◄** and notice that the edit cursor moves to the left of **Y1** onto an icon that looks like a small line segment, \.

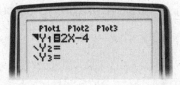

Now press the **ENTER** key several times and notice the different icons that are displayed. Choose the icon that looks like a shaded region above a line. Press **GRAPH** to display the shaded region. Any point, (*x, y*) not on the line that is in the shaded region is a solution of $y > 2x - 4$.

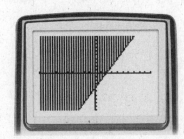

Holt Mathematics

Technology Lab

LESSON 12F

Graph Inequalities In Two Variables, continued

Think and Discuss

1. What inequality would the graph with all points below the *x*-axis shaded represent?

   _____

2. How would you use your calculator to display a graph of the region that is the intersection of the solution graphs of **both** $y > x - 2$ and $y < x + 3$.

   _____

   _____

   _____

   _____

Try This

Use a graphing calculator to graph each inequality.

1. $y < x - 4$
2. $y > 4 - x$
3. $y < 2x - 5$

4. $2x - 5y < 10$
5. $x + y < 4$
6. $3x + y > 6$

Holt Mathematics

Review for Mastery

LESSON 12F

Graphing Inequalities in Two Variables

A **boundary line** divides the coordinate plane into two *half-planes*.

When $y = -x + 4$ is a boundary line:

All the points on the line satisfy the equation.

    $(5, -1)$ is on the line since $-1 = -5 + 4$.

All the points in the half-plane <u>above the line</u> satisfy the linear inequality $y > -x + 4$.

    $(5, 3)$ is in the half-plane above the line since $3 > -5 + 4$.

All the points in the half-plane <u>below the line</u> satisfy the linear inequality $y < -x + 4$.

    $(-2, 1)$ lies in the half-plane below the line since $1 < -(-2) + 4$.

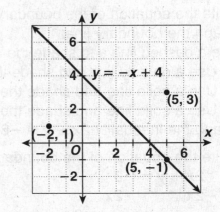

When a boundary line is in the form $y = mx + b$,

points in the half-plane above the line satisfy the inequality $y > mx + b$ and points in the half-plane below the line satisfy the inequality $y < mx + b$.

Complete the linear inequality that each point satisfies.

1. $(1, -2)$ is in the half-plane below the boundary line $y = 3x - 4$.

The boundary line is in the form $y = mx + b$; so, $(1, -2)$ satisfies the linear inequality y _____ $3x - 4$.

2. $(-3, 7)$ is in the half-plane below the boundary line $y = -2x + 6$.

The boundary line is in the form $y = mx + b$; so, $(-3, 7)$ satisfies the linear inequality y _____ $-2x + 6$.

Write the linear inequality whose solution set is shaded on each graph. The dashed boundary line is not included in the solution set.

3.

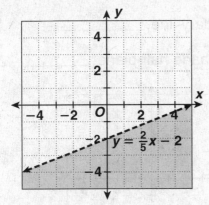

$y = \frac{2}{5}x - 2$

_____

4.

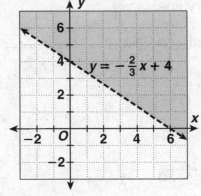

$y = -\frac{2}{3}x + 4$

_____

Holt Mathematics

Review for Mastery

Graphing Inequalities in Two Variables (continued)

To graph the solution set of a linear inequality:

Write the equation of the boundary line in the form $y = mx + b$.
Graph the boundary line.
Use a dashed line and shade the region above if $y > mx + b$.
 Use a dashed line and shade the region below if $y < mx + b$.
 Use a solid line and shade the region above if $y \geq mx + b$.
 Use a solid line and shade the region below if $y \leq mx + b$.
Graph the inequality $2x + y \leq -6$:

Write the equation of the boundary line in $y = mx + b$ form.

$$2x + y = -6$$
$$\underline{-2x \qquad\quad -2x}$$
$$y = -2x - 6$$
$$\overline{\text{slope} = -2,\ y\text{-intercept} = -6}$$

Since the inequality uses $\leq$,
draw a solid boundary line and
shade the half-plane below.

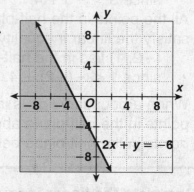

Graph the solution set of each inequality.

5. $3x + y \geq 4$

Rewrite equation $3x + y = 4$.

$y =$ _____

slope = _____, y-intercept = _____

Given symbol is $\geq$, so draw

boundary line _____

and shade half-plane _____.

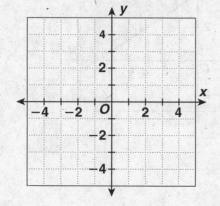

6. $2y - x < 6$

Rewrite equation $2y - x = 6$.

$y =$ _____

slope = _____, y-intercept = _____

Given symbol is $<$, so draw

boundary line _____

and shade half-plane _____.

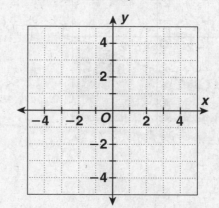

Holt Mathematics

Homework and Practice

LESSON
12F *Graphing Inequalities in Two Variables*

Graph each inequality.

1. $y \leq 3x - 4$

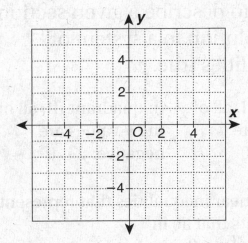

2. $y + 2x > 5$

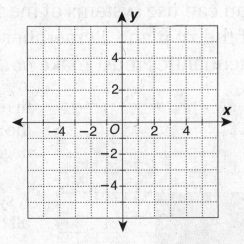

3. $x - 3y > 9$

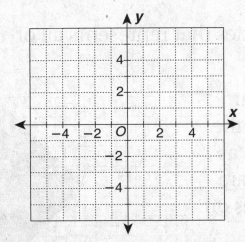

4. $-3x - y \leq 1$

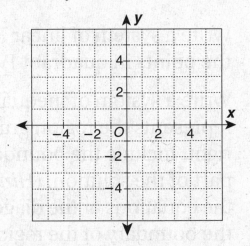

5. Richard must buy clothes for his new job. He has a budget of $250. The shirts he plans on buying cost $15 and the slacks costs $30. Let *x* equal the number of shirts and *y* equal the number of pairs of slacks Richard can buy with his clothes allowance. Write an inequality for this information.

_____

6. If Richard buys 4 pairs of slacks, what is the most number of shirts he can buy?

_____

Holt Mathematics

EXPLORATION

12G Solving Systems of Inequalities

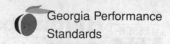

Georgia Performance
Standards

M8A5.a, M8A5.c,
M8A5.d

You can use systems of inequalities to describe a given section of the *xy*-plane. Remember that a solution to a system of inequalities must make *both* inequalities true.

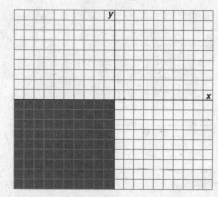

In quadrant III, all of the *x*-values are negative: $x < 0$

In quadrant III, all of the *y*-values are negative: $y < 0$

A system of linear inequalities that represents all of the points that lie in quadrant III is $\begin{cases} x < 0 \\ y < 0 \end{cases}$.

1. Write a system of linear inequalities that represents all of the points in quadrant IV.

2. Write a system of inequalities that represents the region graphed at the right. Include the boundary lines as part of the solution. (*Hint*: What are the equations of the diagonal lines on the boundary of the region?)

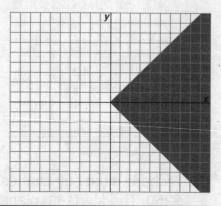

Think and Discuss

3. **Explain** why the graphs on this page cannot actually show all of the solutions to their systems of inequalities.

4. **Discuss** with your classmates when to include a boundary line as part of the solution to a system of inequalities.

408

Holt Mathematics

Review for Mastery

Solving Systems of Linear Equalities

You can graph a system of linear inequalities by combining the graphs of the inequalities.

Graph of $y \le 2x + 3$

Graph of $y > -x - 6$

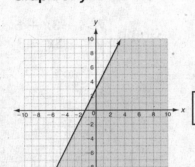

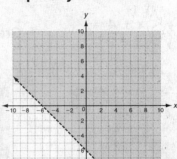

Graph of the system

$\begin{cases} y \le 2x + 3 \\ y > -x - 6 \end{cases}$

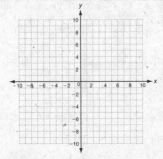

All solutions are in this double shaded area.

Two ordered pairs that are solutions: (3, 4) and (5, −2).

For each system below, give two ordered pairs that are solutions and two that are not solutions.

1.

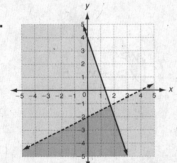

_____

_____

2.

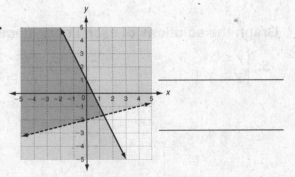

_____

_____

Graph each system of linear inequalities

3. $\begin{cases} y > x - 3 \\ y \ge -x + 6 \end{cases}$

4. $\begin{cases} y < x \\ y > -2x + 1 \end{cases}$

Holt Mathematics

Review for Mastery

LESSON 12G *Solving Systems of Linear Equalities (continued)*

A system of equations with parallel lines has no solutions.
Parallel lines in a system of inequalities might have solutions.

Graph $\begin{cases} y < x + 4 \\ y > x - 2 \end{cases}$.

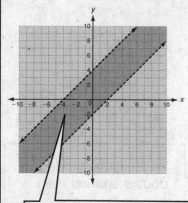

Solutions are in the double shaded area between the parallel lines.

Graph $\begin{cases} y \geq 2x + 4 \\ y > 2x - 1 \end{cases}$.

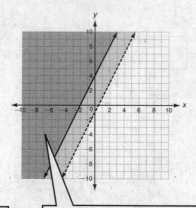

Solutions are in the double shaded area to one side of the line.

Graph $\begin{cases} y > -3x + 5 \\ y < -3x - 3 \end{cases}$.

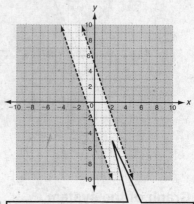

There are no overlapping areas. There are no solutions.

Graph the solutions of each linear inequality.

5. $\begin{cases} y \leq x - 3 \\ y > x + 3 \end{cases}$

6. $\begin{cases} y > 2x - 2 \\ y \leq 2x + 3 \end{cases}$

7. $\begin{cases} y > -x - 1 \\ y > -x - 5 \end{cases}$

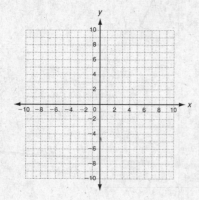

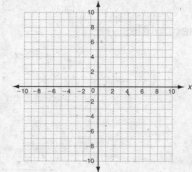

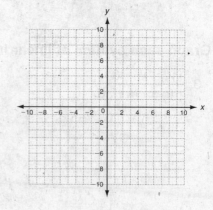

Holt Mathematics

Name _____ Date _____ Class _____

Homework and Practice
Solving Systems of Linear Equalities

Tell whether the ordered pair is a solution of the given system.

1. $(4, 5);$ $\begin{cases} y \leq x + 2 \\ y \geq x - 1 \end{cases}$

2. $(1, 3);$ $\begin{cases} y > 3x \\ y < x + 2 \end{cases}$

3. $(2, 3);$ $\begin{cases} y < 5x - 3 \\ y \geq -x \end{cases}$

_____ _____ _____

Graph the system of linear inequalities. a. Give two ordered pairs that are solutions. b. Give two ordered pairs that are not solutions.

4. $\begin{cases} y \geq x + 1 \\ y \leq -2x \end{cases}$

5. $\begin{cases} y < 2x + 4 \\ y > x - 1 \end{cases}$

6. $\begin{cases} y > -x \\ y > -x + 3 \end{cases}$

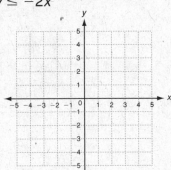
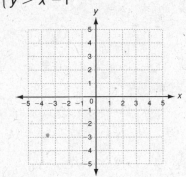
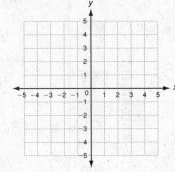

a. _____   a. _____   a. _____

b. _____   b. _____   b. _____

7. Lou is buying macaroni salad and potato salad for a picnic. Macaroni salad costs \$4 per pound and potato salad costs \$2 per pound. Lou would like to buy at least 6 pounds of salads and wants to spend no more than \$20.

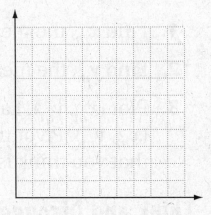

   a. Write a system of linear equations.
     Let x = pounds of macaroni salad
     Let y = pounds of potato salad

   _____

   b. Graph the solutions of the system.

   c. Describe all the possible combinations of pounds of salads that Lou could buy.

_____

_____

   d. List two possible combinations. _____

_____

Holt Mathematics

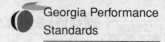

Georgia Performance
Standards

M8A3.i, M8A4.c,
M8A4.d, M8A4.f,
M8A4.g, M8D4.b

12H Lines of Best Fit

The table shows student enrollment at a college by year. The enrollment numbers are graphed below.

Year	2001	2002	2003	2004	2005	2006	2007	2008
Enrollment	950	995	1011	1020	1035			

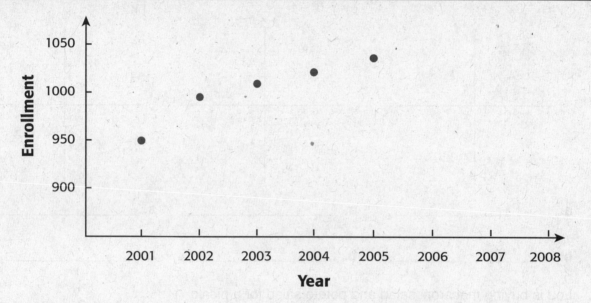

1. Find x_m, the mean of the x-values of the points on the graph.

2. Find y_m, the mean of the y-values of the points on the graph.

3. Plot (x_m, y_m). Lay the edge of a ruler on the graph through (x_m, y_m). Pivot the ruler around (x_m, y_m) and draw the line that you think is closest to the line of best fit.

Think and Discuss

4. **Predict** the enrollment for 2006, 2007, and 2008 by using the line of best fit.

Holt Mathematics

Name _____ Date _____ Class _____

Hands-On Lab
Lines of Best Fit

Activity

The table below shows the number of hours 10 students studied for a test and the scores they got on the test. Plot the data on the graph below.

Study Hours	1	5	4	3	1	2	2	4	5	3
Test Score	50	95	85	80	60	75	80	95	100	75

Find a line of best fit for the data.

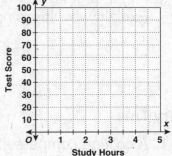

Step 1 Calculate the mean of the *x*-coordinates, indicating the study hours.

$$\frac{1 + 5 + 4 + 3 + 1 + 2 + 2 + 4 + 5 + 3}{10}$$

What is the mean of the *x*-coordinates? _____

Step 2 Calculate the mean of the *y*-coordinates, indicating the test scores.

$$\frac{50 + 95 + 85 + 80 + 60 + 75 + 80 + 95 + 100 + 75}{10}$$

What is the mean of the *y*-coordinates? _____

Step 3 Plot the point (*x*, *y*), where *x* is the mean of the *x*-coordinates and *y* is the mean of the *y*-coordinates.

Step 4 Estimate and plot the coordinates of another point on the line. Find the slope of the line as $\frac{y_2 - y_1}{x_2 - x_1}$. *m* =

_____

Step 5 Use point-slope form, $y - y_1 = m(x - x_1)$,. Substitute one of the points on the line for x_1 and y_1. Simplify to find the equation of a line of best fit.

_____

Holt Mathematics

Name _____ Date _____ Class _____

Think and Discuss

1. Can there be only one line of best fit for a graph? Explain why or why not.

_____

_____

_____

2. According to a line of best fit for the scatter plot on the previous page, to get a 100 on the test, a student needs to study 5 hours. Explain why this is not true for every student.

_____

_____

Try This

1. A college compared high-school grade point averages of ten of its freshman students with their grade point averages their first year of college. The data is shown in the scatterplot.

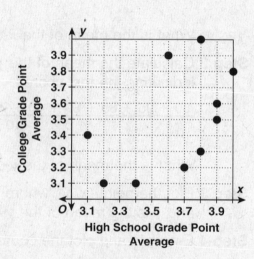

The data is

High School GPA	3.9	3.1	3.2	3.4	3.9	4.0	3.6	3.8	3.7	3.8
College GPA	3.5	3.4	3.1	3.1	3.6	3.8	3.9	4.0	3.2	3.3

Draw a line of best fit for the graph and find the equation of the line.

_____

Equation of the line:

_____

_____

_____

Holt Mathematics

Name _____ Date _____ Class _____

Line of best fit: a line drawn near the points on a scatter plot to show the trend between two sets of data

To draw a line of best fit:
    Draw the line through as many points as you can.
    Try to get an equal number of points above the line as below.
    Ignore any outliers.
    It may happen that none of the points lie on the line.

The line of best fit for the data in the scatter plot below slants up, indicating a positive correlation.

The slope of this line of best fit is positive and its *y*-intercept is about 3.

The line of best fit for the data in the scatter plot below slants down, indicating a negative correlation.

The slope of this line of best fit is positive and its *y*-intercept is about 28.

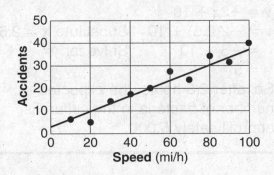

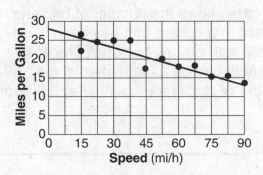

Draw a line of best fit for each graph.
Describe the slope and find an approximate
value for the *y*-intercept of the line of best fit.

1.

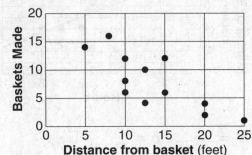

2.

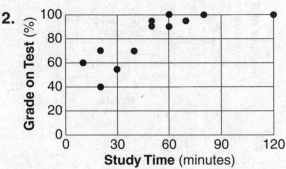

The line of best fit slants _____.

The slope of the line is _____.

The *y*-intercept is approximately _____.

The line of best fit slants _____.

The slope of the line is _____.

The *y*-intercept is approximately _____.

Holt Mathematics

Name _____ Date _____ Class _____

Review for Mastery
Lines of Best Fit (continued)

To write an equation for a line of best fit, you can use the slope-intercept form, $y = mx + b$.

After you have drawn the line of best fit, estimate its slope from any two points on the line whose coordinates you can read.

Draw a right triangle with the hypotenuse on the line of best fit.

$$\text{slope} = \frac{\text{length of vertical leg}}{\text{length of horizontal leg}}$$

$\text{slope} = -\frac{2}{1}$, y-intercept $= 10$

equation for the line of best fit:
$$y = -2x + 10$$

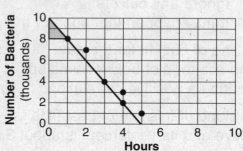

The data shows the number of bacteria present in a culture that has been treated with an anti-bacterial. The line of best fit can be used to predict the number of bacteria present after 2.5 hours.

$y = -2x + 10$
$y = -2(2.5) + 10$ Substitute $x = 2.5$.
    $= -5 + 10$ Solve for y.
    $= 5$

So, after 2.5 hours, the expected number of bacteria in the culture is approximately 5,000.

Find an equation for each line of best fit.
Use the equation to answer the question.

3.

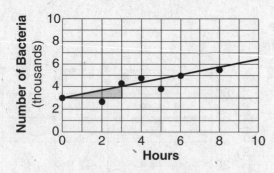

$m = $ _____ , $b = $ _____ ,

equation: _____

The expected number of bacteria after 10 hours is about _____.

4.

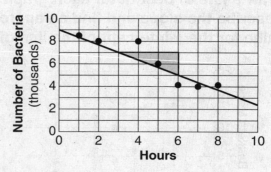

$m = $ _____ , $b = $ _____ ,

equation: _____

The expected number of bacteria after 10 hours is about _____.

Holt Mathematics

Name _____ Date _____ Class _____

Homework and Practice

Lines of Best Fit

Plot the data and find a line of best fit.

1.

x	2	4	6	8	10	12	14	16
y	12	14	18	16	20	21	25	26

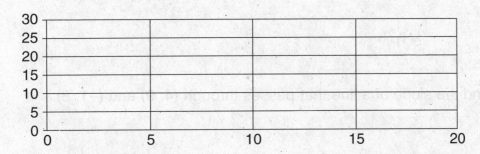

2.

x	5	10	18	20	25	30	35	40
y	135	120	105	90	94	56	50	30

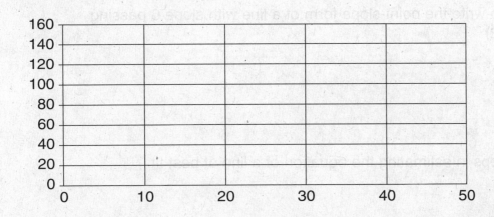

3. Nuxhall Company wants to predict their payroll costs for the next
two years based on the salary cost over the past six years. Use
the information in the table below and a line of best fit to
estimate the payroll costs for the next two years.

x	Year 1	Year 2	Year 3	Year 4	Year 5	Year 6
y	$96,750	$104,490	$112,925	$125,150	$131,650	$148,825

417

Holt Mathematics

Big Ideas

Answer these questions to summarize the important concepts from Chapter 12 in your own words.

1. Tell whether $y = -5x + 4$ is a linear equation. Explain.

2. Explain how to find the slope of a line that passes through $(4, 9)$ and $(-1, 8)$.

3. Explain how to write the point-slope form of a line with slope 6 passing through $(5, -2)$.

4. Explain the steps in estimating the equation of a line of best fit.

For more review of Chapter 12:

- Complete the Chapter 12 Study Guide and Review on pages 670–672 of your textbook.

- Complete the Ready to Go On quizzes on pages 648 and 664 of your textbook.

Holt Mathematics

Project
Sequences and Functions: Growing and Growing

Career: Bacteriologist

Bacteriologists study the growth and characteristics of microorganisms. They generally work in the fields of medicine and public health. Bacteria colonies grow very quickly. The rate at which bacteria multiply depends upon temperature, nutrient supply, and other factors.

In this chapter project...you will draw and analyze a fractal pattern. You will:

• Learn about microorganisms that grow exponentially.

• Research common fractals, such as the Koch snowflake or the Sierpinski triangle.

• Draw several stages of the fractal you chose and decorate them. Keep track of how each fractal grows at each stage, and graph the number of line segments or triangles at each stage.

To get started, work through the Addition by Division worksheet on the next page.

This chapter project reinforces your understanding of these Georgia Performance Standards:

M8A3.d Recognize functions in a variety of representations and a variety of contexts.

M8P5.a Create and use representations to organize, record, and communicate mathematical ideas.

---

go.hrw.com
Chapter Project Online
KEYWORD: MT7 Ch13

Holt Mathematics

CHAPTER **13**	# Project Recording Sheet
	Sequences and Functions

Addition by Division

Bacteriologists study the growth and characteristics of microorganisms, the way they interact with their environment including human beings.

Bacteria are one-celled organisms which grow in number by the division of individual cells. Although some bacteria create illness and even death in people, bacteria have important roles in many natural cycles. How long it takes a bacteria population to grow depends upon factors such as temperature and nutrient supply. Doubling time is the time it takes a population to double at a constant rate of growth. The number of bacteria is 2^n where n is the number of times the population has doubled.

E. coli bacterium	
Conditions	**Doubling Time (min)**
Optimum temperature (37°C) and growth medium	20
Low Temperature (below 37°C)	40
Low Growth Medium	60
Low Temperature, Low Growth Medium	120

B. anthracis bacterium	
Conditions	**Doubling Time (min)**
Optimum temperature (37°C) and growth medium	45
Low Temperature (below 37°C)	75
Low Growth Medium	90
Low Temperature, Low Growth Medium	120

Create a graph that compares the growth of E. coli and B. anthracis for 12 hours under optimum conditions. Extend the curves to estimate the differences in the numbers of bacteria after one day.

_____

Research: What other things can you discover that show geometric sequences of growth?

_____

Holt Mathematics

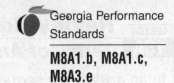

13A Terms of Arithmetic Sequences

Georgia Performance Standards

M8A1.b, M8A1.c, M8A3.e

In an *arithmetic sequence,* the difference between one term and the next is always the same.

The table shows the first four terms of an arithmetic sequence.

Term 1	Term 2	Term 3	Term 4	Term 5	Term 6	Term 7
10	16	22	28			

1. Find the difference between two consecutive terms.

2. Find the next three terms.

3. Find a short way to find the 20th term.

The table shows an arithmetic sequence with the first three terms missing.

Term 1	Term 2	Term 3	Term 4	Term 5	Term 6	Term 7
			88	84	80	76

4. Find the difference between two consecutive terms.

5. Find the first three terms.

Think and Discuss

6. **Discuss** the similarities and differences between the two sequences.

7. **Explain** your strategy for finding the 20th term in the first sequence.

Holt Mathematics

Name _____ Date _____ Class _____

Review for Mastery
Terms of Arithmetic Sequences

In an **arithmetic sequence,** the difference between terms
is constant. The difference is called the **common difference.**

This is an arithmetic sequence with a common difference of 3.	This is not an arithmetic sequence since there is no common difference.
2, 5, 8, 11, 14, ...	2, 5, 9, 14, 20, ...
3 3 3 3	3 4 5 6

Complete to determine if each sequence is arithmetic.

1. 20, 16, 12, 8, 4, ...

−4 ___ ___ ___

arithmetic? _____

2. 1, 2, 4, 8, 16, ...

1 ___ ___ ___

arithmetic? _____

3. 0.1, 0.2, 0.3, 0.4, ...

___ ___ ___

arithmetic? _____

4. $\frac{1}{2}$, 1, $\frac{3}{2}$, 2, $\frac{5}{2}$, ...

___ ___ ___ ___

arithmetic? _____

5. 2, $\frac{3}{2}$, 1, $\frac{1}{2}$, 0, ...

___ ___ ___ ___

arithmetic? _____

6. 3, 1, 0, $-\frac{1}{2}$, $-\frac{1}{4}$, ...

___ ___ ___ ___

arithmetic? _____

You can use the common difference to find any term in an arithmetic sequence.

4, 6, 8, 10, 12, ...This arithmetic sequence has a common difference of 2.

2 2 2 2

This is the 1st term of the sequence.	4
For the 2nd term, add the common difference × 1	4 + 2 × 1 = 6
For the 3rd term, add the common difference × 2	4 + 2 × 2 = 8
For the 4th term, add the common difference × 3	4 + 2 × 3 = 10
For the 5th term, add the common difference × 4	4 + 2 × 4 = 12
For the nth term, add the common difference × $(n − 1)$	4 + 2 × $(n − 1)$

Complete to find the given term of the arithmetic sequence
4, 6, 8, 10, 12, ...

7. the 9th term

4 + 2 × ___ = ___

8. the 20th term

4 + 2 × ___ = ___

9. the 100th term

4 + 2 × ___ = ___

Holt Mathematics

Name _____ Date _____ Class _____

Review for Mastery
Terms of Arithmetic Sequences (continued)

You can use a formula to find the nth term, a_n, of an arithmetic sequence with common difference d. $\quad a_n = a_1 + (n - 1)d$

Find the 20th term of this arithmetic sequence: 2, 5, 8, 11, 14, …

$a_n = a_1 + (n - 1)d$
$a_{20} = 2 + (20 - 1)3$
$a_{20} = 2 + (19)3 = 2 + 57 = 59$

Complete to find the given term of each arithmetic sequence.

10. 28, 34, 40, 46, 52, …
Find the 18th term.

$n =$ _____, $a_1 =$ _____, $d =$ _____

$a_{18} =$ _____ $+ ($ _____ $- 1)$ _____

$=$ _____ $+$ _____ $=$ _____

11. $\frac{1}{8}, \frac{1}{4}, \frac{3}{8}, \frac{1}{2}, \frac{5}{8}, …$
Find the 25th term.

$n =$ _____, $a_1 =$ _____, $d =$ _____

$a_{25} =$ _____ $+ ($ _____ $- 1)$ _____

$=$ _____ $+$ _____ $=$ _____

You can use the same formula to find other missing information.

What term of the arithmetic sequence 0.25, 0.50, 0.75, … is 6.5?

Assign values to the variables.	$a_1 = 0.25,\ d = 0.25,\ a_n = 6.5,\ n = ?$
Substitute into the formula.	$a_n = a_1 + (n - 1)d$
Solve for n.	$6.5 = 0.25 + (n - 1)0.25$
Multiply.	$6.5 = 0.25 + 0.25n - 0.25$
Combine like terms.	$6.5 = 0.25n$
Divide.	$\dfrac{6.5}{0.25} = \dfrac{0.25n}{0.25}$

So, 6.5 is the 26th term. $\qquad\qquad 26 = n$

Complete to answer the question.

12. What term of the arithmetic sequence 8, 16, 24, 32, … is 112?

$a_n = a_1 + (n - 1)d$

_____ $=$ _____ $+ (n - 1)$ _____ Substitute.

$a_1 =$ _____

_____ Solve for n.

$d =$ _____

_____

$a_n =$ _____

_____

So, 112 is the _____ term

_____ $= n$

Holt Mathematics

LESSON 13A **Homework and Practice**

Arithmetic Sequences

Determine if each sequence could be arithmetic. If so, give the common difference.

1. −19, −16, −13, −10, −7, …

2. 7, 14, 28, 56, 112, …

3. 8, 1, −6, − 13, − 20, …

_____

_____

_____

4. 1, 2.2, 4.84, 10.648, 23.4256 …

5. $\frac{1}{10}$, $\frac{3}{5}$, $\frac{11}{10}$, $\frac{8}{5}$, $\frac{21}{10}$, …

6. −10.4, −8.7, −7.1, −5.4, −3.7, …

_____

_____

_____

7. $\frac{1}{8}$, $\frac{1}{4}$, $\frac{3}{8}$, $\frac{1}{2}$, $\frac{5}{8}$, …

8. 91, 42, −7, −56, −105, …

9. −25.3, −18.5, −11.7, −4.9, 1.9, …

_____

_____

_____

Find the given term in each arithmetic sequence.

10. 15th term: 35, 42, 49, 56, 63, …

11. 28th term: −41, −29, −17, −5, 7, …

_____

_____

12. 32nd term: 204, 158, 112, 66, 20, …

13. 97th term: −8, −22, −36, −50, −64, …

_____

_____

14. 45th term: 3, 5.9, 8.8, 11.7, 14.6, …

15. 61st term: 49, 31, 13, −5, −23, …

_____

_____

16. 74th term: 84, 62, 40, 18, −4, …

17. 37th term: $\frac{1}{9}$, $\frac{4}{9}$, $\frac{7}{9}$, $1\frac{1}{9}$, $1\frac{4}{9}$, …

_____

_____

18. Write the first six terms in an arithmetic sequence that begins with −8.7 and has a common difference of −3.9.

_____

19. Corrine starts a book collection by purchasing seven books. Each week she adds two new books. How many weeks before Corrine has 75 books in her collection?

_____

Holt Mathematics

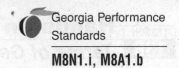

Georgia Performance
Standards
_____
M8N1.i, M8A1.b

13B Terms of Geometric Sequences

In a *geometric sequence,* the ratio of one term to the next is always the same.

The table shows the first four terms of a geometric sequence.

Term 1	Term 2	Term 3	Term 4	Term 5	Term 6	Term 7
10	20	40	80			

1. Find the ratio between two consecutive terms.

2. Find the next three terms.

3. Find a short way to find the 20th term.

The table shows a geometric sequence with the first three terms missing.

Term 1	Term 2	Term 3	Term 4	Term 5	Term 6	Term 7
			150	75	37.5	18.75

4. Find the ratio between two consecutive terms.

5. Find the first three terms.

Think and Discuss

6. **Discuss** the similarities and differences between the two sequences.

7. **Explain** your strategy for finding the 20th term in the first sequence.

Holt Mathematics

Hands-On Lab
Terms of Geometric Sequences

Activity 1

What is the common ratio of the geometric sequence in the table?
Complete the table.

Term Number	a_1	a_2	a_3	a_4	a_5	a_6	a_7	a_8
Term	1	4	16	64				

Step 1 Divide the second term by the first term.

$4 \div 1 =$ _____

Step 2 Divide the third term by the second term.

$16 \div 4 =$ _____

Step 3 Divide the fourth term by the third term.

$64 \div 16 =$ _____

What is the common ratio? _____

Step 4 To complete the table, multiply a_4 by the common ratio to get a_5.
Then multiply a_5 by the common ratio and so on.

Activity 2

Find the 12th term in the geometric sequence: 1, 3, 9, 27 ...

Step 1 Find the common ratio, r, of the sequence.

$r = 3 \div 1 =$ _____

Step 2 Use the formula $a_n = a_1 \times r^{n-1}$ to find the 12th term.

$a_{12} = 1 \times 3^{11}$.

Step 3 Use a calculator to find 3^{11}.

$a_{12} =$ _____

Holt Mathematics

Name _____ Date _____ Class _____

Hands-On Lab

LESSON
13B *Terms of Geometric Sequences, continued*

Think and Discuss

1. Could the following sequence be geometric? Explain how you know.

   512, 128, 32, 8, …

   _____

   _____

Try This

1. Could the following sequence be geometric? If so, what is the common ratio?

   2, 5, 8, 11, 14, …

   _____

2. Find the next 4 terms in the sequence shown in the table.

Term Number	a_1	a_2	a_3	a_4	a_5	a_6	a_7	a_8
Term	2	$\frac{1}{2}$	$\frac{1}{8}$	$\frac{1}{32}$				

3. Find the 18th term of the geometric sequence. Show your work.

   160, 80, 40, 20 …

Holt Mathematics

LESSON 13B **Technology Lab 1**
Generate Arithmetic and Geometric Sequences

Graphing calculators can be used to explore arithmetic and
geometric sequences.

Activity

1 The command **seq(** is used to generate a sequence.

a. Press **2nd** **STAT** OPS 5:seq.

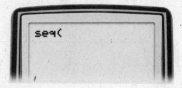

The **seq(** command is followed by the rule for generating
the sequence, the variable used in the rule, and the
positions of the first and last terms in the sequence. To
find the first 20 terms of the arithmetic sequence
generated by the rule
$5 + (x - 1) \cdot 3$, enter **seq($5 + (x - 1) \cdot 3, x, 1, 20$):**

5 **+** **(** **X,T,θ,n** **−** 1 **)** **×**

3 **,** **X,T,θ,n** **,** 1 **,** 20 **ENTER**

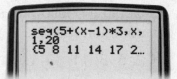

b. You can see all 20 terms by pressing the right arrow
key repeatedly. From the calculator display, the first
term is 5, the second is 8, the third is 11, the fourth is
14, and so on.

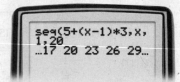

2 Consider the *geometric* sequence whose *n*th term is

$3\left(\dfrac{1}{4}\right)^{n-1}$. To use a graphing calculator to find the first 15

terms in fraction

form, press **2nd** **STAT** **>** 5:seq 3 **×** **(** 1 **÷** 4 **)**

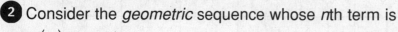

∧ **(** **X,T,θ,n** **−** 1 **)** **,** **X,T,θ,n** **,** 1 **,** 15 **MATH**

1:Frac **ENTER** .

To see all 15 items, press the right arrow key repeatedly.

Holt Mathematics

Technology Lab 1

LESSON 13B

Generate Arithmetic and Geometric Sequences

Think and Discuss

1. Why is the seventh term of the sequence in ❷ *not* displayed as a fraction?

_____

_____

_____

Try This

Find the first 15 terms of each sequence. Tell if the consecutive terms increase or decrease.

1. $-4 + (n - 1) \cdot 7$

_____

2. $2\left(\frac{1}{5}\right)^{n-1}$

_____

_____

3. 9, 14, 19, 24...

_____

4. $2, \frac{2}{3}, \frac{2}{9}, \frac{2}{27}...$

_____

_____

_____

Holt Mathematics

Technology Lab 2
Terms of Geometric Sequences

Activity

Consider the following sequence of tile groupings.

Write down the number of tiles in each grouping.

_____

Starting with the single tile, as you look from one tile grouping to
the next, what pattern do you see?

_____

What type of sequence do these tile groupings represent? Why?

_____

_____

How many tiles will be in the next two tile groupings in the
sequence?

_____

How many tiles will the 10th tile grouping have? Justify your answer.

_____

_____

Holt Mathematics

LESSON 13B | Technology Lab 2
Terms of Geometric Sequences, continued

Think and Discuss

1. Do geometric sequences always increase? Justify your answer.

_____

_____

2. What is the 10th term in the geometric sequence that begins with

   $1, \frac{1}{2}, \frac{1}{4}, ...$?

_____

Try This

1. Use circles, squares or other shapes to represent the first three
   terms of a geometric sequence. The sequence begins with the
   number $a_1 = 2$, and has a common ratio $r = 3$.

_____

2. Find the 4th, 5th, and 10th terms in the sequence.

_____

_____

3. What is the nth term? Use the formula for the nth term: $a_n = a_1 r^{n-1}$.

_____

_____

4. What is the 20th term?

_____

Holt Mathematics

LESSON 13B Review for Mastery
Terms of Geometric Sequences

In a **geometric sequence,** the ratio of one term to the next is constant.
The ratio is called **common ratio.**

This is a geometric sequence
with a common ratio of $\frac{3}{1} = 3$.

2, 6, 18, 54, 162, ...

$\frac{3}{1}$ $\frac{3}{1}$ $\frac{3}{1}$ $\frac{3}{1}$

This is not a geometric sequence
since there is no common ratio.

2, 4, 2, 4, 2, ...

$\frac{2}{1}$ $\frac{1}{2}$ $\frac{2}{1}$ $\frac{1}{2}$

Complete to determine if each sequence is geometric. Write *yes* or *no*.

1. $\frac{1}{125}$, $\frac{1}{25}$, $\frac{1}{5}$, 1, 5, ...

$\frac{5}{1}$ ___ ___ ___

geometric? _____

2. $\frac{1}{8}$, $\frac{1}{4}$, $\frac{3}{8}$, $\frac{1}{2}$, $\frac{5}{8}$, ...

$\frac{2}{1}$

geometric? _____

3. 4, −2, 1, $-\frac{1}{2}$, $\frac{1}{4}$ ...

geometric? _____

You can use the common ratio to find any term in a geometric
sequence.

2, 8, 32, 128, ...This geometric sequence has a common ratio of $\frac{4}{1}$ or 4.

4 4 4 4

This is the 1st term of the sequence.   2
Multiply it by the common ratio to get the 2nd term. $2 \times 4 = 8$
Multiply it by the square of the common ratio to get the 3rd term. $2 \times 4^2 = 32$
Multiply it by the cube of the common ratio to get the 4th term. $2 \times 4^3 = 128$
To get the *n*th term, multiply the 1st term by the common ratio $2 \times 4^{n-1}$
raised to the $(n − 1)$ power.

**Complete to find the given term of the geometric
sequence 2, 8, 32, 128, ...**

4. 5th term

$2 \times 4^{} = $ _____

5. 7th term

$2 \times 4^{} = $ _____

6. 6th term

$2 \times 4^{} = $ _____

7. 10th term

$2 \times $ ___ $ = $ _____

8. 8th term

$2 \times $ ___ $ = $ _____

9. 9th term

$2 \times $ ___ $ = $ _____

Holt Mathematics

LESSON 13B

Review for Mastery

Terms of Geometric Sequences (continued)

You can use a formula to find the nth term,
a_n, of a geometric sequence with common ratio r: $\quad \boldsymbol{a_n = a_1 \cdot r^{n-1}}$

Find the 7th term of this geometric sequence: 3, 6, 12, 24, 48, ...

$a_n = a_1 \cdot r^{n-1}$ Find r. $r = \dfrac{6}{3} = 2$

$a_7 = 3 \cdot 2^{7-1}$ Substitute $n = 7$, $a_1 = 3$, $r = 2$.

$a_7 = 3 \cdot 2^{7-1} = 3 \cdot 2^6 = 3 \cdot 64 = 192$ The 7th term is 192.

Find the given term of each geometric sequence.

10. 1, 10, 100, 1000, ...
Find the 9th term.

$n = 9$, $a_1 = 1$, $r = \dfrac{10}{1} =$ _____

$a_9 = 1 \cdot$ _____ $^{9-1} = 1 \cdot$ _____

$a_9 = 1 \cdot$ _____

$=$ _____

11. 1.1, 1.21, 1.331, 1.4641, ...
Find the 7th term.

$n = 7$, $a_1 = 1.1$, $r = \dfrac{1.21}{1.1} =$ _____

$a_7 = 1.1 \times$ _____ $= 1.1 \times$ _____

$a_7 = 1.1 \times$ _____

$=$ _____

Which sequence has the greater 20th term? by how much?

1000, 1050, 1100, 1150, ...
arithmetic sequence, $d = 50$

$a_{20} = 1000 + (20 - 1)50$

$a_{20} = 1000 + (19)50 = 1000 + 950$

$a_{20} = 1950$

2, 4, 8, 16, ...
geometric sequence, $r = 2$

$a_{20} = 2 \cdot 2^{20-1}$

$a_{20} = 2 \cdot 2^{19} = 2 \cdot 524{,}288 = 1{,}048{,}576$

$a_{20} = 1{,}048{,}576$

The 20th term of this geometric sequence is greater by 1,046,626.

**Determine whether each sequence is arithmetic or geometric
and find its 15th term.**

12. $2, 1, \dfrac{1}{2}, \dfrac{1}{4}, \ldots$

sequence is _____

_____

_____

$a_{15} =$ _____

13. $\dfrac{5}{2}, 3, \dfrac{7}{2}$

sequence is _____

_____

_____

_____ $a_{15} =$ ____

Holt Mathematics

LESSON 13B Homework and Practice
Geometric Sequences

Determine if each sequence could be geometric. If so give the common ratio.

1. 3, 15, 75, 375, 1,875, ...

2. −36, −30, −24, −18, −12, ...

3. 3, $\frac{3}{2}$, $\frac{3}{4}$, $\frac{3}{8}$, $\frac{3}{16}$, ...

_____

_____

_____

4. 850, 170, 34, 6.8, 1.36, ...

5. 6, 33, 171, 861, 4,311, ...

6. 14, 98, 686, 4,802, 33,614, ...

_____

_____

_____

7. 999, 333, 111, 99, 33, ...

8. 95, 38, $15\frac{1}{5}$, $6\frac{2}{25}$, $2\frac{54}{125}$, ...

9. 4, 22, 121, 665.5, 3,660.25, ...

_____

_____

_____

Find the given term in each geometric sequence. If necessary, round to the nearest hundredth.

10. 8th term; 4, 12, 36, 108, 324, ...

11. 5th term; $a_1 = 155$, $r = 0.6$

_____

_____

12. 7th term; 4, 14, 49, 171.5, 600.25, ...

13. 12th term; $a_1 = 0.05$, $r = 9$

_____

_____

14. 16th term; $\frac{1}{3125}$, $\frac{1}{625}$, $\frac{1}{125}$, $\frac{1}{25}$, $\frac{1}{5}$, ...

15. 9th term; $\frac{7}{9}$, $2\frac{1}{3}$, 7, 21, 63, ...

_____

_____

16. Nicholas has a picture that is 3 in. × 5 in. If he enlarges the photo by 25% five times, what are the dimensions of the new photo? Round to the nearest tenth of an inch?

_____

Holt Mathematics

EXPLORATION

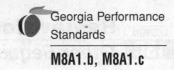

Georgia Performance
Standards

M8A1.b, M8A1.c

13C Other Sequences

The table shows a sequence that is determined by the sum of consecutive odd numbers.

Term 1	Term 2	Term 3	Term 4	Term 5	Term 6	Term 7
1	1 + 3 = 4	1 + 3 + 5 = 9				

1. Find the next four terms.

2. Is the difference between consecutive terms a constant?

The table shows a sequence that is determined by the sum of consecutive even numbers.

Term 1	Term 2	Term 3	Term 4	Term 5	Term 6	Term 7
2	2 + 4 = 6	2 + 4 + 6 = 12				

3. Find the next four terms.

4. Is the difference between consecutive terms a constant?

Think and Discuss

5. Describe the sequence created by the differences of consecutive terms in the first table above.

6. Describe the sequence created by the differences of consecutive terms in the second table above.

Holt Mathematics

Name _____ Date _____ Class _____

LESSON 13C Review for Mastery
Other Sequences

Differences can help you find patterns in some sequences.

Find the next number in the sequence: 1, 6, 15, 28, 45, ...

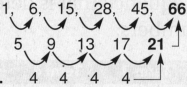

Find the **first differences.**   5   9   13   17   **21**

Find the **second differences.**   4   4   4   4

Use the second and first diffences to calculate the next term.

Complete to find the next term in each sequence.

1. 1, 4, 9, 16, 25, ...

   3   5   7   9

   2   2   2

The next term in the sequence is:

25 + _____ = _____

2. 1, 8, 21, 40, 65, ...

   7   13   19   25

   6   6   6

The next term in the sequence is:

65 + _____ = _____

A rule is used to define a sequence.

Write a rule for this sequence: $\frac{1}{2}, \frac{2}{3}, \frac{3}{4}, \frac{4}{5}, \frac{5}{6}, \ldots$

A possible rule is that the numerator of a term is the number of that terms position, and the denominator is 1 more than the numerator.

This can be written algebraically as $a_n = \frac{n}{n+1}$.

Using this rule, the 10th term of the sequence is $a_{10} = \frac{10}{10+1} = \frac{10}{11}$.

Use the given rule to write the 5th and 10th terms.

3. 1, 8, 27, 64, ...

$a_n = n^3$

$a_5 = ($_____$)^3 = $_____

$a_{10} = ($_____$)^3 = $_____

4. 1, 3, 6, 10, ...

$a_n = \frac{n(n+1)}{2}$

$a_5 = \frac{(\ \ )(\ \ +1)}{2} = $_____

$a_{10} = \frac{(\ \ )(\ \ +1)}{2} = $_____

5. 1, −3, 1, −3, ...

$a_n = 2(-1)^{n+1} - 1$

$a_5 = 2(-1)^{-+1} - 1$

$= $_____

$a_{10} = 2(-1)^{-+1} - 1$

$= $_____

Holt Mathematics

Homework and Practice

LESSON 13C *Other Sequences*

Use first and second differences to find the next three terms in each sequence.

1. 12, 13, 16, 21, 28, …

2. 4, 6, 10, 16, 24, …

_____

_____

3. $\frac{3}{4}$, $2\frac{3}{4}$, $5\frac{1}{4}$, $8\frac{1}{4}$, $11\frac{3}{4}$, …

4. 3.6, 4.1, 6.1, 9.6, 14.6, …

_____

_____

Give the next three terms in each sequence using the simplest rule you can find.

5. 1, 2, 4, 7, 11, …

6. 6, 7, 10, 15, 22, …

_____

_____

7. 2, 5, 10, 17, 26, …

8. 32, 50, 72, 98, 128, …

_____

_____

9. 400, 361, 324, 289, 256, …

10. 2.5, 10, 22.5, 40, 62.5, …

_____

_____

Find the first five terms of each sequence defined by the given rule.

11. $a_n = \frac{n^2}{2n}$

12. $a_n = \frac{n^2 + 5}{2n}$

13. $a_n = \frac{6n - 2}{n^2 + 1}$

_____   _____

_____

14. Suppose *a, b,* and *c* are three consecutive numbers in the Fibonacci sequence. Complete the following table and guess the pattern.

a, b, c	ac	b^2
1, 1, 2		
2, 3, 5		
5, 8, 13		
13, 21, 34		
34, 55, 89		

_____

Holt Mathematics

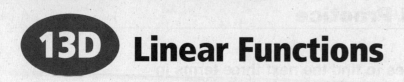

13D Linear Functions

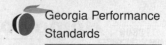

Georgia Performance
Standards

M8A3.d, M8A3.e,
M8A3.f, M8A3.g,
M8A3.i, M8A4.e,
M8A4.f

Many everyday situations can be represented with *linear functions.*

For each situation, write a rule and complete the table.

1. A car beginning at time = 0 hours travels 60 miles per hour.

Input x (hr)	Rule $y = $ _____	Output y (mi)
0	60 · 0	0
1	60 · 1	60
2		120
3		
4		

2. A club that has $2000.00 in its treasury plans to spend $150.00 per week.

Input x (weeks)	Rule $y = $ _____	Output y ($)
0		2000
1		1850
2		1700
3		
4		

Think and Discuss

3. **Explain** how you determined the rules in Problems 1 and 2.

Holt Mathematics

Name _____ Date _____ Class _____

Review for Mastery
Linear Functions

The graph of a **linear function** is a straight line, so you can write a **rule** for a linear function in slope-intercept form. Use function notation to show that the output value, $f(x)$, corresponds to the input value, x.

$$f(x) = mx + b$$

slope y-intercept

You can find the slope and y-intercept of a linear function in a graph of the function or in a table of its x-values and y-values.

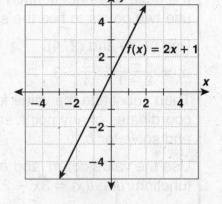

The table shows the y-intercept, 1. $b = 1$

Substitute 1 for b into the slope-intercept form. $f(x) = mx + 1$

Substitute a pair of x- and y-values and solve. $5 = m \cdot 2 + 1$

$$4 = 2m$$

$$2 = m$$

x	y
−1	−1
0	1
1	3
2	5

So, the rule for the function is $f(x) = 2x + 1$.

Write the rule for the linear function.

1.
x	y
−2	−1
−1	1
0	3
1	5

$$f(x) = mx + b$$

$$f(x) = mx + \underline{\quad}$$

$(x, y) = (1, 5)$ $5 = m(\underline{\quad}) + \underline{\quad}$

$$\underline{\quad} = m$$

$$f(x) = \underline{\qquad\qquad}$$

2.
x	y
−1	3
0	−1
1	−5
2	−9

$$f(x) = mx + b$$

$$f(x) = mx \underline{\quad}$$

$(x, y) = (−1, 3)$ $\underline{\quad} = m(\underline{\quad}) \underline{\quad}$

$$\underline{\quad} = m$$

$$f(x) = \underline{\qquad\qquad}$$

Holt Mathematics

LESSON 13D Review for Mastery

Linear Functions (continued)

If a table does not contain the y-intercept, use two points to find the slope.

Use (1, 1) and (2, 4).

$$m = \frac{4 - 1}{2 - 1} = \frac{3}{1} = 3$$

Then substitute the value for m and the coordinates of any point, say (1, 1), and solve for b.

Use the values of m and b to write the function rule: $f(x) = 3x - 2$

x	y
−2	−8
−1	−5
1	1
2	4

$f(x) = mx + b$

$1 = 3(1) + b$

$1 = 3 + b$

$\underline{-3 \;\; -3}$

$-2 = b$

Write the rule for the linear function.

3.

x	y
−3	−17
−1	−7
1	3
3	13

Using (1, 3) and (3, 13);

$m =$ _____ = _____ = ___

Using your value for m and (1, 3):

$f(x) = mx + b$

___ = ___ + b

___ = b

$f(x) =$ _____

Use the graph to write the function rule.

4. From point B, read the y-intercept.

$b =$ ___

Write the coordinates of two points on the line.

$A($ ___ $)$, $C($ ___ $)$

Use these points to find the slope.

$m =$ _____ = _____ = ___

$f(x) =$ _____

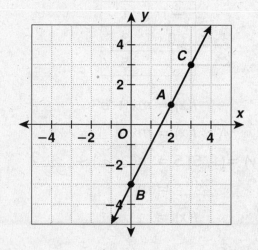

LESSON **Homework and Practice**
13D **Linear Functions**

Write a rule for each linear function.

1.
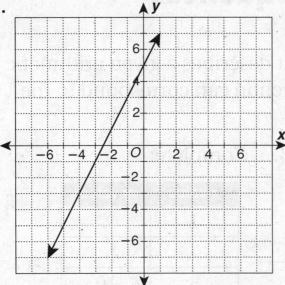

2.
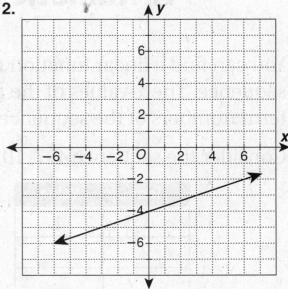

_____

3.

x	−4	−2	3	5
$f(x)$	13	7	−8	−14

_____

4.

x	−6	−4	2	8
$f(x)$	−10	−9	−6	−3

_____

5. A salesperson is paid a base salary of $300 plus 8% of their sales. Write a function rule for the salary. Graph the function.

6. If a salesperson has $900 in sales, what is the salesperson's salary?

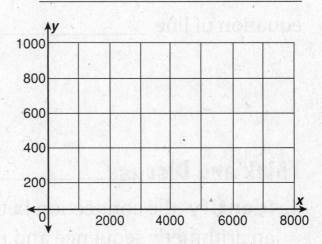

_____

441   **Holt Mathematics**

Georgia Performance
Standards

M8A3.g

13E Linear Functions and Arithmetic Sequences

You can find a linear function that describes a given arithmetic sequence. The *x*-values of the function can correspond to the term numbers of the sequence.

Consider the sequence 4, 7, 10, 13…. Complete:

Term	Value
1	4
2	

→

x-value	*y*-value
1	
3	10

common difference _____   slope of line _____

Graph the ordered pairs from the table on the right. Draw a straight line through the points.

equation of line _____

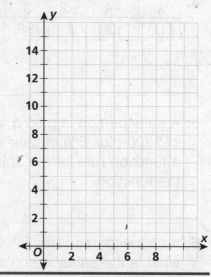

Think and Discuss

1. **Identify** the connection between the common difference of an arithmetic sequence and the slope of its associated linear function.

2. **Discuss** how you could use your graph to determine the 7th and 8th terms of the sequence above.

Holt Mathematics

Review for Mastery

LESSON 13E Linear Functions and Arithmetic Sequences

**Find the associated linear function for the arithmetic sequence.
Then use it to find the 7th term of the sequence.**

$$-12, -6\tfrac{1}{2}, -1, 4\tfrac{1}{2}, \ldots$$

Since the sequence is arithmetic, determine the common difference:

$$\text{Common difference} = -6\tfrac{1}{2} - (-12) = 5\tfrac{1}{2}$$

The slope of the associated linear function is $5\tfrac{1}{2}$, or $\tfrac{11}{2}$.

Use the point $(1, -12)$, since term 1 is -12, and the slope.
Determine the y-intercept of the associated linear function.

$$y = mx + b$$
$$-12 = \tfrac{11}{2}(1) + b$$
$$b = -\tfrac{17}{2}$$

The associated linear function is $y = \tfrac{11}{2}x - \tfrac{17}{2}$. To find the 7th term
of the sequence, let $x = 7$:

$$y = \tfrac{11}{2}(7) - \tfrac{17}{2} = \tfrac{77}{2} - \tfrac{17}{2} = \tfrac{60}{2} = 30$$

The 7th term of the sequence is 30.

**Find the associated linear function for the arithmetic sequence.
Then use it to determine the 10th term of the sequence.**

1. 2, 8, 14, 20, . . .

2. −3.5, 1, 5.5, 10, . . .

Holt Mathematics

Review for Mastery

LESSON 13E *Linear Functions and Arithmetic Sequences (cont.)*

You can interpret the common difference of an arithmetic sequence as the slope of its associated linear function.

For any two consecutive terms of an arithmetic sequence,

common difference = $(n + 1)^{th}$ term − n^{th} term

For any two points (x_1, y_1) and (x_2, y_2) of the associated linear fuction,

$$\text{slope} = \frac{y_2 - y_1}{x_2 - x_1}$$

Find the missing terms of the arithmetic sequence. Then determine the common difference.

$$4, \underline{\quad}, \underline{\quad}, 25, \ldots$$

Consider the slope of the associated linear function. Since the 1st and 4th terms are given, the slope is

$$\frac{y_2 - y_1}{x_2 - x_1} = \frac{25 - 4}{4 - 1} = \frac{21}{3} = 7$$

This is also the common difference. The missing terms are found by adding the common difference to the previous terms:

$$4 + 7 = 11; 11 + 7 = 18$$

So, the missing terms are 11 and 18, and the common difference is 7.

Find the missing terms of the arithmetic sequence. Then determine the common difference.

3. 6, _____, _____, −3

4. 80, _____, _____, 212

Holt Mathematics

Homework and Practice

Linear Functions and Arithmetic Sequences

Find the common difference of the arithmetic sequence. Then write the associated linear function. Use the function to determine the 8th term of the sequence.

1. 13, 4, −5, −14, . . .

Common difference _____

Associated linear function:

_____

8th term: _____

2. $\frac{10}{3}$, 3, $\frac{8}{3}$, $\frac{7}{3}$ . . .

Common difference _____

Associated linear function:

_____

8th term: _____

3. −4.5, −1, 2.5, 6, . . .

Common difference _____

Associated linear function:

_____

8th term: _____

4. 20, 25, 30, 35, . . .

Common difference _____

Associated linear function:

_____

8th term: _____

Find the missing terms of the arithmetic sequence. Then determine the common difference.

5. 4, ___, ___, ___, 25, . . .

6. −11, ___, ___, ___, 1, . . .

7. 3, ___, ___, ___, −4.5, . . .

8. 0, ___, ___, ___ 2, . . .

9. An arithmetic sequence has a common difference of 5. What is the slope of the associated linear function for this sequence?

_____

Holt Mathematics

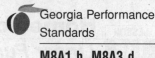Georgia Performance
Standards

13F Exponential Functions

M8A1.b, M8A3.d,
M8A3.i, M8N1.i

Scientists use *exponential functions* to make predictions about populations. Consider the model for a deer population, which begins with 1000 deer in year 0.

1. Use a calculator to complete the table.

Input x (year)	Rule: $1000(1.1)^x$	Output y (number of deer)
0	$1000(1.1)^0$	1000
1	$1000(1.1)^1$	1100
2	$1000(1.1)^2$	
3		
4		
10		

2. Determine the year in which the deer population will be greater than 3000 for the first time.

Think and Discuss

3. **Discuss** the difference between a linear function and an exponential function.

4. **Explain** what percent increase per year in the deer population the exponential model shows.

Holt Mathematics

Technology Lab
Exponential Functions

The pitch of a note—how high or low it sounds—is the frequency of that note, measured in *hertz.* For example, the pitch of the lowest note A on a piano is 27.5 hertz. The pitch of the A that is one octave (8 whole notes) higher has a frequency of 55 hertz. For every octave you go up, the frequency doubles. (This is true for every note and its corresponding octaves.) Therefore, the frequency of each A, starting with the lowest A on the piano, can be found using the exponential function $f(x) = 27.5(2)^x$ where the values of x are whole numbers from 0 of 7 because of the number of octaves on a piano.

Activity

Use the above information to find the pitch of A, starting from the lowest octave to the highest. Create a spreadsheet for your data. Enter the formula =(27.5)(2^A1) into cell **B1**. To have the spreadsheet calculate the values of the function for each value of x, do the following:

1) highlight cell **B1**;
2) place cursor over box in lower left of this highlighted cell;
3) select and drag this box down to the cell **B9**;
4) release the mouse button and the values will fill in.

	A	B
1	0	27.5
2	1	55
3	2	110
4	3	220
5	4	440
6	5	880
7	6	1760
8	7	3520

Technology Lab
Exponential Functions, continued

Think and Discuss

1. What type of sequence is formed by the output values you just calculated?

_____

2. What does the value 2 represent in this sequence?

_____

Try This

1. Use the above information to find an exponential function that represents the pitch of C, given that the frequency of the lowest C is 32.

_____

2. Create a spreadsheet for your data.

3. Compare the function for finding the frequencies of C with the function for finding the frequencies of A. What is the same and what is different? Explain.

_____

_____

_____

_____

Holt Mathematics

LESSON 13F
Review for Mastery
Exponential Functions

A function that has the input value *x* in the exponent is called an **exponential function.** The base number *a* is positive.

$$f(x) = a^x$$

<u>Situation 1</u>   *a* > 1, say *a* = 3

$$f(x) = 3^x$$

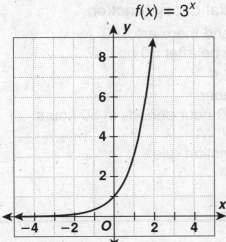

This graph rises from left to right.

<u>Situation 2</u>   *a* < 1, say *a* = $\frac{1}{3}$

$$f(x) = \left(\frac{1}{3}\right)^x$$

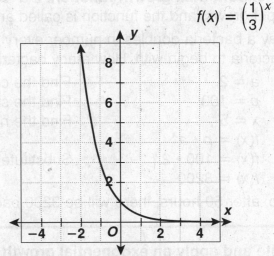

This graph falls from left to right.

For both situations: The domain is the set of all real numbers.
The range is the set of positive real numbers.
The *y*-intercept is 1.

Complete the table for each function.
Graph both functions on the same grid. Label each function.

1. $f(x) = 2^x$

x	y
−2	$2^{-2} = \frac{1}{2^2}$
	=
−1	$2^{-1} = \frac{1}{2^1}$
	=
0	$2^0 = \frac{1}{2^0}$
	=
1	$2^1 =$
2	$2^2 =$

2. $f(x) = \left(\frac{1}{2}\right)^x$

x	y
−2	$\left(\frac{1}{2}\right)^{-2} = \left(\frac{2}{1}\right)^2$
−1	$\left(\frac{1}{2}\right)^{-1} = \left(\frac{2}{1}\right)$
	=
0	$\left(\frac{1}{2}\right)^0 =$
1	$\left(\frac{1}{2}\right)^1 =$
2	$\left(\frac{1}{2}\right)^2 =$

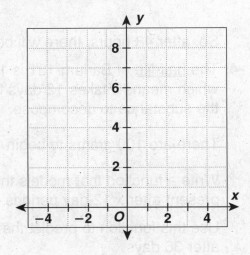

Holt Mathematics

Name _____ Date _____ Class _____

LESSON 13F Review for Mastery
Exponential Functions (continued)

When an exponential function has a **starting number** p, its rule
can be written $f(x) = p \cdot a^x$.

If $a > 1$, the output grows as the input grows, and the function is called
an **exponential growth function**. If $a < 1$, the output shrinks as the
input grows, and the function is called an **exponential decay function**.

Say a bacteria doubles in number every 10 hours, and there are 100
bacteria to begin with. How many bacteria will there be after 50 hours?

$a = 2$	Find the common ratio.
$p = 100$	Find the starting number.
$x = 5$	Find the number of 10-hour periods in 50 hours.
$f(x) = p \cdot a^x$	
$f(x) = 100 \cdot 2^5$	Substitute into the function rule.
$f(x) = 3200$	

So, after 50 hours, there will be 3200 bacteria.

Write and apply an exponential growth function.

3. Consider a bacteria that triples in number every 24 hours. $a = $ _____

   Suppose there are 40 bacteria to begin. $p = $ _____

   Write a function that models the number of bacteria
   present after x 24-hour periods. $f(x) = $ _____

   Use this function to predict the number of bacteria
   present after 48 hours. $x = $ _____

   $f(x) = $ _____

   So, after 48 hours, there will be _____ bacteria present.

4. The <u>half-life</u> of Barium-131 is 12 days,
   which means it takes 12 days for half of
   the substance to decompose. $a = $ _____

   There are 100 grams to begin. $p = $ _____

   Write a function that models the number of grams
   present after x 12-day periods. $f(x) = $ _____

   Use this function to predict the number of grams present
   after 36 days. $x = $ _____

   = =

   $f(x) = $ _____

   So, after 36 days, there will be _____ grams of Barium-131 remaining.

Holt Mathematics

Homework and Practice
LESSON 13F
Exponential Functions

Create a table for each exponential function, and use it to graph the function.

1. $f(x) = 0.25 \cdot 5^x$

x	y
−1	$y = 0.25 \cdot 5^{-1} = 0.05$
0	
1	
2	

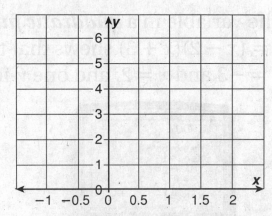

2. $f(x) = \frac{1}{4} \cdot 6^x$

x	y
−1	
0	
1	
2	

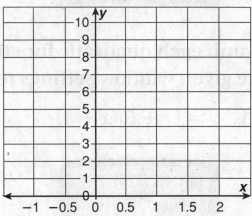

3. A lawyer opens a new office with 28 clients. She intends to increase her clientele 30% each year for the next 4 years. How many clients can she expect to have at the end of 4 years? Round the answer to the nearest whole number?

_____

4. A company owns office cars worth a total of $587,000. The cars are depreciated by 12% a year for 10 years. What is the expected value of the cars at the end of 10 years? Round the answer to the nearest cent.

_____

5. Clayton earns $725 a week at his job. He is given a 6% annual increase in pay. How much will Clayton earn per week after 3 years? Round the answer to the nearest cent.

_____

Holt Mathematics

EXPLORATION

13G Quadratic Functions

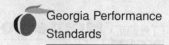

Georgia Performance Standards

M8A1,b, M8A3.d, M8A3.i, M8N1.i

The variable in a *quadratic function* is squared. The graph of $y = (x - 2)(x + 3)$ shows that the function has two x-intercepts, $x = -3$ and $x = 2$, and one y-intercept, $y = -6$.

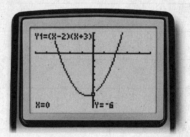

Graph each quadratic function on a graphing calculator. Use the given window settings to find the x- and y-intercepts.

1. $y = (x + 5)(x + 1)$　　　**2.** $y = (x - 4)(x - 2)$

Think and Discuss

3. Discuss the relationship between the function rule and the intercepts, the points where the graph crosses the x- and y-axes.

Holt Mathematics

Name _____ Date _____ Class _____

Hands-On Lab 1
Quadratic Functions

Aristotle thought that heavier objects fall faster, but Galileo conducted a series of experiments showing that all objects accelerate at the same rate as they fall. The rate at which falling objects accelerate is known as the acceleration due to gravity.

Activity

1. Drop pairs of objects from the same height at the same time and see if they hit the floor at the same time. You can drop coins, pens, slips of paper, marbles, feathers, etc.

2. Drop a flat piece of notebook paper and a piece of notebook paper that has been crumpled up into a small ball.

3. Most objects fall too quickly to compare their rates of fall. Galileo got around this problem by allowing objects to roll down a smooth ramp. Construct a ramp by propping one end of a smooth board on a pencil or by lifting one side of your desk or table by a small amount. Allow various-sized marbles to roll down this ramp. To compare pairs of marbles, you will need to use a "starting gate" so that the marbles begin to roll at the same time. You can use a ruler or anything else that is straight. Place the marbles behind the gate and lift the gate.

4. Since objects accelerate as they fall, they fall farther during each second. The distance an object has fallen is related to the time of fall by $d = 4.9t^2$, with d in meters and t in seconds. Suppose a small, round, dense object is dropped from a tall tower. How far does it fall in each interval? Complete the following table.

t	1	2	3	4	5
t^2	1				
$d = 4.9t^2$	4.9				

5. Construct a graph of distance versus time for this object.

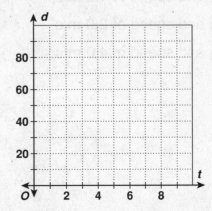

Name _____ Date _____ Class _____

Hands-On Lab 1
Quadratic Functions, continued

Think and Discuss

1. Do all objects fall at the same rate?

   _____

   _____

2. Did the flat sheet of paper and the crumpled sheet of paper fall
   at the same rate?

   _____

   _____

3. Do all small, dense objects fall at the same rate?

   _____

   _____

4. Did all of the marbles roll down the ramp at the same rate?

   _____

   _____

   _____

Try This

The kinetic energy of an object is given by the relation $KE = \frac{1}{2}mv^2$.

When the mass is given in kg and the speed is given in m/s, the
kinetic energy will be in joules (J). Calculate the kinetic energy of the
following objects.

1. mass of 1.0 kg and speed of 1.0 m/s   _____

2. mass of 3.5 kg and speed of 2.0 m/s   _____

3. mass of 3.5 kg and speed of 4.0 m/s   _____

454   **Holt Mathematics**

Hands-On Lab 2
LESSON 13G *Quadratic Functions*

Activity

All graphs of quadratic functions are related to the basic function $f(x) = x^2$, which is shown at the right. Create a table for each quadratic function below. Use the tables to graph the functions Compare the graphs.

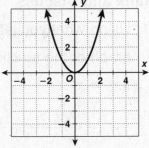

Step 1 Find $f(x)$ for each x value to complete the tables.

x	$f(x) = 2x^2$
−3	
−2	
−1	
0	
1	
2	
3	

x	$f(x) = x^2 + 2$
−3	
−2	
−1	
0	
1	
2	
3	

Step 2 Plot the points for each parabola on a separate sheet of graph paper or as a separate plot using a graphing calculator.

Step 3 Compare each graph to the graph of $f(x) = x^2$.

How does multiplying x^2 by 2 affect the parabola of the function $f(x) = x^2$?

_____

_____

How does adding 2 to the function $f(x) = x^2$ change the parabola?

_____

_____

Holt Mathematics

Hands-On Lab 2
Quadratic Functions, continued

Think and Discuss

1. Using what you learned on the previous page, predict what the graph of the function $f(x) = \frac{1}{2}x^2$ will look like compared to $f(x) = x^2$.

_____

_____

2. Predict what the graph of the function $f(x) = x^2 - 2$ will look like compared to $f(x) = x^2$.

_____

_____

Try This

The cross-section of the bottom of a boat is approximated by the graph of $f(x) = \frac{1}{2}x^2$. Complete the table for the function and use it to make a graph of the function.

x	$f(x) = \frac{1}{2}x^2$
-3	
-2	
-1	
0	
1	
2	
3	

If the boat is 4 m across, how deep is it?

_____

LESSON 13G Technology Lab
Quadratic Functions

Activity

A square has sides with length *x*. How does the area of the square change when the length of the side is changed? Make a table of values.

Length *x* (cm)	area *y* (cm^2)
0	_____
1	_____
2	_____
3	_____
4	_____
5	_____

Write an equation expressing the relationship between the length of the side and the area of the square.

_____

Use a graphing calculator or graphing software to graph the function, using only positive values for *x* (since the length of a square's side will always be positive).

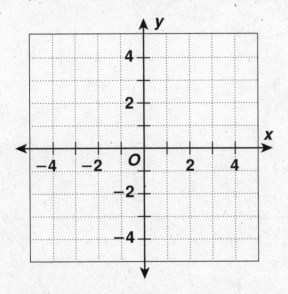

Notice that the graph of this line is curved, not straight. It is not a linear equation.

Holt Mathematics

Technology Lab

13G *Quadratic Functions, continued*

Think and Discuss

1. What if the equation in the activity above were not being used to describe the relationship between the length of a square's side and its area? How would the graph be different?

   _____

   _____

   _____

   _____

Try This

1. Graph the function $y = \frac{1}{2}x^2 + x$. Give the y–coordinate for point A (1, ?).

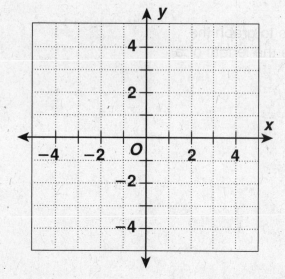

   _____

Holt Mathematics

Review for Mastery

LESSON 13G *Quadratic Functions*

A **quadratic function** has a variable that is squared.

general quadratic function $f(x) = ax^2 + bx + c$

square term   *y*-intercept

$f(x) = x^2 - 4x + 3$

The graph of a quadratic function is a **parabola,** a curve that falls on one side of a turning point and rises on the other. You can make a table of a function's values and use them to graph the function.

x	$f(x) = x^2 - 4x + 3$
−1	$f(-1) = (-1)^2 - 4(-1) + 3 = 8$
0	$f(0) = 0^2 - 4(0) + 3 = 3$
1	$f(1) = 1^2 - 4(1) + 3 = 0$
2	$f(2) = 2^2 - 4(2) + 3 = -1$
3	$f(3) = 3^2 - 4(3) + 3 = 0$
4	$f(4) = 4^2 - 4(4) + 3 = 3$
5	$f(5) = 5^2 - 4(5) + 3 = 8$

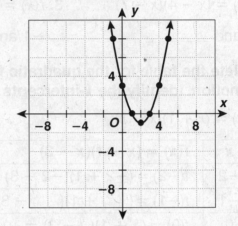

Complete the table for the quadratic function and use it to graph the function.

1. $f(x) = x^2 - 2x - 3$

x	$f(x) = x^2 - 2x - 3$
−2	$f(-2) = (\quad)^2 - 2(-2) - 3 =$
−1	$f(-1) = (\quad)^2 - 2(-1) - 3 =$
0	$f(0) = (\quad)^2 - 2(0) - 3 =$
1	$f(1) = (\quad)^2 - 2(1) - 3 =$
2	$f(2) = (\quad)^2 - 2(2) - 3 =$
3	$f(3) = (\quad)^2 - 2(3) - 3 =$
4	$f(4) = (\quad)^2 - 2(4) - 3 =$

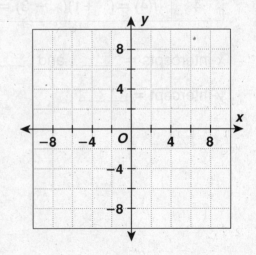

Holt Mathematics

Review for Mastery

LESSON 13G *Quadratic Functions (continued)*

When a quadratic function is written as the product of two differences, you can read the two *x*-intercepts.

$$f(x) = (x - r)(x - s)$$

x-intercepts

For the quadratic function $f(x) = (x - 3)(x + 4)$, the *x*-intercepts are 3 and −4.

Identify the *x*-intercepts for each function.

2. $f(x) = (x - 4)(x - 7)$ **3.** $f(x) = (x + 1)(x - 5)$ **4.** $f(x) = (x + 2)(x + 4)$

4 and _____   −1 and _____   _____ and _____

Complete the table for the quadratic function and use it to graph the function. Identify the *x*-intercepts and the *y*-intercept.

5. $f(x) = (x + 1)(x - 3)$

x	f(x) = (x + 1)(x − 3)
−2	$f(-2) = (-2 + 1)(-2 - 3) = 5$
−1	$f(-1) = (\quad + 1)(\quad - 3) =$
0	$f(0) = (\quad + 1)(\quad - 3) =$
1	$f(1) = (\quad + 1)(\quad - 3) =$
2	$f(2) = (\quad + 1)(\quad - 3) =$
3	$f(3) = (\quad + 1)(\quad - 3) =$
4	$f(4) = (\quad + 1)(\quad - 3) =$

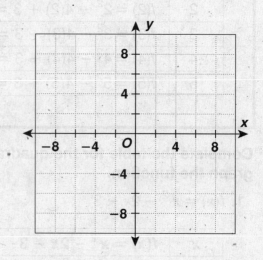

x-intercepts = _____ and _____

y-intercept = _____

Holt Mathematics

Name _____ Date _____ Class _____

Homework and Practice
Quadratic Functions

Create a table for each quadratic function and use it to make a graph.

1. $f(x) = x^2 - 6$

x	$f(x) = x^2 - 6$
−3	$f(-3) = (-3)^2 - 6 = 3$
−1	
0	
2	
3	

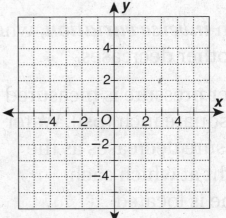

2. $f(x) = (x - 5)(x - 3)$

x	$f(x) = (x - 5)(x - 3)$
6	
5	
4	
3	
2	

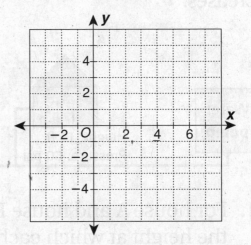

3. $f(x) = x^2 - 3x - 2$

x	$f(x) = x^2 - 3x - 2$
3	
2	
1	
0	
−1	

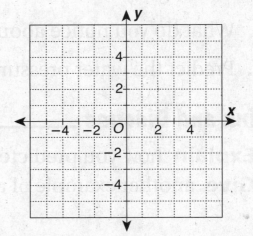

4. If the perimeter of a rectangle is 124 cm, find the dimensions of the rectangle with the greatest possible area? What is the greatest possible area?

Holt Mathematics

EXPLORATION

13H Inverse Variation

Georgia Performance Standards

M8A3.d, M8A3.i

In an *inverse variation,* when one quantity increases, the other decreases.

Water pressure is measured in pounds per square inch (psi). Water pressure decreases as the height at which each home is located increases.

Water pump

A
Height: 15 ft
Pressure: 60 psi

B
Height: 30 ft
Pressure: 30 psi

C
Height: 60 ft
Pressure: ?

1. For house A and house B, multiply the water pressure by the height at which each house is located.

2. What do you notice about the products in Problem 1?

3. Predict the water pressure for house C.

Think and Discuss

4. **Explain** how you predicted the water pressure for house C.

5. **Give** another example of an inverse variation.

Review for Mastery

LESSON 13H

Inverse Variation

Two quantities **vary inversely** if their product is constant.

y varies inversely as x. $xy = k$ ←—— constant of variation

$y = \dfrac{k}{x}$ ←—— function of inverse variation

To determine if two data sets vary inversely, check for a constant product.

x	1	2	4	8	−1	−2	−4	−8
y	8	4	2	1	−8	−4	−2	−1

$xy = 1(8) = 2(4) = 4(2) = 8(1) = -1(-8)$
$\quad = -2(-4) = -4(-2) = -8(-1) = 8$

So, y varies inversely as x.

The constant of variation is 8.

The function of inverse variation is $y = \dfrac{8}{x}$.

The graph of an inverse variation is two curves and is not defined for $x = 0$.

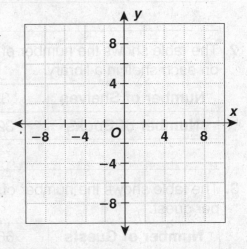

Tell whether the data shows inverse variation. If there is a constant product, identify it and write the function of inverse variation.

1.

x	5	4	2	1	−1	−2
y	20	16	8	4	−4	−8

2.

x	1	2	3	−3	−2
y	12	6	4	−4	−6

constant product? _____   constant product? _____

If yes, function. _____   If yes, function. _____

Write the function of inverse variation. Then graph it.

3.

x	1	2	3	6
y	6	3	2	1
x	−1	−2	−3	−6
y	−6	−3	−2	−1

function: _____

Holt Mathematics

Name _____ Date _____ Class _____

LESSON 13H Homework and Practice
Inverse Variation

Tell whether each relationship is an inverse variation. If yes, write an equaiton.

1. The table shows the length and width of a parallelogram.

Length	4	8	10	12	36
Width	18	9	7.2	6	2

_____

2. The table shows the number of shelves and the number of books on each shelf in a library.

Number of Shelves	3	4	6	12	16
Number of Books	32	24	16	8	6

_____

3. The table shows the number of guests at a party and the cost per guest.

Number of Guests	66	75	96	100	150
Cost per Guest	9	8	6.25	6	4

_____

Graph each inverse variation.

4. $f(x) = \dfrac{6}{x}$

5. $f(x) = \dfrac{-4}{x}$

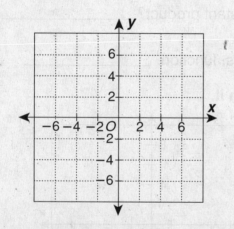

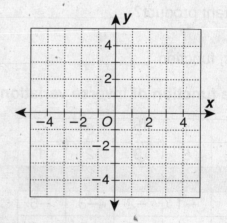

6. Hertz, abbreviated Hz, is a unit of frequency equal to 1 cycle per second. The pitch of a musical instrument is measured in vibrations per second or Hertz. If the pitch of a panpipe 2 feet long is 282 Hz, what is the length of pipe with a pitch of 376 Hz?

_____

Holt Mathematics

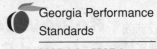

Georgia Performance Standards

M8D1.b, M8D1.c

131 Sets and Subsets

A *set* is a collection of objects called *elements*. Elements can be numbers, letters, shapes, songs on an mp3 player, or a coin collection.

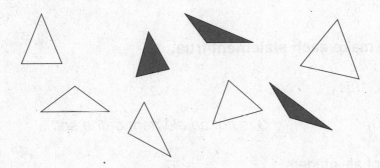

1. How would you describe the set shown above?

2. How many elements does the set have?

3. Is  an element of the set?

4. Is ▊ an element of the set?

Think and Discuss

5. **Explain** whether or not the number 5 would be in the set containing all even numbers.

6. **Describe** an example of a set from your real life.

Holt Mathematics

Name _____ Date _____ Class _____

Review for Mastery
Sets and Subsets

Sets can be described with words, such as "the set of all even numbers," or they can be represented by listing their elements between curly brackets { }. For example, the set of the colors of the rainbow could be written as

$$C = \{red, orange, yellow, green, blue, indigo, violet\}$$

The symbol $\in$ means "is an element of," and the symbol $\notin$ means "is not an element of."

Insert $\in$ or $\notin$ to make each statement true.

3 ☐ {2, 4, 6, 8, 10}

$3 \notin \{2, 4, 6, 8, 10\}$ *3 is not an element of the set.*

−6 ☐ the set of all integers

$-6 \in$ the set of all integers   *−6 is an integer, so it is an element of the set.*

Insert $\in$ or $\notin$ to make each statement true.

1. 3 ☐ {2, 4, 6, 1, 3, 5}

2. 7.3 ☐ the set of all integers

Sets can also be described by *roster notation*. $R = \{x \mid x < 5\}$ means that R is the set of all numbers x such that $x < 5$.

$R = \{x \mid x < 5\}$ and $S = \{x \mid x > 7\}$

$-6 \in R$ *−6 is less than 5, so −6 is an element of R.*
$-6 \notin S$ *−6 is not greater than 7.*

$A = \{x \mid x < 0\}$ and $B = \{x \mid x \geq -1\}$. **Insert $\in$ or $\notin$ to make each statement true.**

3. −2 ☐ A

4. 3 ☐ A

5. −1 ☐ A

6. −2 ☐ B

7. 3 ☐ B

8. −1 ☐ B

Holt Mathematics

Name _____ Date _____ Class _____

Review for Mastery

LESSON 13-1 *Sets and Subsets (continued)*

Set *A* is called a *subset* of *B* if every element in *A* is also an element of *B*.

The symbol $\subset$ means "is a subset of."
The symbol $\not\subset$ means "is not a subset of."

Insert $\subset$ or $\not\subset$ to make each statement true.

$A = \{1, 3, 5\}$

$B = \{1, 2, 3, 4, 5, 6\}$

$A \boxed{} B$

$A \subset B$ All elements of A are elements of B.

$C = \{-2, 1, 2\}$

$D = \{x \mid x > 0\}$

$C \boxed{} D$

$C \not\subset B$ -2 is not an element of D, so C is not a subset of D.

Insert $\subset$ or $\not\subset$ to make each statement true.

9. $A = \{$ $,$ ⬭ $\}$
   $B =$ the set of all quadrilaterals

   $A \boxed{} B$

10. $P = \{$ ⋁ $,$ ⯃ $\}$
    $Q =$ the set of all polygons

    $P \boxed{} Q$

11. $S = \{x \mid 0 \le x \le 5\}$
    $T = \{3, 7\}$

    $S \boxed{} T$

12. $D = \{x \mid 0 \le x \le 5\}$
    $E = \{x \mid 1 < x < 4\}$

    $D \boxed{} E$

13. $G = \{2, 4, 6\}$
    $H =$ the set of all even numbers

    $G \boxed{} H$

14. $R = \{3, 7, 9, 13\}$
    $S =$ the set of all prime numbers

    $R \boxed{} S$

15. Describe a subset of the set of triangles on the Exploration page.

Holt Mathematics

LESSON 13| Homework and Practice
Sets and Subsets

Insert ∈ or ∉ to make each statement true.

1. 6 ☐ the set of all even numbers

2. 6 ☐ the set of all odd numbers

3. 9 ☐ {0, 2, 4, 5, 6, 8, 10}

4. 0 ☐ the set of all integers

5. −7.1 ☐ {−8.4, −7.9, −7.1, −6.6}

6. 8.5 ☐ the set of all integers

$C = \{x \mid x > 0\}$ and $D = \{x \mid x \le -1\}$. **Insert ∈ or ∉ to make each statement true.**

7. −4 ☐ C

8. 0 ☐ C

9. 5 ☐ C

10. −1 ☐ C

11. 2 ☐ D

12. −1.3 ☐ D

13. −1 ☐ D

14. 7.8 ☐ D

15. 0 ☐ D

Insert ⊂ or ⊄ to make each statement true.

16. E = { △ , ⊙ }
    F = the set of all triangles
    E ☐ F

17. M = { ⬠ , ⬡ }
    N = the set of all pentagons
    M ☐ N

18. G = { ▱ , ▱ }
    H = the set of all polygons
    G ☐ H

19. S = { ☐ , ▱ }
    T = the set of all quadrilaterals
    S ☐ T

20. A = {x | 0 ≤ x < 6}
    B = {x | −4 < x ≤ 6}
    A ☐ B

21. P = {1, 3, 5, 7, 8, 9}
    Q = the set of all odd numbers
    P ☐ Q

22. H = {x | −1 ≥ x > −10}
    J = {−6, −5, −2, −1}
    H ☐ J

23. K = {x | 2 > x ≥ −1}
    L = {−1, 1}
    K ☐ L

Holt Mathematics

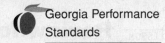
Georgia Performance
Standards

13J Intersections and Unions M8D1.a, M8D1.b, M8D1.c

The *intersection* of sets A and B is the set of all elements that are in both A and B. You can also think of the intersection of two sets as where the two sets "overlap."

$$A = \{1, 2, 3, 4, 5, 6, 7, 8, 9, 10\}$$

$$B = \{2, 3, 5, 7, 11, 13\}$$

1. Which elements are in both sets A and B? Write them in the area where the two circles overlap in the Venn diagram below.

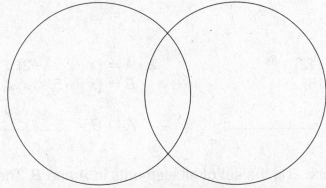

2. Fill in the circles with the rest of the elements of each set. Remember: An element only goes in the overlap if it is in both sets.

3. A *union* of sets A and B is the set of elements that are in set A or set B. You can also think of the union of two sets as the collection of all the elements from both sets. What is the union of sets A and B?

Think and Discuss

4. **Describe** what a Venn diagram of two sets that have no common elements would look like.

Holt Mathematics

LESSON 13J — Review for Mastery

Intersections and Unions

The *intersection* of sets A and B is the set of all elements that are common to both A and B. The symbol ∩ means intersection.

Find $P \cap Q$.

$P = \{3, 6, 9, 12, 15\}$
$Q = \{x \mid x \geq 9\}$ *The intersection contains all of the elements*
$P \cap Q = \{9, 12, 15\}$ *of P that are greater than or equal to 9.*

If two sets have no elements in common, their intersection is the empty set, or *null set*. The symbol for the null set is ∅.

Find $X \cap Y$.

$X = \{x \mid x \leq 0\}$
$Y = \{x \mid x > 3\}$
$X \cap Y = \varnothing$ *X and Y have no elements in common.*

Find $A \cap B$.

1. $A = \{2, 4, 6, 8, 10, 12\}$
   $B = \{1, 2, 3, 4, 8, 16\}$

   $A \cap B =$ _____

2. $A = \{x \mid x \leq -2\}$
   $B = \{x \mid -5 < x < 2\}$

   $A \cap B =$ _____

The *union* of sets A and B is the set of all elements in A and B. The symbol ∪ means union.

Find $D \cup E$.

$D = \{1, 2, 3, 5, 7\}$
$E = \{2, 4, 6, 8\}$ *2 is an element of both sets, but list it*
$D \cup E = \{1, 2, 3, 4, 5, 6, 7, 8\}$ *only once.*

Find $A \cup B$.

3. $A = \{-2, -1, 0, 1, 2\}$
   $B = \{0, 1, 2, 3, 4\}$

   $A \cup B =$ _____

4. $A =$ all positive integers and 0
   $B =$ all negative integers

   $A \cup B =$ _____

Holt Mathematics

Review for Mastery

13J Intersections and Unions (continued)

You can use Venn diagrams to represent intersections and unions of sets.

Use the Venn diagram to identify the intersection and union of sets *D* and *E*.

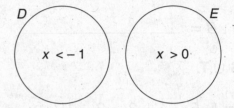

$D \cap E = \{8, 9\}$

$D \cup E = \{5, 6, 7, 8, 9, 10, 11, 12\}$

$D \cap E = \emptyset$

$D \cup E = \{x \mid x < -1 \text{ or } x > 0\}$

Draw a Venn diagram to represent sets *H* and *J* and write the intersection and union of the two sets.

$H = \{x \mid x \le 5\}$
$J = \{x \mid x > -2\}$

$H \cap J = \{x \mid -2 < x \le 5\}$
$D \cup J = \text{all real numbers}$

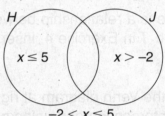

$-2 < x \le 5$

Use the Venn diagram to identify the intersection and union of sets *A* and *B*.

5.

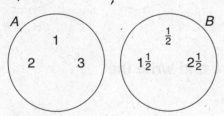

$A \cap B = $ _____

$A \cup B = $ _____

6.

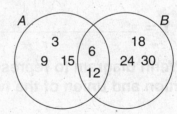

$A \cap B = $ _____

$A \cup B = $ _____

Holt Mathematics

Name _____ Date _____ Class _____

LESSON 13J **Homework and Practice**
Intersections and Unions

Find A ∩ B.

1. $A = \{2, 4, 8, 16\}$

   $B = \{3, 9, 27, 81\}$

   $A \cap B =$ _____

2. $A = \{1, 2, 3, 4, 5\}$

   $B =$ the set of all factors of 12

   $A \cap B =$ _____

Find S ∪ T.

3. $S = \{-5, -4, -3, -2, -1\}$

   $T = \{-3, -2, -1, 0, 1\}$

   $S \cup T =$ _____

4. $S = \{x \mid x > 10\}$

   $T = \{x \mid x > 5\}$

   $S \cup T =$ _____

5. There is a relationship between sets
   S and T in Exercise 4. Insert the correct symbol: S ▢ T

6. Use the Venn diagram at right to identify
   the intersection and union of sets X and Y.

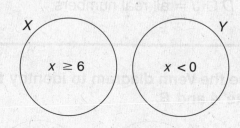

   $X \cap Y =$ _____

   $X \cup Y =$ _____

**Draw a Venn diagram to represent sets K and L and write the
intersection and union of the two sets.**

7. $K =$ the set of all factors of 18
   $L =$ the set of all factors of 21

   $K \cap L =$ _____

   $K \cup L =$ _____

8. $K = \{x \mid x < 3\}$
   $L = \{x \mid x > -3\}$

   $X \cap L =$ _____

   $K \cup L =$ _____

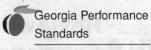

Georgia Performance Standards

M8D1.a, M8D1.b, M8D1.c

13K Complement of a Set

The *complement* of a set A is the set of all elements that are not in A. You write the complement of set A as A^C.

To describe A^C, you need to know the *universe* from which A is a subset. This universal set is often written as U. Assume that U contains all the elements of every set.

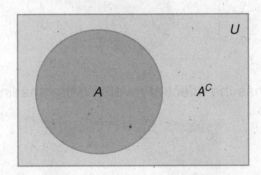

1. Let $U = \{3, 4, 6, 8, 11, 13, 15\}$ and $A = \{4, 8, 11, 15\}$. Find the complement of A, A^C.

2. Let U = the set of all whole numbers, and B = the set of all positive integers. Find the complement of B, B^C.

3. Describe the set B^C if $U = \{$beverages in your refrigerator$\}$ and $B = \{$milk$\}$. Would you expect to have the same answer as your classmates? Explain.

Think and Discuss

4. **Discuss** what each of the following notations means. Then write each one in a more simple way.

$$A \cup A^C \qquad A \cap A^C \qquad (A^C)^C$$

Holt Mathematics

Name _____ Date _____ Class _____

Review for Mastery
Complement of a Set

You can use a Venn diagram to show unions, intersections, and complements of more complicated sets. Consider the set

$$(B \cup C)^C \cap A$$

To show this set, begin with a Venn diagram that has 3 sets. Shade $B \cup C$.

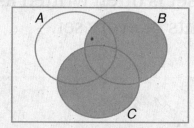

Next, find $(B \cup C)^C$. This has the effect of reversing the shading.

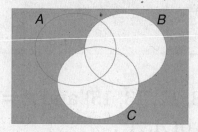

Finally, find the intersection of $(B \cup C)^C$ and A. This will leave only parts of set A that are already shaded.

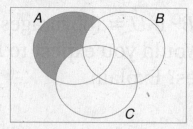

Draw a Venn diagram to show the following sets.

1. $(B^C \cap C) \cap A^C$

2. $A^C \cup B$

Holt Mathematics

Review for Mastery

LESSON 13K *Complement of a Set (continued)*

You can determine the complement of a set when the universal set is small by listing the elements in the universe. Then cross out elements that are in the set.

Find the complement of set A, A^C.

> U = the set of positive integers less than 10
> A = the set of multiples of 3

First, write out the universal set.

$$U = \{1, 2, 3, 4, 5, 6, 7, 8, 9\}$$

Next, look for elements that are in the set A, or multiples of 3. Cross these out so that only elements in A^C remain. Notice that multiples of 3 outside of the set U are not considered.

1 2 3̸ 4 5 6̸ 7 8 9̸

So, $A^C = \{1, 2, 4, 5, 7, 8\}$.

Write out the universal set, U. Then cross off elements that are in the given set, and write the complement of the set.

3. U = the set of multiples of 5 less than 50
   B = the set of multiples of 10

4. U = the set of prime numbers less than 12
   A = the set of odd numbers

5. U = the set of integers whose absolute value is less than 4
   A = the set of counting numbers

Holt Mathematics

Name _____ Date _____ Class _____

LESSON 13K **Homework and Practice**
Complement of a Set

Shade the region of the Venn diagram that represents the given set.

1. $(A \cap B)^C$

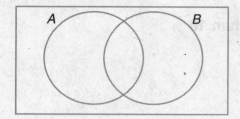

2. $A^C \cup B^C$

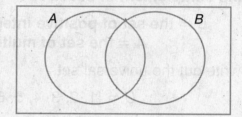

3. $(A \cap B)^C \cup B$

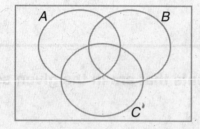

4. $(A \cup B)^C \cap C$

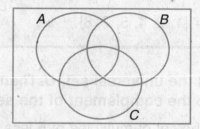

Find the complement of set B, B^C.

5. $U = \{s, w, t, u, k, z\}$
$B = \{s\}$

6. $U = $ the set of the factors of 60
$B = $ the set of multiples of 3

7. $U = $ the set of positive integers
$B = \{7, 8, 9, 10, ...\}$

Holt Mathematics

Answer these questions to summarize the important concepts from Chapter 13 in your own words.

1. Explain how to determine if the sequence is arithmetic.

   5, 7, 9, 11, 13, 15, …

2. Explain how to determine if the sequence is geometric.

   120, 60, 30, 15, …

3. Explain the difference between an exponential growth function and an exponential decay function.

4. Explain how to determine if a relationship is an inverse variation.

For more review of Chapter 13:

• Complete the Chapter 13 Study Guide and Review on pages 722–724 of your textbook.

• Complete the Ready to Go On quizzes on pages 698 and 718 of your textbook.

Project
Polynomials: The Algebra of Profit

Career: Financial Analyst

Financial analysts can be found in many business settings. They can help determine the cost of each product a company makes. Financial analysts use polynomials to calculate the relationships between production costs, selling price, total sales, and profits.

In this chapter project...you will design a CD for a real or imaginary band and calculate the costs of producing the CD. You will:

- Write a polynomial that shows the relationship between sales, costs, and profit.

- Choose what features your CD will have. Will there be elaborate artwork? A larger booklet? A plastic or cardboard case? Make estimates for how much your choices will cost, both in terms of setup and overhead and in cost per CD.

- Decide on a price for each CD. Make a presentation showing your CD design, the costs involved, and a table showing the cost for each feature, the total costs, and the total profit per CD.

To get started, work through the What Did We Make? worksheet on the next page.

This chapter project reinforces your understanding of these Georgia Performance Standards:

M8A1.a Represent a given situation using algebraic expressions or equations in one variable.

M8P5.a Create and use representations to organize, record, and communicate mathematical ideas.

---

go.hrw.com
Chapter Project Online
KEYWORD: MT7 Ch14

Name _____ Date _____ Class _____

Project Recording Sheet
Polynomials

What Did We Make?

How much should we charge for our product or service? This is the question that every business must answer correctly to find and keep customers and make a profit. A financial analyst can help the make pricing decisions that create a profit in a competitive market.

What are the factors that affect sales? Most customers look for quality, value, and service.

1. Which has more effect on the total cost, fixed costs or variable costs? _____

2. Does the size of the production run make any difference? _____

CD Production Costs				
Fixed		**Variable (for each CD produced)**		
Setup	Overhead	Blank CD	Packaging	Maintenance
$100	$97	51¢	19¢	18¢

3. Use the data in the table to determine what would happen if:

   a. the fixed costs doubled _____

   b. the cost of CD blanks rose to $1 _____

   c. no packaging was needed _____

Price ($)	2.00	2.25	2.50	3.00	4.00
% Purchase	100	90	80	60	50

4. Check this data of the sales in the table above. What happens to the amount purchased as the price goes up?

   _____

5. If 5000 CDs would be sold at $2.00 how many would be sold at $4.00? _____

6. Sales is equal to the number of CDs sold times the price of the individual CD. Show this relationship in an equation.

   _____

7. Write an equation to show the relationship between sales, costs, and profit.

   _____

Holt Mathematics

EXPLORATION

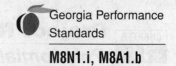
Georgia Performance
Standards

M8N1.i, M8A1.b

14A Polynomials

An object is dropped from an initial height of 144 feet. The graph shows its height versus time.

Height of Falling Object

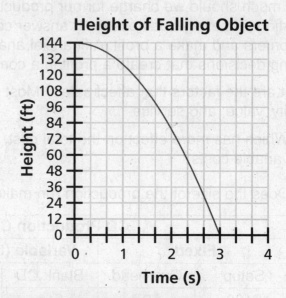

Time (s)	Equation	Height (ft)
x	$y = 144 - 16x^2$	y
0	$y = 144 - 16(0)^2 = 144$	144
1		
2		
3		

1. What does the point (0, 144) represent?

2. When does the object reach the ground?

3. You can use the equation $y = 144 - 16x^2$ to model the object's fall. Complete the table and label the points on the graph.

Think and Discuss

4. **Explain** why the graph of a falling object is not a straight line.

Holt Mathematics

Review for Mastery

LESSON 14A *Polynomials*

Expressions such as $2x$ and $4y^2$ are called **monomials.** A monomial has only one term. Monomials do <u>not</u> have fractional exponents, negative exponents, variable exponents, roots of variables, or variables in a denominator.

Determine whether each expression is a monomial.

1. $3x - 5$ **2.** $-9a^4$ **3.** $21m^{0.5}$ **4.** $7m^3n^2$

_____   _____   _____   _____

A monomial or a sum or difference of monomials is called a **polynomial.** Polynomials can be classified by the number of terms. A monomial has 1 term, a **binomial** has 2 terms, and a **trinomial** has 3 terms.

Classify each expression as a monomial, a binomial, a trinomial, or not a polynomial.

5. $7y + 3x^2 + 5$ **6.** $6y + \sqrt{x}$

_____   _____

7. m^2n **8.** $-6a + 2b^4$

_____   _____

The degree of a polynomial is the degree of the term with the greatest degree. The **degree** of a term is the greatest value of a variable's exponent.

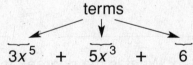

$$\underset{\text{5th degree}}{\overbrace{3x^5}} \ + \ \underset{\text{3rd degree}}{\overbrace{5x^3}} \ + \ \underset{\text{0 degree}}{\overbrace{6}}$$

The above polynomial is a 5th degree trinomial.

Find the degree of each polynomial.

9. $5x + 3x^3 + 2x^2$ **10.** $-3m^4 + m^2 + 2$ **11.** $4y + 2y^3 + y^5$ **12.** $7a^2 + 8a$

_____   _____   _____   _____

 Holt Mathematics

LESSON 14A

Homework and Practice
Polynomials

Determine whether each expression is a monomial.

1. $-xyz$

2. u^3

3. $-8q^3$

_____   _____   _____

4. $\left(\dfrac{3}{5}\right)rs^2t^3$

5. $a^{2.2}$

6. $\left(\dfrac{7}{9}\right)x^{\frac{7}{9}}$

_____   _____   _____

Classify each expression as a monomial, a binomial, a trinomial, or not a polynomial.

7. $5a - 4.9b + \left(\dfrac{1}{3}\right)$

8. $9pq^{-1}r^{-4}$

9. $9 + r^2 + 2r$

_____   _____   _____

10. $-1.077p^5r$

11. $-1.1q + p^{0.6}$

12. $-7.55r^{75} - 1$

_____   _____   _____

Find the degree of each polynomial.

13. $z^0 + y^9 - x$

14. $2k + 7k^2 - 4k^3$

15. $-1p^2 - 2q - p^3 - 8q^2$

_____   _____   _____

16. 2

17. $\left(\dfrac{9}{8}\right)ab^8c^2 + d^{11}$

18. $\left(\dfrac{4}{5}\right)c - c^7 + 2$

_____   _____   _____

19. Look at the polynomial $2x^3 + x^2 - x$. What is the degree? Is the polynomial a monomial, binomial, or trinomial? What is the value of the polynomial if $x = 2$?

_____

20. The volume of a box with width x, length $x + 2$, and height $3x - 2$ is given by the trinomial $3x^3 + 4x^2 - 4x$. What is the volume of the box if its width is 4 feet?

_____

Holt Mathematics

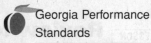
Georgia Performance
Standards

14B Simplifying Polynomials M8N1.i, M8A1.b

You can use algebra tiles to model polynomials. The polynomial $2x^2 + 2x + 2 + x^2 - x - 3$ is modeled below.

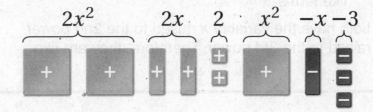

1. Use tiles to show that $2x^2 + 2x + 2 + x^2 - x - 3 = 3x^2 + x - 1$.

Use algebra tiles to simplify each expression.

2. $4x^2 - 2x - 5 - 3x^2 + x - 4$

3. $3x^2 - x + 1 - x^2 - x + 3$

Think and Discuss

4. **Explain** how you can use tiles to simplify polynomials.
5. **Explain** why you cannot simplify the polynomial $3x^2 + 4x - 9$.

Holt Mathematics

Review for Mastery

14B *Simplifying Polynomials*

You can simplify a polynomial by combining like terms. Like terms
have the same variables raised to the same powers. All constants
are like terms.

$$9 + 6y^3 - 8 + 7x^2y^3 + 3x^2y^3$$

like terms · like terms

$7x^2y^3$ and $3x^2y^3$ both have the variable x raised to the 2nd power
and the variable y raised to the 3rd power. Therefore, they are like
terms.

Identify the like terms in each polynomial

1. $m + 3m^2 - 2m + 6 + 2m^2$

2. $b - a^2b^2 - 2 + a^2 + 2a^2b^2$

_____

3. $x^3 + 2 + 4x^3 - 9 + x$

4. $9 + 4dg^2 + 4 + 6dg^2 + d^2$

_____

To simplify a polynomial, combine like terms. To combine like
terms, add or subtract the coefficients. The variables and the
exponents
do not change.

$\left(7x^2y^3\right) - 6y^3 + \left(3x^2y^3\right)$

$\mathbf{7}x^2y^3 + 6y^3 + \mathbf{3}x^2y^3$ Identify like terms.

$\mathbf{10}x^2y^3 + 6y^3$ Combine coefficients of like terms.

$7 + 3 = 10$

Simplify.

5. $8a + 3ab^2 + 3a + 2ab^2$

6. $x^3 + 1 + 2x^3 + 3xy^2 - 3$

_____

7. $y^4 + 2x^2y^3 - 3x^2 + 2y^4$

_____

LESSON 14B — Review for Mastery
Simplifying Polynomials (continued)

To simplify some polynomials, you first need to use the Distributive Property.

Distributive Property: $a(b + c) = a \cdot b + a \cdot c$

Simplify the polynomial.

$3(4y^2 + x^2) + 5x^2$

$3(4y^2 + x^2) + 5x^2 = (3 \cdot 4y^2) + (3 \cdot x^2) + 5x^2$ Apply the Distributive Property.

$\qquad\qquad\qquad\;\; = 12y^2 + 3x^2 + 5x^2$

$\qquad\qquad\qquad\;\; = 12y^2 + \boxed{3x^2} + \boxed{5x^2}$ Combine like terms.

like terms

$\qquad\qquad\qquad\;\; = 12y^2 + 8x^2$

So, $3(4y^2 + x^2) + 5x^2$ simplified is $12y^2 + 8x^2$.

Simplify.

8. $2(2a^2 - b^2) + 3a^2$

9. $4(3x^2y + 2x) + 3x^2 + 5x$

10. $-6mn + 3(m^4 + 3mn) - 2n^2$

11. $8(y - 5) + 3y + 6y^2$

12. $2(x^2 + 3x - 6) + 5(y + 2)$

13. $4(xy^2 + 2y + 3) + 2(x^2 - 2xy^2)$

Holt Mathematics

CHAPTER 14B Homework and Practice
Simplifying Polynomials

Identify the like terms in each polynomial.

1. $6x - x^5 + 2x^3 - 2x$

2. $2c^2 - d^3 + 4 + 3d^3 - c + 8$

_____   _____

3. $3a^2 + b + a^2$

4. $3x^2 - 2x + x^2 + 9 + x$

_____   _____

5. $c^2 - 2d^3 + 5d^3 - 9 + 2c^2$

6. $2 - 9 + x^2 - 3x^2 + x$

_____   _____

7. $5m - 9m^2 + 3m^2 + 6 - m$

8. $6x - x^5 + 2x^3 - 8x$

_____   _____

Simplify.

9. $m - 2(9mn + 3n - 2m)$

10. $9(a^2 + 2ab - b^2) - 2(a^2 + ab)$

_____   _____

11. $-d^2e^3 + 2(d^2e^3 - 8d^3e^2)$

12. $2v + 3v^2 + 2(v^2 - 8 + v + 7)$

_____   _____

13. $xy + 2xy - 2x - 3xy$

14. $7(1 - x) + 5(2 - 2x) + 3(x + 4)$

_____   _____

15. $2(c - 3cd - 9d) + 4(9cd + 3d + 4c)$

16. $bc - 3b^2 + 6c^2 - 2(b^2 + 3bc)$

_____   _____

17. Mr. Rose wrote the following expression on the board:
$3(8 + 9a) + 2(9a + a^2) + 9a^2 + a^3$. Use the Distributive
Property to simplify the expression.

_____

Holt Mathematics

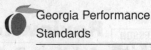

Georgia Performance
Standards

**M8N1.i, M8A1.b,
M8A1.c**

14C Adding Polynomials

You can use algebra tiles to model addition of polynomials. The
addition problem $(2x^2 + 2x - 2) + (x^2 - 4x - 3)$ is modeled
below.

$$2x^2 + 2x - 2 \qquad x^2 - 4x - 3$$

1. Use tiles to show that
$(2x^2 + 2x - 2) + (x^2 - 4x - 3) = 3x^2 - 2x - 5$.

You can use a graphing calculator to check. Enter the left side of
the equation in **Y1** and the right side in **Y2**, and compare tables.

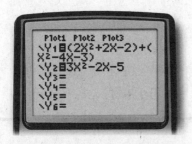

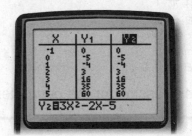

**Use algebra tiles to add each pair of polynomials. Check your
answers with a graphing calculator.**

2. $(x^2 + 7x) + (3x^2 - 7x - 5)$

3. $(-3x^2 - x - 1) + (4x^2 - 3x - 2)$

Think and Discuss

4. Explain how you can use tiles to add polynomials.

Holt Mathematics

LESSON
14C
Review for Mastery
Adding Polynomials

Adding polynomials is like simplifying polynomials.
You can regroup the terms and then combine like terms. Or you cn
place the polynomials in columns and then combine like terms.

Find an expression for the perimeter of the triangle below.

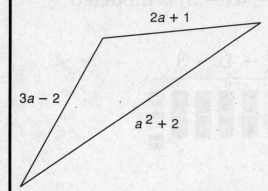

To find an expression for the perimeter, add the polynomials.

$(2a + 1) + (3a - 2) + (a^2 + 2)$

like terms   like terms

Place like terms in columns and combine them.

$$\begin{array}{r} 2a + 1 \\ 3a - 2 \\ + \quad a^2 \qquad + 2 \\ \hline a^2 + 5a + 1 \end{array}$$

So, an expression for the perimeter of the triangle is $a^2 + 5a + 1$.

Add.

1. $(3x^2 + 3xy^3 + 5y + 2) + (4xy^3 - 3y)$

$$\begin{array}{l} \quad 3x^2 + 3xy^3 + 5y + 2 \\ + \qquad\quad 4xy^3 - 3y \\ \hline \\ \hline \end{array}$$

2. $(4a^2b - 3a^2 + 3b) +$
$(6a^2b + 4ab - 2b)$

$$\begin{array}{l} \quad 4a^2b - 3a^2 \qquad\quad + 3b \\ + \; 6a^2b \qquad\quad + 4ab - 2b \\ \hline \\ \hline \end{array}$$

3. $(4mn + 5n^3 + 3n) + (3m^2 + 5n)$

4. $(-5r^3 + 2r + 7) + (2r^3 + 4r^2 - 6r + 1)$

Holt Mathematics

Name _____ Date _____ Class _____

Homework and Practice
Adding Polynomials

Add.

1. $(2b^2 + b + 3) + (5b^2 + 5b + 7)$

2. $(3y + 9y^2) + (3y - 12y^2)$

_____

3. $(-a^2 + 9a - 6) + (12a^2 - a + 2)$

4. $(6h^2 + 2h) + (10h^2 + 11)$

_____

5. $(2s + 3t + 8u) + (s + 4t + 7u) + (u - 3t)$

_____

6. $(4xw - 2x^2w + 9xw^2) + (15x^2w - 7xw^2) + (3xw^2 - 15xw + 6x^2w)$

_____

7. $(3b^2c^2 - 3b^2c + 3bc) + (5b^2c^2 - bc + 2) + (2b^2c - 3bc - 8)$

_____

8. $(7e^2 + 3e + 2) + (9 - 6e + 4e^2) + (9e + 2 - 6e^2) + (4e^2 - 7e + 8)$

_____

9. $(f^4g - fg^3 + 2fg - 4) + (3fg^3 + 3) + (4f^4g - 5fg) + (3 - 12fg^3 + f^4g)$

_____

10. Each side of an equilateral triangle has length $2m + 3$. Each
side of a square has length $3m - 2$. Write an expression for the
sum of the perimeter of the equilateral triangle and the perimeter
of the square.

_____

Holt Mathematics

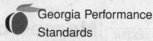
Georgia Performance
Standards

14D Subtracting Polynomials M8N1.i, M8A1.a, M8A1.b, M8A1.d

You can use algebra tiles to find the opposite of a polynomial.
To do this, replace each tile with its opposite.

The opposite of

$x^2 + 3x - 2$

is

$-x^2 - 3x + 2.$

Use algebra tiles to find the opposite of each polynomial.

1. $4x^2 - 2x - 5$

2. $-x^2 - 7x + 3$

3. $2x^2 + 3x - 3$

Think and Discuss

4. **Explain** how you can use tiles to find opposites.

5. **Discuss** how opposites of polynomials might be useful if you were subtracting polynomials.

Holt Mathematics

LESSON 14D — Review for Mastery

Subtracting Polynomials

When subtracting polynomials, you can distribute a factor of −1.

Subtract. $(5x^2 + 7x + 3) - (4x^2 + 3x - 5)$.

Rewrite the expression. $(5x^2 + 7x + 3) + (-1)(4x^2 + 3x - 5)$.

Apply the Distributive Property.

$-1(4x^2 + 3x - 5) = (-1 \cdot 4x^2) + (-1 \cdot 3x) + (-1 \cdot -5) = -4x^2 - 3x + 5$

Distributing the −1 changes the sign of each term.
$(5x^2 + 7x + 3) + (-4x^2 - 3x + 5)$

Use the Associative Property to remove parentheses and combine like terms.

$5x^2 + 7x + 3 - 4x^2 - 3x + 5 = x^2 + 4x + 8$

Subtract.

1. $(3b^3 + 4b^2 + 6) - (b^3 - 5b - 3)$

$3b^3 + 4b^2 + 6 + -1(b^3 - 5b - 3)$ Rewrite the expression.

$3b^3 + 4b^2 + 6 + (-b^3 + 5b + 3)$ Apply the Distributive Property.

$3b^3 + 4b^2 + 6 - b^3 + 5b + 3$ Remove the parentheses.

_____

2. $(3m^2n^2 - 4m^2n + m^2) - (m^2n^2 + 5m^2n - 5)$

_____

3. $(2x^3y^2 + x^2y - 4) - (x^2y - 8x + 3)$

_____

4. $(6y^2 + 3xy - 9x^2) - (-4y^2 + 8xy + x^2)$

_____

Holt Mathematics

Homework and Practice
LESSON 14D *Subtracting Polynomials*

Find the opposite of each polynomial.

1. $18xy^3$

2. $-9a + 4$

3. $6d^2 - 2d - 8$

Subtract.

4. $(4n^3 - 4n + 4n^2) - (6n^3 + 3n - 8n^2)$

5. $(2b^2 - 4b + 6) - (-b^2 - 3b - 5)$

6. $(9y^2 + y - 6) - (4y^2 - 7y - 2)$

7. $(17x^2 - x + 3) - (14x^2 + 3x + 5)$

8. $(9r^3s - 3rs + 4rs^3 + 5r^2s^2) - (2rs^3 - 2r^2s^2 + 6rs + 7r^3s)$

9. $w - (3w^4 + 5w^3 + 2w - 10)$

10. $(3qr^2 - 2q^3 + 14q^2r^2 - 9qr) - (-10qr + 4q^3 - 5qr^2 + 6q^2r^2)$

11. The volume of a rectangular prism, in cubic yards, is given by the expression $x^4 + 3x^3 + 2x^2$. The volume of a smaller rectangular prism is given by the expression $x^4 - 3x^3 + 2x^2$. How much greater is the volume of the larger rectangular prism?

12. Alice has a closet with an area of $5y^2 + 10y - 15$ square feet. She has a piece of carpet with an area of $2y^2 + 2y - 4$ square feet. She wants the carpet to cover the closet floor. What is the expression that represents the number of square feet of additional carpet she needs to cover the closet floor?

Holt Mathematics

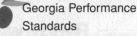

14E Multiplying Polynomials by Monomials

Georgia Performance Standards

M8N1.i, M8A1.b

You can use algebra tiles to model multiplication. The model shows that $2(-3) = -6$.

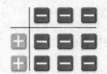

Find each product.

1. $2(2x - 3)$

2. $x(2x - 3)$

Use algebra tiles to model and find each product.

3. $2(3x + 2)$

4. $2x(3x - 1)$

Think and Discuss

5. Explain how area applies to modeling multiplication.

6. Write the factors and product modeled by the tiles shown.

Holt Mathematics

Review for Mastery
Multiplying Polynomials by Monomials

To multiply a monomial by a monomial, follow the steps used in the example below.

$(7x^2y^3)(3xy^4)$

1. Multiply the coefficients.

$(7)(3) = 21$

2. Multiply the variables.

To multiply two powers with the same base, you keep the base and **add** the exponents.

$(x^2)(x) = (x^2)(x^1) = x^3$ $\qquad$ $(y^3)(y^4) = y^7$

3. Write the monomial product.

$21x^3y^7$

Remember: If a variable has no exponent, the exponent is 1.

$x = x^1$

Multiply.

1. $(3x^2)(4x^3y^2)$ $\qquad$ **2.** $(6a^3b)(2a^3b^4)$ $\qquad$ **3.** $(2m^4n^2)(-5m^2n^2)$

_____ _____ _____

To multiply a polynomial by a monomial, multiply each term of the polynomial by the monomial.

$$
\begin{array}{r}
4a^2 + 2ab + 6b^2 \\
\times \qquad\qquad 3a^3 \\
\hline
12a^5 + 6a^4b + 18a^3b^2
\end{array}
$$

Multiply.

4. $\begin{array}{r} 3r^2s^3 - 2r^2 + 10 \\ \times \qquad\qquad 2s \end{array}$ $\qquad$ **5.** $\begin{array}{r} 5x^5 + x^2 - 3x \\ \times \qquad\qquad 4x^3 \end{array}$

_____ $\qquad\qquad$ _____

_____ $\qquad\qquad$ _____

6. $\begin{array}{r} m^2n - 3mn^2 - 8n^3 \\ \times \qquad\qquad -3mn \end{array}$

_____

_____

Holt Mathematics

Homework and Practice

Multiplying Polynomials

Multiply.

1. $(a)(-9a)$

2. $(-8bc^2)(d^2e^2)$

3. $(2ef^4)(2ef)$

4. $(2hk^2)(-h^2k^2)$

5. $6k(2m^3 - 2k)$

6. $p^2(2 + n^2 - 10n)$

7. $\left(\dfrac{1}{2}\right)q(2q - 4q^2 - 8q^3 - 16q^4)$

8. $6rs(3r^2 - rs + 2s^3)$

9. $-4u^5v^2\left(-u^4v^7 + \left(\dfrac{1}{4}\right)u - 2v\right)$

10. $(w^2 + (xyz) + w^4)(-w^8)$

11. $\left(\dfrac{3}{4}\right)a^2b^2(4 + 16ab + 8ab^3)$

12. $(-d^8)(-d^2 - 28e + 17d - 5e^2)$

13. $4gh^2\left(h + \left(\dfrac{1}{2}\right)gh - 2g^2 - 4gh\right)$

14. $(2k)(7k^2 - 2k + 3)(-k)$

15. $(-12k^3m^2)\left(\left(\dfrac{1}{3}\right)m - \left(\dfrac{5}{6}\right)k^5m^5 + km\right)$

16. $(p)(3n)(np - np^2 + 4n^4)$

17. The volume of a rectangular prism is given by the expression $(s + 14)(s)(2s)$. Simplify the expression.

Holt Mathematics

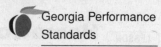

Georgia Performance Standards

14F Multiplying Binomials

M8N1.i, M8A1.b

You can use algebra tiles to model multiplication of binomials. The model shows the product of $(x + 2)(x + 4)$.

1. Use the model to find the product of $(x + 2)(x + 4)$.

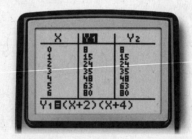

Use a graphing calculator to check your answer. Enter $(x + 2)(x + 4)$ for **Y1** and your answer for **Y2**, and compare tables.

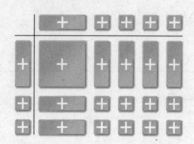

Use algebra tiles to model and find each product. Check your answers with a graphing calculator.

2. $(x + 2)(x + 1)$

3. $(x + 2)(x + 3)$

Think and Discuss

4. Write the factors and product modeled by the tiles shown.

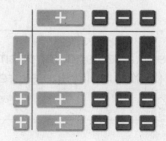

Holt Mathematics

LESSON 14F **Technology Lab**
Evaluate and Compare Polynomials

You can check the result of a polynomial operation by comparing the result to the original expression or expressions.

Activity

1 Multiply $(x + 3)^2$. Suppose your answer is $x^2 + 9$. Press
$\boxed{\text{Y=}}$, and enter $(x + 3)^2$ as Y_1 and $x^2 + 9$ as Y_2, as shown.

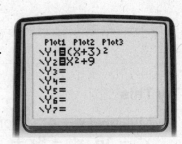

Press $\boxed{\text{2nd}}$ $\boxed{\text{GRAPH}}$. You can see that the values of Y_1 and Y_2 are not equal, so $(x + 3)^2 \neq x^2 + 9$.

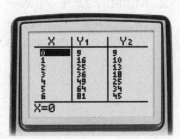

Press $\boxed{\text{Y=}}$, and change Y_2 to $x^2 + 6x + 9$. When you press
$\boxed{\text{2nd}}$ $\boxed{\text{GRAPH}}$, you can see that the values of Y_1 and Y_2 are equal for all values shown in the table.

$(x + 3)^2 = x^2 + 6x + 9$

Holt Mathematics

LESSON 14F Technology Lab
Evaluate and Compare Polynomials, continued

Think and Discuss

1. How could you use a table to subtract $x^2 - 3x + 2$ from $2x^2 + 3x - 1$ and verify that the difference is correct?

_____

_____

Try This

1. Multiply $(x - 4)^2$. Compare each of the following to $(x - 4)^2$: $x^2 - 16$, $x^2 - 8x + 16$, and $x^2 - 8x - 16$.
   Which expression is the product?

_____

2. Multiply $(x + 7)(x - 7)$. Compare each of the following to $(x + 7)(x - 7)$: $x^2 - 7$, $x^2 - 49$, and $x^2 + 49$.
   Which expression is the product?

_____

Name _____ Date _____ Class _____

Review for Mastery
Multiplying Binomials

To multiply a binomial by a binomial, multiply each term of the first binomial by each term of the second binomial.

$$(a + b)(c + d) = ac + ad + bc + bd$$

You can remember the product as FOIL: First terms, Outer terms, Inner terms, and Last terms.

$(5x + 3)(3x - 2)$

Multiply the **F**irst terms.	$(5x)(3x) = 15x^2$
Multiply the **O**utside terms.	$(5x)(-2) = -10x$
Multiply the **I**nside terms.	$(3)(3x) = 9x$
Multiply the **L**ast terms.	$(3)(-2) = -6$
Add the products.	$15x^2 - 10x + 9x - 6$
Combine like terms.	$15x^2 - x - 6$

You can also multiply binomials vertically.

Align the binomials.	$5x + 3$
Multiply each term of one	$\times\ 3x - 2$
binomial by each term of the	$-10x - 6$
other binomial.	$15x^2 + 9x$
Combine like terms.	$15x^2 - x - 6$

Multiply.

1. $(4x + 3)(2x + 5)$

_____

2. $(7t - 4)(2t + 3)$

_____

3. $(3 + 5b)(2b - 3b^2)$

_____

4. $(x - 1)(x + 5)$

_____

5. $(6m - 3n)(2m + 3n)$

_____

6. $(c + 7)(c + 1)$

_____

7. $\quad 6n - 3$
$\underline{\times\ 3n + 3}$

_____

8. $\quad 2y + 4$
$\underline{\times\quad y + 6}$

_____

Holt Mathematics

Name _____ Date _____ Class _____

LESSON 14F — Homework and Practice
Multiplying Binomials

Multiply.

1. $(a + 4)(a + 2)$

2. $(7 + b)(2 + b)$

3. $(4c + 1)(2c - 1)$

4. $(d - 1)(d - 3)$

5. $(3e + 1)(e - 1)$

6. $(3g + 2f)(2g - 3f)$

7. A square garden is 6 meters across. The drainage strip that runs around the garden is h meters wide. What expression gives the combined area of the garden and the drainage strip?

Multiply.

8. $(x - 5)^2$

9. $(3 + k)^2$

10. $(k + 8)(k - 8)$

11. $(2m - 6)(2m + 6)$

12. $(n - p)(n + p)$

13. $(2q + 3r)(2q - 3r)$

14. $(s - 2t)^2$

15. $(-2u + 4)(12u - 1)$

16. $(20 + w)^2$

17. $(9y - 2)(-2 + 9y)$

18. $(z^3 - 1)^2$

19. $(a^2 - b^2)(a^2 - b^2)$

20. A rectangular swimming pool is 30 feet long and 15 feet wide. It is surrounded by a deck of width c feet. What expression gives the total area of the pool and deck?

21. A circular pond with a radius of 21 ft is surrounded by a stone walkway with width b. What expression gives the total area of the pond and the walkway? Use $\frac{22}{7}$ for pi.

500

Holt Mathematics

Answer these questions to summarize the important concepts from Chapter 14 in your own words.

1. Explain why $2\sqrt{x}$ is not a monomial.

2. Explain how to simplify the polynomial.
$a^3 + 4a^5 - 3a^2 + 2 - 6a^2 + 8a^5$

3. Explain how to subtract the polynomials horizontally.
$(b^3 - 7 + b^2) - (4b + 3 - 3b^3)$

4. Explain how to multiply the polynomial by the monomial.
$0.5y^2(yz^5 - 8xy^3)$

5. Explain how to multiply the binomials using the FOIL method.
$(7c - 3)(c + 9)$

For more review of Chapter 14:

• Complete the Chapter 14 Study Guide and Review on pages 772–774 of your textbook.

• Complete the Ready to Go On quizzes on pages 744 and 766 of your textbook.

Holt Mathematics

Big Ideas

Answer these questions to summarize the important concepts from Chapter 14 in your own words.

1. Explain why $2\sqrt{x}$ is not a monomial.

2. Explain how to simplify the polynomial
$$5^3 + 4a^3 - 9a^2 - 2 - 4a^2 - 8a^3$$

3. Explain how to subtract the polynomial horizontally.
$$(a^2 - 7b^2) - (6b - 3 - 3b^2)$$

4. Explain how to multiply the polynomial by the monomial.
$$-4x^2(x^2 - 8x + 4)$$

5. Explain how to multiply the binomials using the FOIL method.
$$(4x - 3)(x - 4)$$

For more review of Chapter 14:

- Complete the Chapter 14 Study Guide and Review on pages 773–774 of your textbook.

- Complete the Ready to Go On quizzes on pages 744 and 766 of your textbook.